Application-Oriented Algebra

APPLICATION-ORIENTED ALGEBRA

An Introduction to Discrete Mathematics

JAMES L. FISHER
University of Alberta

Thomas Y. Crowell
HARPER & ROW, PUBLISHERS
New York   Philadelphia   San Francisco   London

APPLICATION-ORIENTED ALGEBRA: An Introduction to Discrete Mathematics

Copyright © 1977 by Harper & Row, Publishers, Inc.

Fisher, James Louis, 1943-
    Application-oriented algebra.

    (The IEP series in mathematics)
    Includes index.
    1. Algebra.   I. Title.
QA154.2.F47   512   77-2311
ISBN 0-7002-2504-8

Contents

* Asterisk indicates optional sections.

* Asterisk indicates optional sections.

* Asterisk indicates optional sections.

Preface

A traditional course in abstract algebra often offers little motivation for students whose primary interest lies outside of pure mathematics. One way to involve these students is through a course that includes topics in discrete mathematics along with substantial and interesting applications of algebra. This text outlines such a course. It offers applications not usually available in conventional algebra texts. Congruences and homomorphisms of groups, rings, and universal algebras are covered because of the importance of congruence in the theory of machines and its natural extension to congruence of universal algebra. In fact, congruence relations provide a unifying theme for many of the seemingly disparate topics that are treated.

The book evolved from lecture notes for a course in applied algebra given at the University of Alberta. The students taking this course come from mathematics, computer science, or engineering and are usually juniors, seniors, or first-year graduate students. The primary prerequisite is a knowledge of matrix theory. The student should know how to multiply matrices, solve sets of linear equations, and find inverses of matrices. In the text, starred sections contain optional material.

The first six chapters can form the basis of a one-semester course in discrete mathematics. The material in Chapter 1 and Chapters 7 through 11 is, except for the optional Sections 7.8 and 9.8, independent of Chapters 2 through 6, and thus is suitable for a one-semester course in algebra.

Chapter 1 introduces the basic concepts of set, relation, and function necessary for understanding the remainder of the material. Chapter 2 considers partially ordered sets, particularly three types—weak order, semi-order, and interval order—that are important in attempts to describe more accurately the notion of preference in economics and political science. The final section of Chapter 2 deals with Kenneth Arrow's proof of the inconsistency of a set of axioms describing voting conditions commonly held to be desirable in a democratic society. Chapter 3 deals with graphs and introduces the concepts and algorithms necessary for applications to language theory, the critical-path method, and flows on networks, the latter two being used extensively in industrial applications. Chapter 4 introduces Boolean algebra and shows how this algebra is used to analyze both switching circuits (to minimize the cost of circuits) and logical statements.

Chapter 5 describes a rather primitive model of a computer—a finite state machine—and shows how to minimize the number of states of the machine. This chapter illustrates the importance of congruence relations to the theory of finite state machines and shows how arbitrary machines can be built from switching circuits and memory elements. Chapters 4 and 5 form a natural link between the discrete and the algebraic. Chapter 6 introduces the theory of languages and presents, first, the algebraic description, then the graph theoretical description, and finally the machine description of various types of languages. Chapter 7 considers group theory and shows the close connections between finite state machines and semigroups. Applications of these concepts include the design of error-correcting codes. Enough material on permutation groups is covered to obtain some rather attractive formulas for counting symmetry classes. Chapter 8 is concerned with modular arithmetic, and the results of this chapter are applied to cryptographic codes, constructing finite fields, and, briefly, to fast integer multiplication.

Chapter 9 on coding theory deals with cryptography—the science of secret code making and breaking—and with error-correcting and error-detecting codes. The final sections of the chapter introduce addressing systems—an area of potential application in data transmission—and K. P. Bogart's description of equivalent codes.

Chapter 10 develops the structure of finite fields and suggests applications to the design of experiments and BCH error-correcting codes. Finally, Chapter 11 unites congruence on finite machines, semigroups, and rings under the general notion of congruence of a universal algebra. The isomorphism theorem is given and is shown to be the expected result in each case.

I would like to express my sincere thanks to B. Allison, H. H. Brungs,

H. Hosli, A. Rhemtulla, and A. Lau for their helpful comments on the material and to K. P. Bogart for showing me several interesting applications. I owe a great deal to my wife for her faith and patience during the writing of this book.

Notes to the Reader

The following diagram shows the dependencies among the sections.

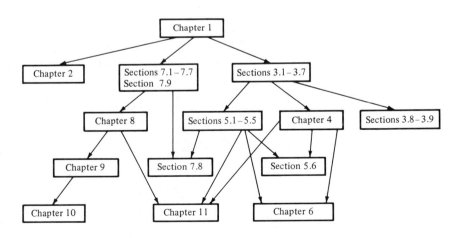

List of Notation and Symbols

Notation	Description	Page
$f(X, \overline{X})$	flow from X to $\overline{X}$	91
g^{-1}	inverse of g	187
$|G|$	order of G	190
$\langle g \rangle$	subgroup generated by g	190
$\gcd\{a, b\}$	greatest common divisor	235
$G(f)$	associated incremental graph	94
$GF(2^k)$	finite field of order 2^k	340
$G_{\mathscr{F}}$	permutations of $\mathscr{F}$ induced by G	206
gH	left coset	190
G/H	group of cosets	226
$[G : H]$	index	192
$G_1 \times G_2$	direct product	189
g^m, g^{-m}	power of g	187
G_M	monoid of the machine	217
$G/\mathscr{P}$	semigroup of congruence classes	224
G_x	stabilizer of x	208
$g(X, Y)$	flow from X to Y	91
$\text{lcm}\{a, b\}$	least common multiple	235
$L(G)$	language	165
$lh(x)$	lower holding	41
$L(u)$	distance to u	77
$l(x)$	left endpoint	25
$\max S$	maximum in S	102
$\min S$	minimum in S	102
$M_G = (G, G, \delta)$	machine of the monoid	217
(N, T, P, σ)	grammar	164
$\mathscr{P}(A)$	power set	3
R/I	ring of cosets	267
R^k	k-tuples	255
$R/\mathscr{P}$	ring of congruence classes	265
$R_1 \oplus \cdots \oplus R_K$	direct product	247
$r(x)$	right endpoint	25
$R[x]$	polynomial ring	248
$\langle S \rangle$	subspace spanned by S	261
$|S|$	number of elements in S	7
$\overline{S}$	complement of S	2
$(\mathscr{S}, \mathscr{I}, \mathcal{O}, \delta, \rho)$	state output machine	146
$(\mathscr{S}, \mathscr{I}, \mathcal{O}, \delta, \theta)$	i/o machine	132
$(\mathscr{S}, \mathscr{I}, \delta)$	state machine	133
$(\mathscr{S}_R, \mathscr{I}, \mathcal{O}, \delta_R, \theta_R)$	reduced machine	153
S_n	symmetric group	193
$S \times T$	Cartesian product	2

Notation	Description	Page
$s \to t$	s maps to t	11
$(s)w$	string w applied to state s	139
S_x	symmetric group	193
$T \backslash S$	complement of S in T	2
$t(v)$	longest distance to v	83
$t^*(v)$	$t(z) - t(v, z)$	83
$t(v, z)$	longest distance from v to z	83
$uh(x)$	upper holding	41
$U(R)$	invertible elements	248
$v(a)$	degree of a	250
$w(\mathbf{x})$	weight of $\mathbf{x}$	295
X^*	finite sequences	138
(X, F)	algebra	350
$Z/(n)$	integers modulo n	244
β_{s_0}	behavior	145
$\beta_s^{-1}(z)$	strings ending at z	175
$\delta(s, a)$	next state	132
$\delta^*(s, w)$	next state	138
$\delta(v)$	degree	63, 75
$\theta(s, a)$	output	132
$\theta(v)$	out-degree	74
$\iota(v)$	in-degree	75
$\lambda(P)$	length of a path	77
$\phi(n)$	number of relatively prime elements	237

Symbol	Description	Page
$\in$	is an element of	1
$\notin$	is not an element of	1
$\cap$	intersect	2
$\cup$	union	2
$\subset$	is a subset of	2
$\varnothing$	empty set	2
$\geq$	greater than or equal	5
$>$	greater than	5
$\ngeq$	not greater than or equal	5
$\not>$	not greater than	5
$\sim$	is equivalent to	8, 112
$\subsetneqq$	is a subset but not equal to	42
$\cong$	is isomorphic to	69, 246
$\wedge$	intersect	101
$\vee$	union	101
$-$	complement	101

	Description	Page
$\rightarrow$	implies	104
$\leftrightarrow$	if and only if	104
$\bigvee m_i$	union	114
$\rightarrow$	directly derives	164
$\Rightarrow$	derives	165
$::=$	is defined to be	170
$\circ$	binary operation	12
$\underset{G}{\sim}$	G-equivalent	195
$\equiv \bmod n$	congruent modulo n	237
$\mid$	divides	233

Application-Oriented Algebra

Basic Concepts

1.1 SETS

The theory of sets and relations on sets is at the core of modern mathematics, hence is important to the mathematician. Furthermore, sets and relations on sets provide conceptual organization for many models used in applications, and thus the theory assumes importance for many users of mathematics.

A set is considered a primitive term and thus formally undefined but, nevertheless, we have an intuitive idea of what constitutes a set. There are many English words that describe sets or special types of sets, for example, collection, bunch, group, herd, crowd, and flock. For all these words, we think of a single aggregate composed of its members. Thus, along with the notion of set, we need the idea of membership in a set, so that a set consists of a collection of elements which intuitively can be thought of as the members of the set or the objects contained in the set. We explicitly assume that the members of a set determine the set. Thus two sets are equal if they contain exactly the same elements. The fact that a is an element in a set S is denoted by $a \in S$. If a is not a member of S, we write $a \notin S$. Often a set is described by listing its elements and enclosing the list in braces or by describing its elements in terms of properties.

A set consisting of the integers 2, 4, 6, and 8 can be described as $\{2, 4, 6, 8\}$ or, alternatively, the set of even integers n such that $1 < n < 9$ can be written $\{\text{even integers } n : 1 < n < 9\}$. Since the elements contained in the set determine it, the order of the listing is immaterial.

The *intersection* of two sets S and T is the set of elements common to both S and T and is written $S \cap T$. Thus $S \cap T = \{a : a \in S \text{ and } a \in T\}$. The *union* of S and T is $S \cup T = \{a : a \in S \text{ or } a \in T\}$. For example, $\{2, 4, \pi, \frac{5}{3}\} \cap \{2, 6, 18, 54\} = \{2\}$ and $\{2, 4, 5, \pi\} \cup \{3, 4, 6, \pi\} = \{2, 4, 5, \pi, 3, 6\}$. The set S is contained in the set T or, alternatively, S is a *subset* of T if every member of S is also a member of T. This is written $S \subset T$. For example, $\{0, 1\} \subset \{x : x$ is an integer and $x^2 - x < 3\}$, since $0^2 - 0 < 3$ and $1^2 - 1 < 3$. The sets S and T will be equal sets if $S \subset T$ and $T \subset S$. If $S \subset T$, the *complement* of S in T is defined as $T\backslash S = \{t \in T : t \notin S\}$. If T is understood from the context, $T\backslash S$ will be denoted by $\bar{S}$. The set that contains no members is called an empty set and is denoted by $\varnothing$. There are many ways of describing $\varnothing$. For example, $\varnothing = \{ \} = \{x : x$ is an integer and $x^2 = -1\} = \{x : x$ is an integer and $\sqrt{5} < x < \sqrt{7}\}$. Note that $\varnothing \subset S$ for every set S.

The *Cartesian product* of the sets S and T is the set of all ordered pairs (s, t), where $s \in S$ and $t \in T$, with $(s, t) = (u, v)$ for $u \in S, v \in T$, if and only if $s = u$ and $t = v$. This Cartesian product is written $S \times T$ and is not necessarily the same set as $T \times S$. If R is the set of real numbers, then the Cartesian product $R \times R$ can be used to represent the points in a plane. If S_i are sets, where $i = 1, 2, \ldots, n$, then $S_1 \times \cdots \times S_n$ is the set of ordered n-tuples $(s_1, s_2, \ldots, s_n)$, where $s_i \in S_i$, with $(s_1, s_2, \ldots, s_n) = (t_1, t_2, \ldots, t_n)$ for $t_i \in S_i$, if and only if $s_i = t_i$, $i = 1, 2, \ldots, n$.

Exercises

1-1 List the elements of the set $\{a/b : a$ and b are prime integers with $1 < a < 10$ and $3 < b < 9\}$.

1-2 List the elements of $S \times T$ and $M \times N$, where $S = \{1, 2\}$, $T = \{a, b, \pi, \alpha\}$, $M = \{1, \pi\}$, and $N = \{\pi, \frac{4}{3}, a\}$. Determine $(M \times N) \cap (S \times T)$.

1-3 Let $A, B, C,$ and U be sets with $A \subset U, B \subset U,$ and $C \subset U$. Prove the following:
  a $A \cap (B \cap C) = (A \cap B) \cap C$
  b $A \cup (B \cup C) = (A \cup B) \cup C$
  c $A \cup B = B \cup A$
  d $A \cap B = B \cap A$
  e $A \cap (B \cup C) = (A \cap B) \cup (A \cap C)$
  f $A \cup (U\backslash A) = U, A \cap (U\backslash A) = \varnothing$.

1-4 Let A_i be a collection of sets—one for each element $i \in I$, where I is some set (e.g., the positive integers). Define $\bigcup_{i \in I} A_i = \{a : a \in A_i \text{ for some } i \in I\}$ and

$\bigcap_{i \in I} A_i = \{a : a \in A_i$ for every $i \in I\}$. If U contains every A_i, prove $U \backslash (\bigcup_{i \in I} A_i) = \bigcap_{i \in I} (U \backslash A_i)$.

1-5 Let A be a set. Define $\mathscr{P}(A)$ as the set of all subsets of A. This is called the power set of A. List $\mathscr{P}(A)$, where $A = \{1, 2, 3\}$. If $\mathscr{P}(A)$ has 256 elements, how many elements are in A?

1-6 If the set A has n elements, formulate a conjecture about the number of elements in $\mathscr{P}(A)$.

1-7 Prove $A \times B$ is not equal to $B \times A$ unless $A = B$ or either A or B is $\varnothing$.

1.2 BINARY RELATIONS

The idea of relationship is very general and, in the case of a binary relationship, corresponds to pairing certain elements of a set (i.e., those that are related).

Definition A relation $\mathscr{R}$ between the sets $A_1, A_2, A_3, \ldots, A_n$ is a subset of $A_1 \times A_2 \times \cdots \times A_n$.

If we have n sets, the relation is called n-ary, with the exception that two-ary is called binary and three-ary is called ternary. Furthermore, in much of the following discussion, all the sets $A_1, \ldots, A_n$ are the same set S; in which case $\mathscr{R}$ is called an n-ary relation on S. Furthermore, since we are essentially considering only binary relations, the adjective "binary" is often omitted and the relation generally means "binary relation on S."

Relations on various sets form an important although not necessarily conscious part of everyday life. For example, the basis of denotation of names in a language is the forming of relations on a set of objects. The name "blue," for instance, is a relation on elements, where two objects are related if they are both blue. Thus the denotation of a name corresponds to a certain relation on a set.

There are certain special types of binary relations which, because of their importance and frequent occurrence, are singled out. These special types correspond to our intuitive notions of preference and equality. Constantly we make choices between alternatives and, if alternative a is preferred to alternative b, then (a, b) is in our preference relation. If a is preferred to b and b to c, then a will be preferred to c. This gives rise to the definition of a transitive relation.

Definition A relation $\mathscr{R}$ is *transitive* if $(a, b) \in \mathscr{R}$ and $(b, c) \in \mathscr{R}$, then $(a, c) \in \mathscr{R}$.

Another example of a type of preference is the natural ordering on the integers, $n \geq m$. This relation is transitive and also satisfies

i $n \geq n$, and
ii If $k \geq j$ and $j \geq k$, then $k = j$.

These notions are formalized by the following definitions.

Definition A relation $\mathscr{R}$ on S is *reflexive* if $(a, a) \in \mathscr{R}$ for all $a \in S$.

Definition A relation $\mathscr{R}$ is *antisymmetric* if $(a, b) \in \mathscr{R}$ and $(b, a) \in \mathscr{R}$ implies $a = b$.

The equality of certain aspects of an element (for example, equality with respect to height in a group of people) leads to a relation. For example, $(a, b) \in \mathscr{R}$ if a and b are equal in that certain aspect. This is not antisymmetric, since for example two distinct people may be the same height. In fact, almost the opposite of antisymmetry is true—if $(a, b) \in \mathscr{R}$, then certainly $(b, a) \in \mathscr{R}$. A relation satisfying this property is called *symmetric*.

If S is a finite set, a binary relation on S can be represented by a matrix. If $|S| = n$, the elements of S can be called $s_1, \ldots, s_n$. If $\mathscr{R}$ is a relation on S, the relation matrix of $\mathscr{R}$ is the $n \times n$ matrix (a_{ij}), $i = 1, 2, \ldots, n$ and $j = 1, 2, \ldots, n$, where a_{ij} is 1 if $(s_i, s_j) \in \mathscr{R}$ and a_{ij} is 0 if $(s_i, s_j) \notin \mathscr{R}$. For example, the set $S = \{1, 2, 3, 4\}$ has the relation $\{(1, 1), (2, 2), (3, 4), (1, 2), (4, 1)\}$, which is represented by the relation matrix

$$\begin{bmatrix} 1 & 1 & 0 & 0 \\ 0 & 1 & 0 & 0 \\ 0 & 0 & 0 & 1 \\ 1 & 0 & 0 & 0 \end{bmatrix}.$$

Conversely, once a labeling $s_1, s_2, \ldots, s_n$ is chosen for the elements of S, an $n \times n$ matrix with each entry from $\{0, 1\}$ yields a binary relation $\mathscr{R}$ on S, where $(s_i, s_j) \in \mathscr{R}$ if and only if the i, j entry of the matrix is 1. Furthermore, each such matrix gives a distinct binary relation.

A binary relation is reflexive if and only if the relation matrix has only 1's on its diagonal. A binary relation is symmetric if and only if the relation matrix M is identical with its transpose M^T. Hence, if S contains n elements, there are 2^{n^2} distinct relation matrices, since there are two choices (namely, 0 and 1) for each of the n^2 entries of the relation matrix. Exactly 2^{n^2-n} of these will be reflexive, and $2^{n(n+1)/2}$ will be symmetric—small fractions of the total number indeed.

Exercises

1-8 Determine whether the following relations are reflexive, symmetric, transitive, or antisymmetric:

a "Is the same height as" on the set of all people.

b $(a, b) \in \mathscr{R}$ if b divides a evenly and a and b are positive integers.

c "Is the brother of" on the set of all people.

d $(x, y) \in \mathscr{R}$ if $x^2 + y^2 = 1$ and x and y are real numbers.

e Let p be a fixed positive integer. The element $(m, n) \in \mathscr{R}$ if p divides $m - n$, where m and n are integers. In this case m is said to be congruent to n modulo p.

f "Has the same blood type as" on the set of all people.

1-9 Show that, if S contains n elements, there are $2^{n^2 - n}$ reflexive relations on S, $2^{n(n+1)/2}$ symmetric relations on S, and $2^{(n-1)n/2}$ relations that are both reflexive and symmetric.

1-10 Determine the relation matrix for the relation $(a, b) \in \mathscr{R}$ if b divides a evenly and a and b are in $\{2, 3, 4, 5, 6, 8, 9, 12\}$.

1.3 PARTIALLY ORDERED SETS

A *partially ordered set* is a set S with a relation $\mathscr{R}$ on S which is reflexive, antisymmetric, and transitive. Denote (a, b) in $\mathscr{R}$ by $a \geq b$. If $a \geq b$ but $a \neq b$, then we write $a > b$. If it is not the case that $a \geq b$, we write $a \not\geq b$. Likewise, not $a > b$ is written $a \not> b$. The phrase "partially ordered set" is commonly abbreviated *poset*. The relation of preference on a set S forms a poset if the relation is supplemented with (a, a) for all $a \in S$. For example, if S is the set of oranges (O), peaches (P), plums (Pl), pears (Pe), bananas (B), and coconuts (C), and preference is with respect to taste, then my preference is (P, B), (P, O), (P, C), (P, Pe), (P, Pl), (O, C), (O, Pe), (O, Pl), (B, C), (B, Pe), (B, Pl), (C, Pl), (C, Pe), (Pe, Pl). This becomes a partially ordered set if we add (P, P), (O, O), (B, B), (C, C), (Pe, Pe), and (Pl, Pl) to it. There is no preference between bananas and oranges.

In addition to preference, a poset can also model the parts of a machine. A machine parts assembly plant has a certain set of parts which it uses to assemble other parts. If one part a is a component of another part b, then $a \leq b$. This relation is transitive, since a being a component of b and b being a component of c means that a is also a component of c. It is also antisymmetric, since if a is a proper component of b and b is a proper component of a, then we will have the physically impossible situation of a containing part b containing part a ad infinitum. The relation is also reflexive if we think of b as being part of b (namely, the whole part). Thus we have a partial ordering.

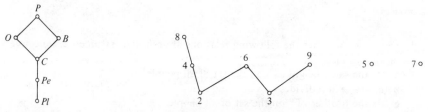

Figure 1.1   Figure 1.2

A finite poset can always be diagramed on the plane. We show this explicitly in Section 2.2. If in a poset, $a > b$ with no c such that $a > c$ and $c > b$, then a is said to *cover* b. Each element of the poset corresponds to an appropriate point in the plane and, if a covers b, then join a and b by a line segment with a above b. If an element e is joined to an element d by a sequence of line segments all going downward, then $c \geq d$, by transitivity. Thus the preceding taste preference is diagramed in Figure 1.1. This poset has a unique largest element (namely, peaches are preferred over all else) and a unique smallest element (namely, plums are preferred over nothing else). This does not have to occur, however. Let $\mathscr{R}$ be the relation a is divisible by b on {integers $n : 2 \leq n \leq 9$}. This poset is diagramed in Figure 1.2. It has several minimal elements [an element a is *minimal* (*maximal*) if there is no c such that $a > c$ ($c > a$)], namely, 2, 3, 5, and 7. The elements 8, 6, 9, 5, and 7 are maximal.

The relation matrix for the poset in Figure 1.1, with (O), (P), (Pl), (Pe), (B), and (C) called 1, 2, 3, 4, 5, and 6, respectively, is

$$\begin{bmatrix} 1 & 0 & 1 & 1 & 0 & 1 \\ 1 & 1 & 1 & 1 & 1 & 1 \\ 0 & 0 & 1 & 0 & 0 & 0 \\ 0 & 0 & 1 & 1 & 0 & 0 \\ 0 & 0 & 1 & 1 & 1 & 1 \\ 0 & 0 & 1 & 1 & 0 & 1 \end{bmatrix}.$$

We can determine from the relation matrix which are the maximal and minimal elements in the poset. An element s_i satisfies $s_i > s_j$ for some $j \neq i$ if and only if the ith row of the relation matrix contains at least two 1's, namely, 1 in the i, i-entry and 1 in the i, j-entry. Thus minimal elements are exactly those s_k such that row k has only one 1. In the above matrix, row 3 and only row 3 contains one 1, so that there is exactly one minimal element, namely, (Pl). It is likewise simple to see for an element s_j that there exists $i \neq j$ with $s_i > s_j$ if and only if the jth column of the relation matrix contains more than one 1. In the preceding example, the second and only the second column has only one 1, hence the second element, namely, P, is maximal.

For Figure 1.2, list the elements 2, 3, 4, 5, 6, 7, 8, and 9. The relation matrix is thus

$$\begin{bmatrix}
1 & 0 & 0 & 0 & 0 & 0 & 0 & 0 \\
0 & 1 & 0 & 0 & 0 & 0 & 0 & 0 \\
1 & 0 & 1 & 0 & 0 & 0 & 0 & 0 \\
0 & 0 & 0 & 1 & 0 & 0 & 0 & 0 \\
1 & 1 & 0 & 0 & 1 & 0 & 0 & 0 \\
0 & 0 & 0 & 0 & 0 & 1 & 0 & 0 \\
1 & 0 & 1 & 0 & 0 & 0 & 1 & 0 \\
0 & 1 & 0 & 0 & 0 & 0 & 0 & 1
\end{bmatrix}.$$

Rows 1, 2, 4, and 6 have exactly one 1, so 2, 3, 5, and 7 are minimal elements. Columns 4, 5, 6, 7, and 8 have exactly one 1, so 5, 6, 7, 8, and 9 are maximal elements.

There are some special types of partial orders. A partially ordered set S is *totally ordered* (commonly shortened to *ordered*) if, for a and b in S, exactly one of $a > b$, $a = b$, or $b > a$ holds. Thus the integers under the usual ordering form a totally ordered set, since for any pair of distinct integers exactly one is larger than the other. The diagram of a totally ordered set S, where $|S| = n$, is exactly one chain with n elements and $n - 1$ links, of the form

If we label the elements of S so that the diagram has the form

then the relation matrix has the very simple form

$$\begin{bmatrix} 1 & 1 & 1 & \cdots & 1 \\ 0 & 1 & 1 & \cdots & 1 \\ 0 & 0 & 1 & \cdots & 1 \\ \vdots & \vdots & \vdots & \cdots & \vdots \\ 0 & 0 & 0 & \cdots & 1 \end{bmatrix}.$$

A finite totally ordered set with n elements corresponds, in essence, to the natural order on the set of integers $\{1, 2, 3, \ldots, n\}$. Thus the ordered sets with diagrams as in Figure 1.3 are in essence the same. We make this notion precise by introducing the concept of isomorphism in Section 2.3.

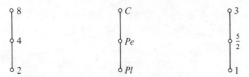

Figure 1.3

Exercises

1-11 Which of the relations in Exercise 1-8 determine a partially ordered set?

1-12 Determine a partial order for a set of six motion pictures you have seen. Diagram this partial order. Determine the relation matrix for the partial order.

1-13 In a finite poset show that there is always at least one maximal element and at least one minimal element.

1-14 A *chain* in a poset is a sequence $a_0, a_1, \ldots, a_n$ of elements such that $a_i > a_{i+1}$. The length of this chain is said to be n. Prove there is always a chain of maximal length in a finite poset.

1.4 EQUIVALENCE RELATIONS

Just as partially ordered sets correspond to preference on a set, equality between certain aspects of objects is formalized in the definition of an equivalence relation.

Definition An *equivalence relation* on a set S is a relation that is reflexive, symmetric, and transitive. If (a, b) is contained in the equivalence relation (written $a \sim b$), a and b are said to be equivalent.

Equality of a certain aspect of elements in a set naturally partitions the set into classes of objects which are equal in this aspect. Thus if the relation "has the same color eyes as" is put on the set of all people, then the human race is divided into classes of blue-eyed people, brown-eyed people, green-eyed people, grey-eyed people, and possibly those with eyes of other hues. If eye color is the only consideration with which one is concerned, instead of considering all individuals, only classes of people with the same eye color need be considered. The number of objects under consideration is dropped, and the new objects will be large sets of people with the same eye color.

This phenomenon is not only true for eye color but for any equivalence relation. If $\mathscr{R}$ is an equivalence relation on S and a is an element of S, define $[a]$ to be the set of all elements in S that are related to a. In other words, $[a] = \{s \in S : s \sim a\}$. This set is called an equivalence class.

Lemma 1.1 If $\mathscr{R}$ is an equivalence relation on S and $a \in S, b \in S$, with $[a] \neq [b]$, then $[a] \cap [b] = \varnothing$.

Proof If $x \in [a] \cap [b]$, then $x \sim a$ and $x \sim b$. For any element y in $[a]$, $y \sim a$. By the symmetry of $\mathscr{R}$, $a \sim x$. Since $y \sim a$ and $a \sim x$, transitivity implies $y \sim x$. Also, $y \sim x$ and $x \sim b$ implies $y \sim b$. Thus $y \in [b]$. This says that $[a] \subset [b]$. A similar argument shows that $[b] \subset [a]$, so $[a] = [b]$. This contradicts our hypothesis that $[a] \neq [b]$, so our initial assumption that $x \in [a] \cap [b]$ is false. Thus $[a] \cap [b] = \varnothing$.

This lemma shows that equivalence classes are always disjoint.

The word "partition" has been used without definition. Let us make the word precise with the following definition.

Definition A *partition* of a set S is a set of subsets $\{S_i \neq \varnothing : S_i \subset S$ and $i \in I$, some index set$\}$ satisfying $\bigcup_{i \in I} S_i = S$, $S_i \cap S_j = \varnothing$, for $i \neq j$.

The first theorem relates equivalence relation and partitions.

Theorem 1.1 An equivalence relation $\mathscr{R}$ on a set $S \neq \varnothing$ partitions S into equivalence classes. Conversely, a partition $\{S_i\}$ of S gives rise to an equivalence relation on S, where the equivalence classes are just the subsets of the partition.

Proof The union of the equivalence classes is a subset of S, since each equivalence class is a subset of S. However, if $s \in S$, $s \sim s$ by reflexivity, so that $s \in [s]$ and S equals the union of the equivalence classes. By Lemma 1.1, distinct equivalence classes are disjoint, so the set of distinct equivalence classes forms a partition.

Suppose now that $\{S_i\}$, $i \in I$, is a partition of S. Let $\mathscr{R} = \{(a, b) : a$ and b are contained in the same set $S_i\}$. If $a \in S$, then $a \in \bigcup_{i \in I} S_i = S$, so that $a \in S_i$ for some $i \in I$. Hence $a \sim a$ and the relation is reflexive. If a and b are in S_i, then b and a are in S_i, so symmetry follows. If $(a, b) \in \mathscr{R}$, $(b, c) \in \mathscr{R}$, then $a \in S_i$, $b \in S_i$ for some $i \in I$, and $b \in S_j$, $c \in S_j$ for some $j \in I$. However, this implies $b \in S_i \cap S_j$, which is empty if i and j are different. Thus $i = j$ and $a \in S_i$, $c \in S_i$, so $a \sim c$. Thus the partition leads to an equivalence relation whose equivalence classes are the sets of the partition.

Equivalence relation is an extremely important concept in mathematics, and equivalence relations are extensively used in building up mathematical structures. The properties of reflexivity, symmetry, and transitivity are relatively easy to work with in formal systems, many of which we meet later. However, in computational problems dealing with equivalence relations, the concept of a partition is paramount. Since writing down every element of an equivalent class, whenever reference is made to this class, is both time-consuming and laborious, a distinguished element in each equivalence class is often picked out, and this element stands for the class. Such a distinguished element is called a *representative* or *leader* of the equivalence class.

Exercises

1-15 A quasi-order is a relation that is reflexive and transitive. If (a, b) is in the quasi-order, then we write $a \geq b$. Define $a \sim b$ when $a \geq b$ and $b \geq a$. Prove that $\sim$ is an equivalence relation. Define, using the quasi-order on the set, a relation on the equivalence classes determined by $\sim$ and prove that the set of equivalence classes under that relation forms a partially ordered set.

1-16 Let S be the set of continuous functions from $\{r \in \text{reals} : 0 \leq r \leq 1\}$ to reals. Define $f(x) \sim g(x)$ for f and g in S if

$$\int_0^1 f(x)\, dx = \int_0^1 g(x)\, dx.$$

Prove that $\sim$ is an equivalence relation and give a rule that determines one and only one representative for each equivalence class.

1-17 Determine the number of equivalence relations on the set $\{1, 2, 3, 4\}$.

1-18 Prove that the relation "is similar to" is an equivalence relation on the set of all triangles in the plane.

1-19 Is $\{(m, n): m$ and n are integers and $m - n$ is odd$\}$ an equivalence relation on the set of integers?

1-20 Let $\mathscr{R}$ be a relation which is symmetric and transitive. If $(a, b) \in \mathscr{R}$, then symmetry implies that $(b, a) \in \mathscr{R}$. However, transitivity now implies that $(a, a) \in \mathscr{R}$. Thus $\mathscr{R}$ is reflexive. Find the fallacy in this proof.

1.5 FUNCTIONS

An even more important relation than partial order or equivalence relation is the concept of function. A function is a special type of binary relation between two sets, say S and T. A computer, for example, takes an input and transforms it to obtain an output, so in a broad sense this is a function. Furthermore, if the computer is in the same initial state each time, a further application of the input results in exactly the same output as that previously obtained. In general, a function is a relation between sets S and T such that each element of S is associated with exactly one element of T. To be precise, we give the following definition.

Definition   A function from S to T is a subset f of $S \times T$ such that, for s in S, there exists t in T with (s, t) in f and, furthermore, if $(s, u) \in f$, then $t = u$.

The element (s, t) in f is often denoted $(s, f(s))$, or just $f(s)$, since t is uniquely determined by f and s. The set S is called the *domain* of f, and the set T is called the *range*. The set of elements t in T such that there is some s in S with (s, t) in f is called the *image* of S under f (or sometimes just the image of f).

There are numerous examples of functions all around us. The age of a person is a function from the set of all people to the set of all integers. The number of people in each classroom is a function from the set of all classrooms to the set of all integers. The price of a commodity is a function from the set of all commodities to the set of all integers. In the above notation for a function, the function determined by commodities bought during a shopping trip may be (bread, 35), (bananas, 60), (milk, 64), (eggs, 80), (hamburger, 180), (cookies, 80), (margarine, 64).

The term mapping is also used to denote a function, even though mapping conjures up dynamic aspects. Thus we sometimes represent (s, t) in a function by $s \rightarrow t$. Thus the above example is illustrated in Figure 1.4.

Domain		Range
Bread	$\longrightarrow$	35
Bananas	$\longrightarrow$	60
Milk	$\longrightarrow$	64
Eggs	$\longrightarrow$	80
Cookies	$\longrightarrow$	80
Hamburger	$\longrightarrow$	180
Margarine	$\longrightarrow$	180

Figure 1.4   Representation of a function.

The representation of a function in Figure 1.4 is not so economical in terms of space, so we often write a function f from the finite set $S = \{s_1, s_2, \ldots, s_n\}$ to R as

$$\begin{pmatrix} s_1 & s_2 & s_3 & \cdots & s_n \\ f(s_1) & f(s_2) & f(s_3) & \cdots & f(s_n) \end{pmatrix}.$$

Numerous functions are common in mathematics. For example, the sine of an angle, the logarithm of a positive number, the area under a curve, the volume of a solid, and the derivative of a differentiable function. In each of these cases see if you can distinguish the domain, the range, and the image of the function.

A function from a set S to a set T is said to be *onto* if for every element $t \in T$ there exists an element $s \in S$ such that (s, t) is in the function. In other words, for each element $t \in T$ there is an element $s \in S$ that is mapped to t. Thus the function that associates the age of a person with each person is not an onto function, since no person has lived for say 10,000 years, except possibly in mythology. However, the function associated with each curve (that is, the graph of a continuous function from the reals to the reals), the area bounded by that curve, the x-axis, and the lines given by the equations $x = 0$ and $x = 1$ is an onto function. A function from the set S to the set T is said to be *one-to-one* if (s, t) and (u, t) being in the function implies that $s = u$. In other words, two distinct elements of S do not map to the same element of T.

For example, the function $(n, 2n)$, where n is any integer, is a one-to-one function, since $2n = 2m$ implies $n = m$, but the function is not onto, since there is no integer n with $2n = 1$, for example. The function

$$\begin{pmatrix} 1 & 2 & 3 & 4 & 5 & 6 \\ T & F & F & T & T & F \end{pmatrix}$$

is a function from $\{1, 2, 3, 4, 5, 6\}$ to $\{T, F\}$ and is onto. It is, however, not one-to-one.

Let g be a function from S to T and f be a function from T to U. The *composition* of f and g is defined to be the function $f \circ g$, where (s, u) is in $f \circ g$ if there is a t in T with (s, t) in g and (t, u) in f. In other words, $t = g(s)$ and $u = f(t) = f(g(s))$. Thus $(f \circ g)(s) = f(g(s))$. The next fact is repeatedly used, so we display it as a proposition.

Proposition 1.1 Let h, g, and f be functions from S to T, T to U, and U to V, respectively. Then $(f \circ g) \circ h = f \circ (g \circ h)$.

Proof We have

$$((f \circ g) \circ h)(s) = (f \circ g)(h(s)) = f(g(h(s))) = f((g \circ h)(s)) = (f \circ (g \circ h))(s).$$

Thus (s, v) is in $(f \circ g) \circ h$ if and only if (s, v) is in $f \circ (g \circ h)$, making the functions equal.

Although general functions are extremely important, we are concerned a great deal with a special class of functions called binary operations. A *binary operation* is a function from the set $S \times S$ into S. Multiplication of two real numbers, addition of two real numbers, subtraction of one real number from another real number, and division of one nonzero real number by another nonzero real number are examples of binary operations. The adjective "binary" refers to the fact that two values of the set S are used to determine a third. This notion can be generalized to an *n*-ary operation which is simply a function from $S \times S \times \cdots \times S$ (where S is taken n times) into S. Thus a unary operation is simply a function from S into S.

Since a function is a relation, a binary operation is also a relation. In fact, a binary operation on S is a special type of subset of $(S \times S) \times S$ and, if we forget the parentheses, $(S \times S) \times S$ becomes $S \times S \times S$, so that a binary operation is a special type of ternary relation on S. An *n*-ary operation on S is a special type of $(n + 1)$-ary relation on S.

If ρ is a binary operation on S, then it is often convenient to denote $\rho((s, t))$ by $s \cdot t$, if no confusion with composition of functions is possible. Binary operations with additional properties are especially important, and we define them now. A binary operation on S is said to be *associative* if $(s \cdot t) \cdot u = s \cdot (t \cdot u)$ for all s, t, and u in S. Thus Proposition 1.1 states that, if $\mathscr{F}$ is the set of functions from S to S, composition of functions is an associative binary operation on $\mathscr{F}$. A binary operation is *commutative* if $s \cdot t = t \cdot s$ for all s and t in S. Composition of functions in $\mathscr{F}$ is not in general commutative. Finally, a binary operation on S has an *identity* (or we say S has an identity) if there is an element e in S such that $e \cdot s = s$ and $s \cdot e = s$ for all s in S. The function $e_X(x) = x$ acts as an identity for the set of all functions from X to X under the binary operation of composition, since $(f \circ e_X)(x) = f(e_X(x)) = f(x)$ and $(e_X \circ f)(x) = e_X(f(x)) = f(x)$, so that $f \circ e_X = f$ and $e_X \circ f = f$.

Exercises

1-21 Show that the composition of functions is a function.

1-22 If f is a one-to-one function from S to T and g is a one-to-one function from T to U, prove that $f \circ g$ is one-to-one.

1-23 If f is an onto function from S to T and g is an onto function from T to U, prove that $f \circ g$ is onto.

1-24 Let f and g be functions from the real numbers to the real numbers. Give an example to show that $f \circ g$ is not in general equal to $g \circ f$. Give an example in which this is the case.

1-25 A function f from S to T is said to have an inverse if there exists a function g from T to S such that $f \circ g = e_T$ and $g \circ f = e_S$. Prove that f has an inverse if and only if f is one-to-one and onto.

1-26 Show that the operation of subtraction on the integers is neither associative nor commutative.

1-27 Let $S = \{x, y\}$ and let $* = \{((x, x), y), ((x, y), x), ((y, x), x), ((y, y), x)\}$, that is, $x * x = y, x * y = x, y * x = x$, and $y * y = x$. Show that $*$ is commutative but not associative.

1-28 Let S be a finite nonempty set containing n elements. Determine the number of distinct binary operations on S. Determine the number of commutative binary operations on S. Determine the number of binary operations on S that have an identity.

1.6 INDUCTION

Mathematical induction is an important tool in mathematics, and we use it often in the proofs that follow. It is also an algorithmic device in the sense that often it gives us a precise method for proving a particular statement. To be more precise, the integers form a totally ordered set under the natural ordering $\cdots < -2 < -1 < 0 < 1 < 2 \cdots$. The positive integers have the property that, if S is any set of positive integers, such that 1 is in S and, whenever an integer k is in S, $k + 1$ is also in S, then S is the set of all positive integers. This claim is called the *principle of mathematical induction* and is made not because we can prove it but because it seems reasonable, and in fact this property is one of the axioms in the construction of the integers from set theory.

The principle of mathematical induction seems reasonable in the following sense. Suppose S is a set of positive integers such that $1 \in S$ and, whenever k is in S, then $k + 1$ is in S. For a particular positive integer n, we can check to see that n is in S, since the following process does exactly that.

1 Set k as 1, and thus $k \in S$.

2 If $k = n$, then $n \in S$; otherwise set k equal to $k + 1$, which by induction is in S, and continue step (2).

Of course we cannot physically check this for the infinite set of all positive integers, so we rely on the principle of mathematical induction.

Another property of the positive integers is the *well-ordering principle*, which states that any nonempty set S of positive integers contains a smallest element. Again this is not an unreasonable assumption since, if we pick an element k of S, there is only a finite number of integers less than k which we must check for membership in S.

The following example illustrates the type of argument that uses induction and also the type of argument that uses well ordering. Note that $1 + 3 = 2^2$, $1 + 3 + 5 = 3^2$, and $1 + 3 + 5 + 7 = 4^2$. This leads to the conjecture that $1 + 3 + 5 + \cdots + (2n - 1) = n^2$ for any positive integer n. Let S be the set of positive integers for which the claim holds true. As we have shown, $1 \in S$. Moreover, if $k \in S$, then $1 + 3 + 5 + \cdots + (2k - 1) = k^2$. But then

$$1 + 3 + 5 + \cdots + (2k - 1) + [2(k + 1) - 1] = k^2 + [2(k + 1) - 1]$$
$$= k^2 + 2k + 1 = (k + 1)^2.$$

Hence $k + 1 \in S$ and, by the principle of mathematical induction, S is the set of all positive integers, proving the conjecture. We can also prove the claim by using well ordering. Let $\bar{S}$ be the set of positive integers such that the claim does not hold. If $\bar{S}$ is not empty, by the well-ordering principle, $\bar{S}$ contains a smallest element, say $k + 1$. Since $2 \cdot 1 - 1 = 1^2$, $k + 1 > k \geq 1$, so that k is a positive integer not in $\bar{S}$. Thus $1 + 3 + 5 + \cdots + (2k - 1) = k^2$ and, as before, we have $1 + 3 + 5 + \cdots + (2k - 1) + [2(k + 1) - 1] = (k + 1)^2$. This contradicts the fact that $k + 1 \in \bar{S}$, which implies that $\bar{S}$ is empty. Hence all integers satisfy the claim.

The above proofs are closely related to one another. In fact, for the positive integers, the well-ordering principle implies the principle of mathematical induction, and vice versa. Thus the two statements are called equivalent. We in fact show that they are equivalent, in Theorem 1.2.

The above proof, by mathematical induction, can be restated in a more familiar form in terms of statements. Namely, let $P(k)$ be a set of statements, one for each positive integer k, which are either true or false. If $P(1)$ is true and, whenever $P(k)$ is true, $P(k + 1)$ is true, then $P(n)$ is true for all positive integers n. In the example given, the statement $P(k)$ could be $1 + 3 + 5 + \cdots + (2k - 1) = k^2$. This principle involving statements $P(k)$ is a seemingly stronger principle than mathematical induction, but it is left to the exercises to show that the two principles are equivalent.

We now show that induction is equivalent to well ordering.

Theorem 1.2 For the set of positive integers, the principle of mathematical induction is equivalent to the well-ordering principle.

Proof Assume induction holds. Let $P(k)$ be the statement that any set of positive integers containing a positive integer $\leq k$ has a smallest element. The statement $P(1)$ is true, since any set of positive integers containing 1 has 1 as its least element. Suppose now that $P(k)$ is true. Since we wish to show that $P(k + 1)$ is true, let S be any set of positive integers that contains an integer $\leq k + 1$. If S does not contain an integer $\leq k$, then $k + 1$ is indeed the smallest element of S, and $P(k + 1)$ is true for the set S. If S does contain an integer $\leq k$, then S is a set in the class described by $P(k)$, so that S indeed has a smallest element. In both cases $P(k + 1)$ is true. Thus $P(n)$ is true for all positive integers n. Now let T be any nonempty set of positive integers. Since T is nonempty, there is some integer m in T. However, we have shown that $P(m)$ is true, so that T contains a smallest element, and the well-ordering principle has been proven using the principle of mathematical induction.

Assume now that the well-ordering principle holds for the positive integers. Suppose that S is a set of positive integers with $1 \in S$ and, whenever k is in S, $k + 1$ is also in S. If $\bar{S}$, the set of positive integers not in S, is nonempty, then it contains a smallest element, say n, by the well-ordering principle. The integer n is not 1, hence $n - 1$ is still a positive integer and $n - 1 < n$. Thus $n - 1 \in S$, which by hypothesis implies that $(n - 1) + 1 = n$ is in S. This is a contradiction, since $S \cap \bar{S} = \varnothing$, so that $\bar{S}$ is indeed empty. Thus S is the set of all positive integers.

Theorem 1.2 shows that induction and well ordering are equivalent for the set of positive integers. The well-ordering principle is easily extended to describe many other totally ordered sets. A totally ordered set is said to be *well ordered* if any nonempty subset contains a smallest element. In the exercises, there are well-ordered sets that do not look like the integers.

The ordering of the integers satisfies for integers a, b, c, and d, with $d > 0$:

i $a > b$ implies $a + c > b + c$.

ii $a > b$ implies $ad > bd$.

These two properties, plus the well ordering for the positive integers, yields the division algorithm for the integers.

Theorem 1.3 (Division Algorithm for the Integers) If a and b are integers, with $b > 0$, then there exist unique integers q and r such that $a = bq + r$, where $0 \leq r < b$.

It is easy to see geometrically why this theorem is true. Simply examine a number line with origin 0 and points nb, where n runs through the set of integers. If a is any particular integer, then a will lie in exactly one interval of

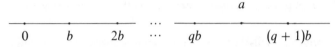

Figure 1.5

the form $qb \leq a < (q + 1)b$ (Figure 1.5). Thus $a = qb + (a - qb)$, where $0 \leq a - qb < b$, and the division algorithm is shown. However, we present a proof that uses the properties of the integers just given.

Proof of Theorem 1.3 Let S be the set of positive integers of the form $a - bx$, where x is any integer. The set S contains $a - b(-a) = a(1 + b)$ if a is positive, $a - ba = a(1 - b)$ if a is negative and $b \neq 1$, or $a - 1(a - 1) = 1$ if $b = 1$, so that S is not empty. By the well ordering of the positive integers, S has a smallest element $r' = a - bq'$. If $r' > b$, then $r' > r' - b = a - b(q' + 1) > 0$, which contradicts the minimality of r'. Hence $0 < r' \leq b$. If $r' < b$, put $r = r'$ and $q = q'$ to obtain the theorem. If $r' = b$, put $r = 0$ and $q = q' + 1$ to obtain the theorem. To show uniqueness, suppose $a = bq + r = bq_1 + r_1$. Thus $b(q - q_1) = r_1 - r$, where we may assume $q - q_1 \geq 0$. If $q - q_1 > 0$, then $b(q - q_1) \geq b > r_1 \geq r_1 - r$, which is impossible. Hence $q = q_1$ and $r = r_1$.

For integers a and b, we say b *divides* a if there exists an integer c such that $a = bc$. If b divides a, then b is called a *divisor* of a. In the division algorithm, b divides a when the remainder r in the expression $a = bq + r$ is zero. An integer p, $p > 1$, is *prime* when any positive divisor of p must be either p or 1. If $a_1, a_2, \ldots, a_n$ are nonzero integers, a positive integer x is a *common multiple* of $a_1, a_2, \ldots, a_n$ if a_i divides x for $i = 1, 2, \ldots, n$. Since a_i divides $a_1 a_2 \cdots a_n$ for $i = 1, \ldots, n$, common multiples exist. Further, since the set of positive integers is well ordered, a least common multiple exists for any finite nonempty set of nonzero integers.

Exercises

1-29 Prove by induction that, for any positive integer n,
  a $1 + 2 + 3 + \cdots + n = n(n + 1)/2$
  b $1 + 4 + 9 + \cdots + n^2 = n(n + 1)(2n + 1)/6$
  c $1 + 8 + 27 + \cdots + n^3 = n^2(n + 1)^2/4$.

1-30 Prove that the set

$$S = \left\{ \frac{2^n - 1}{2^n}, 1 + \frac{2^n - 1}{2^n} : n \text{ is a non-negative integer} \right\}$$

is well ordered under the usual ordering of the rationals but does not in general have a finite number of element $x \in S$ satisfying $0 \leq x \leq c$ for c in S.

1-31   Prove that the set of positive rational numbers under the usual ordering is not well ordered.

1-32   Show that the principle of mathematical induction is equivalent to the following. Let $P(k)$ be a statement for each positive integer k such that $P(k)$ is either true or false. If $P(1)$ is true and, whenever $P(k)$ is true, $P(k + 1)$ is true, then $P(n)$ is true for all positive integers n.

1-33   Show that the principle of mathematical induction is equivalent to the following. Let $P(k)$ be a statement for each positive integer k such that $P(k)$ is either true or false. If $P(1)$ is true and, whenever $P(i)$ is true for all positive integers $i \leq k$, $P(i)$ is true for all positive integers $i \leq k + 1$, then $P(n)$ is true for all positive integers n.

1-34   Let T be the set of all integers $\geq m$, where m is a fixed integer. Let S be a nonempty subset of T such that $m \in S$ and, whenever $k \in S$, $k + 1 \in S$. Use induction or equivalent to prove that $S = T$. In particular, note that this says that induction works for the set of non-negative integers.

1-35   Let T be any totally ordered set. Give a definition for an inductive set, which extends the idea of the principle of mathematical induction for the positive integers. Is the set of non-negative rationals one of the inductive sets? Is the set S in Exercise 1-30 one of the inductive sets?

1-36   Use induction to prove the binomial theorem for positive integers n, namely,

$$(a + b)^n = \sum_{i=0}^{n} \binom{n}{i} a^i b^{n-i},$$

for all real numbers a and b, where

$$\binom{n}{i} = \frac{n(n-1) \cdots (n-i+1)}{1 \cdot 2 \cdots \cdot i} \quad \text{and} \quad \binom{n}{0} = 1.$$

1.7   ALGORITHMS

A function from S to T associates with each element of S an element of T. In many cases, the function f is explicit in the sense that the value $f(s)$ may be theoretically computed for any s in S. For example, multiplication of integers is a function from $Z \times Z$ to Z, where Z is the set of integers and, although we assume for simplicity that $m \times n$ is at our disposal for all integers m and n, in reality the value is known only after going through a long computation. If the integers are expressed in decimal notation, then the product can be found by a finite procedure, familiar to all. Such a procedure is an example of an algorithm, and those functions whose values can be determined by an algorithm form an important special class.

Step	Instruction	i	x	d_i	c	d_3	d_2	d_1
1	1	1			0			
2	2		1	3				
3	3				1			3
4	4 $(1 \neq 3)$	2						
5	2		0	5				
6	3				0		5	3
7	4 $(2 \neq 3)$	3						
8	2		1	0				
9	3				1	0	5	3
10	4 $(3 = 3)$							

Figure 1.6

This section explores the concept of algorithm. Intuitively, an algorithm is any well-defined, finite procedure for obtaining the desired result. The recipes in a well-written cookbook are examples of algorithms. If the recipes are followed to the letter, then the desired result will be obtained. Multiplication of integers represented in decimal form is another example of an algorithm. A properly written program for a computer constitutes an algorithm and is of fundamental importance in computing. In these examples, there is a sequence of instructions, each of which specifies an elementary task. In the cookbook recipe, an elementary task may involve a measurement of material, a combination of materials, a temperature setting, and the like. In a multiplication algorithm, the elementary tasks may be multiplying two single-digit integers, writing down an integer, carrying an integer, and adding a column of integers. The last task is not really elementary and can itself be described by elementary tasks consisting of adding two single-digit integers, carrying an integer, and writing down (or otherwise remembering) an integer. A computer program can likewise be broken down into a sequence of elementary tasks.

Addition of two n-digit decimal integers can be accomplished by the following algorithm. Let the integers be $a_n a_{n-1} \cdots a_1$ and $b_n b_{n-1} \cdots b_1$.

Instruction 1: Set $i = 1$ and $c = 0$.

Instruction 2: Add a_i, b_i, and c to obtain $x d_i$.

Instruction 3: Store d_i and replace c by x.

Instruction 4: If $i = n$, then $c d_n d_{n-1} \cdots d_1$ is the required sum, so halt. If $i \neq n$, then replace i by $i + 1$ and return to instruction (2).

For example, addition of 329 and 724 according to the above algorithm gives the sequence of steps in Figure 1.6.

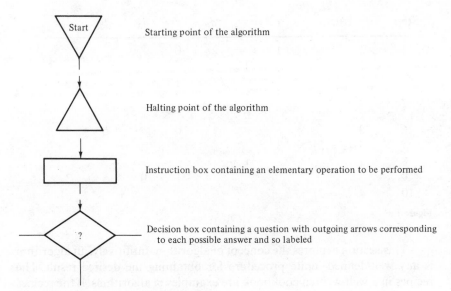

Starting point of the algorithm

Halting point of the algorithm

Instruction box containing an elementary operation to be performed

Decision box containing a question with outgoing arrows corresponding to each possible answer and so labeled

Figure 1.7 Symbols used in flowcharts.

The list of instructions that constitutes an algorithm can be conveniently represented by a flowchart. A flowchart is a diagram consisting of the symbols in Figure 1.7 interconnected by arrows. The arrows joining the symbols give the sequence of the operations.

The addition algorithm described previously has the flowchart in Figure 1.8. The notation $a \leftarrow b$ means a is replaced by b.

A rigorous treatment of algorithm is beyond the scope of this book. However, we can be somewhat more precise. An algorithm begins with a finite set of quantities, usually taken from an infinite set. At successive discrete intervals of time, new finite sets of quantities are obtained by means of a definite program which relies only on the set of quantities available at the preceding instant in time. The algorithm must end in a finite number of steps. The last requirement is certainly desirable but has not been proscribed for our idea of algorithm as yet.

To be precise, let S be a set and let I (for possible inputs) and O (for possible outputs) be subsets of the set S. An algorithm f is a function from S into S, which leaves O fixed pointwise; that is, for x in O, $f(x) = x$, and for x in I, the sequence x_i, defined by $x_0 = x$, $x_1 = f(x_0)$, ..., $x_{k+1} = f(x_k)$, ..., must be in the set O eventually, that is, there exists an integer n depending on x such that $x_n \in O$. The set S represents the state of the computation, the set I represents the input or starting state of the computation, and the set O

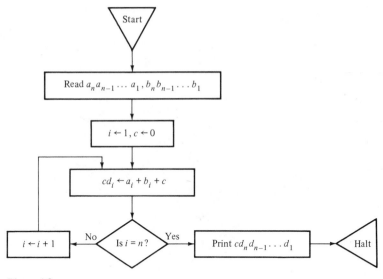

Figure 1.8

represents the output or finished state of the computation. Since $f(y) = y$ for each y in O, the sequence is stationary once it is inside the set O.

As an example suppose we wish to evaluate the polynomial $p(x) = 2x^2 + 3x + 5$, when x can be any real number. One way is by the expression $(2x + 3)x + 5$. In other words, multiply x by 2, then add 3, then multiply by x, and then add 5. There are four steps, so take S to be $\{(i, r, s): i \in \{0, 1, 2, 3, 4\}, r, s$ are real numbers$\}$. The number i refers to the step being executed; r refers to the input x, and s is the result so far obtained. Thus

$$f(0, r, s) = (1, r, 2 \cdot r)$$
$$f(1, r, s) = (2, r, s + 3)$$
$$f(2, r, s) = (3, r, s \cdot r)$$
$$f(3, r, s) = (4, r, s + 5)$$
$$f(4, r, s) = (4, r, s),$$

and it is clear that f is an algorithm as was formally defined. Furthermore, each sequence beginning with $(0, r, s)$ eventually reaches $[4, r, (2 \cdot r + 3) \cdot r + 5]$, at which point it becomes stationary. Thus $I = \{(0, r, s): r, s$ are real numbers$\}$ and $O = \{(4, r, s): r$ and s are real numbers$\}$.

The above algorithm is described by the flowchart in Figure 1.9.

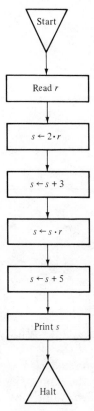

Figure 1.9

This last notion of algorithm guarantees termination but neglects the problem of determination of $f(x_k)$. We ignore this and simply assume that the determination is a consequence of some undefined elementary operation.

Chapter **2**

Partially Ordered Sets

2.1 INTRODUCTION

Partially ordered sets (posets) have a long history beginning with the first recognition of ordering in the integers. In the early nineteenth century, properties of the ordering of the subsets of a set were investigated by De Morgan, and in the late nineteenth century partial ordering by divisibility was investigated by Dedekind. It remained until the 1930s for the subject of lattice theory to blossom as an independent entity under Birkhoff, and it has only been in the last three decades that posets and their relationship to political science, economics, and sociology have been extensively investigated.

In Chapter 1, the concept of relation on a set is introduced, and this concept then specializes to three restricted types of relations, namely, partial orderings, equivalence relations, and functions. Each of these subclasses represents an important and naturally occurring subdivision of the concept of relation. This process of specialization is a common one in mathematics, and a large part of this chapter considers naturally occurring specialized types of posets.

An example of a specialized type of poset is a totally ordered set, that is, a partially ordered set with the additional property that either $a \geq b$ or $b \geq a$ for each a and b in the set. The set of integers under natural ordering is a totally ordered set, as is the set of rational numbers and the set of real numbers. In fact, any nonempty subset of the real numbers (and this includes the rationals and the integers as examples) forms a totally ordered set under the natural ordering. A tournament ranking (with ties being broken by points for and against, coin tossing, or some other method) forms a totally ordered set on the set of competitors.

　　Similar to a tournament ranking with no ties is a tournament ranking with ties allowed. If ties occur, the set is no longer totally ordered but nevertheless has some nice properties. For example, two players are either tied or else one is ranked higher than the other, and being tied is an equivalence relation. In the terminology of posets, a and b being tied means that $a \not> b$ and $b \not> a$. In this case a and b are said to be *indifferent*, and we write a I b. Thus a *weak order* is a partial order that has indifference as an equivalence relation. Besides tournament rankings, a preference relation by price only is a weak order. For example, a person may rank breakfast cereal by the price per gram, the cheapest being most preferred. If this is the only consideration, then breakfast cereals a and b having the same price will be tied, in other words a I b. Having the same price is an equivalence relation, hence we have a weak order. All totally ordered sets are examples of weakly ordered sets, since $a \neq b$ always implies that either $a > b$ or $b > a$. Thus a is indifferent only to itself, which is an equivalence relation. Section 2.4 investigates weak orders and characterizes them in several different ways.

　　The relation of indifference in a poset is always reflexive and symmetric. Indifference in a weak order is also transitive. In many posets, indifference is not transitive, but in some special situations the poset is still closely related to weak ordering and total ordering. The following classic example illustrates this. Suppose a person prefers coffee with two lumps of sugar to coffee with one lump and can tell the difference in taste between the two. We assume this taste preference is transitive, so that in general if coffee A is preferred to coffee B and coffee B to coffee C, then coffee A is preferred to coffee C. Thus for any set of cups of coffee an individual can form a partial ordering of the set. However, suppose we have 21 cups of coffee with cup i having $1 + (i - 1)/20$ cubes of sugar in it, $i = 1, 2, \ldots, 21$. An individual's taste buds are unlikely to discriminate between 1 cube and 1.05 cubes of sugar in the coffee. In this case, cup i is rated indifferent to cup $i + 1$ for $i = 1, \ldots, 20$. If indifference were transitive, cup 1 would be indifferent to cup 21, which is not the case. Thus even though the cups are in some sense totally ordered, indifference is not transitive. In fact, there may be some threshold amount of sugar such that a person can differentiate sweetness between cups of coffee differing by that amount of sugar, but is not able to differentiate sweetness between cups of coffee differing by some amount less than the threshold level. In such a model, indifference is not transitive but does satisfy the following. If $a > b$, b I c, but $c > d$, then $a > d$, since in the example, indifference implies a certain closeness of b and c. Also, if $a > b$, $b > c$, but b I d, then either $a > d$ or $d > c$. A poset that satisfies these two properties is called a *semiorder*. It is left to the exercises to show that a weak order (and thus a total order) is a semiorder. Section 2.5 discusses semiorders and their relationship to weak orders.

Another type of poset arises in the testing of components. For example, suppose a manufacturer produces electronic tubes and tests each one for voltage output. Because of imprecision in the testing equipment and the tube t, the output is known only to within some margin of error. Thus the output voltage is expressed as $v_t \pm \varepsilon_t$, which means that the output is some value in the interval $[v_t - \varepsilon_t, v_t + \varepsilon_t]$. The tubes can be partially ordered by output by saying $t_1 > t_2$ if each value in the output interval of t_1 is greater than each value in the output interval of t_2. The posets arising in this fashion again form a special class of posets which have the property that $a > b$, b I c, and $c > d$ implies $a > d$. If the interval x has a left end point $l(x)$ and a right end point $r(x)$, then $a > b$ means $r(b) < l(a)$, as real numbers. Likewise, $c > d$ means $r(d) < l(c)$. However, b I c implies that $l(c) \not> r(b)$. Thus $l(c) \leq r(b)$, and we have $r(d) < l(c) \leq r(b) < l(a)$, so that $a > d$. A poset such that $a > b$, b I c, and $c > d$ implies $a > d$ is called an *interval order*. Since a semiorder satisfies this condition, a semiorder is always an interval order. Section 2.5 characterizes interval orders and shows why the name is appropriate.

The final section of the chapter is concerned with the problem of finding a partial order compatible with a given set of partial orders. This problem lies at the foundation of democratic and economic choice procedures. In fact, what we discover is that, if we insist that the final result be a weak order, then the only possibilities are either a yes-no type of partial ordering or a dictatorship. This is Arrow's fundamental contribution to mathematical politics and leads to the result known as the voting paradox. If the final partial order is not restricted to being a weak order, there is a further possibility of partial order by consensus of a governing council.

Sections 2.2 and 2.3 develop the techniques needed in analyzing the types of partial orders introduced and in developing the results on social choice. In particular, Section 2.2 develops the techniques related to Hasse diagrams and gives an explicit algorithm for determining the Hasse diagram from the relation matrix.

The various special classes of posets introduced have been described in terms of the natural properties the class possesses. There may be in general many different types of descriptions—possibly in terms of properties, in terms of internal structure, or in terms of functions such as price function for weak orders or interval function for interval orders. Section 2.3 introduces the concepts of restriction, isomorphism, and homomorphism of posets, which form the key elements in later descriptions of the various types of posets. Furthermore, the section develops several tools for constructing new posets from old posets.

Exercises

2-1 Determine which of the following posets are total orders, weak orders, semiorders, or interval orders.

    a The set of integers with the partial order $n \geq m$ if $n^2 \geq m^2$ under the natural order.

    b The set of positive integers less than 100 with the partial order $n \geq m$ if m divides n.

    c The poset with diagram

    d The poset with diagram

    e The set $\{a, b, c, d\}$ with partial order $\{(a, a), (b, b), (c, c), (d, d), (a, b), (a, c), (b, c)\}$.

    f The partial order with relation matrix

$$\begin{bmatrix} 1 & 0 & 0 & 0 \\ 1 & 1 & 1 & 0 \\ 1 & 0 & 1 & 0 \\ 1 & 1 & 1 & 1 \end{bmatrix}.$$

    g The partial order with relation matrix

$$\begin{bmatrix} 1 & 1 & 1 & 1 & 1 & 1 \\ 0 & 1 & 0 & 1 & 0 & 1 \\ 0 & 0 & 1 & 1 & 1 & 1 \\ 0 & 0 & 0 & 1 & 0 & 1 \\ 0 & 0 & 0 & 0 & 1 & 1 \\ 0 & 0 & 0 & 0 & 0 & 1 \end{bmatrix}.$$

2-2 Prove that a weak order is always a semiorder.

2.2   HASSE DIAGRAMS

In Section 1.3, the diagram of a finite partially ordered set is described. This section investigates the matrix associated with a diagram (the covering matrix) and gives an algorithm to produce this matrix from the relation matrix of the poset.

Recall that an element a in a poset is said to cover an element b in the poset if $a > b$ and there is no element c with $a > c > b$.

Definition   The covering matrix of a finite poset $P = \{p_1, p_2, \ldots, p_n\}$ is the matrix (b_{ij}), $i = 1, 2, \ldots, n$, $j = 1, 2, \ldots, n$, where $b_{ij} = 1$ if p_i covers p_j or $i = j$, and $b_{ij} = 0$ otherwise.

The covering matrix (b_{ij}) of the poset $P = \{p_1, p_2, \ldots, p_n\}$ contains as much information as the relation matrix (a_{ij}), and vice versa. The covering matrix can be calculated from the relation matrix, since b_{ij} is 0 if either a_{ij} is 0 or there exists $k \neq i$, $k \neq j$ with $a_{ik} = 1$, $a_{kj} = 1$. Otherwise, b_{ij} is 1.

For example, if (a_{ij}) is

$$\begin{bmatrix} 1 & 1 & 1 & 1 & 1 \\ 0 & 1 & 1 & 1 & 1 \\ 0 & 0 & 1 & 1 & 0 \\ 0 & 0 & 0 & 1 & 0 \\ 0 & 0 & 0 & 1 & 1 \end{bmatrix},$$

then the covering matrix will be (b_{ij}) equal to

$$\begin{bmatrix} 1 & 1 & 0 & 0 & 0 \\ 0 & 1 & 1 & 0 & 1 \\ 0 & 0 & 1 & 1 & 0 \\ 0 & 0 & 0 & 1 & 0 \\ 0 & 0 & 0 & 1 & 1 \end{bmatrix}.$$

The matrix (a_{ij}) can be found from the $n \times n$ matrix $B = (b_{ij})$ by computing $B^{n-1} = (d_{ij}^{(n-1)})$ and putting $a_{ij} = 1$ if $d_{ij}^{(n-1)} > 0$, and otherwise $a_{ij} = 0$.

In the example,

$$B^2 = \begin{bmatrix} 1 & 2 & 1 & 0 & 1 \\ 0 & 1 & 2 & 2 & 2 \\ 0 & 0 & 1 & 2 & 0 \\ 0 & 0 & 0 & 1 & 0 \\ 0 & 0 & 0 & 2 & 1 \end{bmatrix}, \qquad B^3 = \begin{bmatrix} 1 & 3 & 3 & 2 & 3 \\ 0 & 1 & 3 & 6 & 3 \\ 0 & 0 & 1 & 3 & 0 \\ 0 & 0 & 0 & 1 & 0 \\ 0 & 0 & 0 & 3 & 1 \end{bmatrix},$$

$$B^4 = \begin{bmatrix} 1 & 4 & 6 & 8 & 6 \\ 0 & 1 & 4 & 12 & 4 \\ 0 & 0 & 1 & 4 & 0 \\ 0 & 0 & 0 & 1 & 0 \\ 0 & 0 & 0 & 4 & 1 \end{bmatrix}.$$

Thus (a_{ij}) is

$$\begin{bmatrix} 1 & 1 & 1 & 1 & 1 \\ 0 & 1 & 1 & 1 & 1 \\ 0 & 0 & 1 & 1 & 0 \\ 0 & 0 & 0 & 1 & 0 \\ 0 & 0 & 0 & 1 & 1 \end{bmatrix}.$$

To see that (a_{ij}) can indeed be obtained from B^{n-1}, we need the fact that, if $p_i > p_j$, then there is a sequence $p_i = p_{i_0} > p_{i_1} > \cdots > p_{i_k} = p_j$, where p_{i_t} covers $p_{i_{t+1}}$, $t = 0, \ldots, k-1$. This is similar to Exercise 1.14 and can be simply proven by induction. The powers of B characterize these sequences by the following theorem.

Theorem 2.1 Let $B = (b_{ij})$ be the $n \times n$ covering matrix of the poset $P = \{p_1, p_2, \ldots, p_n\}$. There is a sequence $p_i = p_{i_0} > p_{i_1} > \cdots > p_{i_k} = p_j$, where p_{i_t} covers $p_{i_{t+1}}$, $t = 0, \ldots, k-1$, for some integer k, $1 \le k \le m \le n-1$, if and only if $d_{ij}^{(m)} \neq 0$, where $B^m = (d_{ij}^{(m)})$, $i \neq j$, $1 \le m \le n-1$.

Proof The idea behind the proof of the theorem is that $B^m = (B^{m-1})B$. The matrix B^{m-1} corresponds to taking the first (at most) $m-1$ elements in the sequence, and multiplying by B just attaches one more covering to the end of the sequence.

Formally, the proof is by induction on m. If $m = 1$, then by definition of $B = B^1$, $p_i = p_{i_0}$ covers $p_{i_1} = p_j$ if and only if $b_{ij} = 1 = d_{ij}^{(1)}$, $i \neq j$. Assume that the theorem holds for m. If $p_i = p_{i_0} > p_{i_1} > \cdots > p_{i_{k-1}} > p_{i_k} = p_j$, where p_{i_t} covers $p_{i_{t+1}}$, $t = 0, \ldots, k-1$, $k \le m+1$, then $p_i = p_{i_0} > \cdots > p_{i_{k-1}}$, with p_{i_t} covering $p_{i_{t+1}}$, $t = 0, \ldots, k-2$, shows that $d_{i i_{k-1}}^{(m)} \neq 0$. Since $b_{i_{k-1} i_k} \neq 0$, $d_{il}^{(m)} \ge 0$ for all i, and the sum $\sum_{l=1}^{n} d_{il}^{(m)} b_{l i_k} = d_{i i_k}^{(m+1)}$ includes the term $d_{i i_{k-1}}^{(m)} b_{i_{k-1} i_k} > 0$, we have $d_{i i_k}^{(m+1)} > 0$. It remains only to prove that, if $d_{ij}^{(m+1)} \neq 0$, $i \neq j$, then there is some sequence $p_i = p_{i_0} > \cdots > p_{i_k} = p_j$ with $k \le m+1$. If $d_{ij}^{(m)} \neq 0$, then by induction the result holds. If $d_{ij}^{(m)} = 0$, since $d_{ij}^{(m+1)} > 0$ and $d_{ij}^{(m+1)} = \sum_{l=1}^{n} d_{il}^{(m)} b_{lj}$, we have, for some $r \neq j$, $d_{ir}^{(m)} b_{rj} > 0$. Thus $d_{ir}^{(m)} \neq 0$ and $b_{rj} \neq 0$. Since $r \neq j$, p_r covers p_j. Since $d_{ir}^{(m)} \neq 0$, by induction either $i = r$, in which case p_i covers p_j and we are finished, or there exists a sequence $p_i = p_{i_0} > p_{i_1} > \cdots > p_{i_k} = p_r$ with p_{i_t} covering $p_{i_{t+1}}$ for $t = 0, \ldots, k-1$, $k \le m$. Thus $p_i = p_{i_0} > p_{i_1} > \cdots > p_{i_k} > p_{i_{k+1}} = p_j$, with p_{i_t} covering $p_{i_{t+1}}$, $t = 0, 1, \ldots, k$, with $k+1 \le m+1$. Thus the theorem is proven.

The calculation of the relation matrix of a poset from the covering matrix now follows from Theorem 2.1. Namely, $p_i > p_j$ if and only if there is a sequence $p_i = p_{i_0} > \cdots > p_{i_k} = p_j$, with p_{i_t} covering $p_{i_{t+1}}$, $t = 0, \ldots, k-1$, $k \leq n-1$, where n is the number of elements in the poset. This sequence exists by Theorem 2.1 if and only if the i, j component of B^{n-1} is nonzero.

A Hasse diagram can be drawn using the covering matrix. We first determine the level of an element of the poset. The sequence $p_0 > p_1 > p_2 > \cdots > p_k$ is said to have *length* k. An element p of a finite poset is on *level* k if there exists a sequence $p_0 > p_1 > \cdots > p_k = p$ and any other sequence has a length less than or equal to k. It is apparent that, if p is on level k and $p_0 > p_1 > \cdots > p_k$, then p_0 is a maximal element of the poset (otherwise a longer sequence would result) and p_i covers p_{i+1} for $i = 0, 1, \ldots, k-1$ (otherwise a longer sequence could again be obtained). Once the level of each element is determined with, say, n_i points, $n_i > 0$, on level i with $i = 0, 1, \ldots, m$, then arrange the n_0 points for elements of level 0 horizontally, arrange the n_1 points for elements of level 1 horizontally but below those of level 0, and for the ith step arrange the n_i points for elements of level i horizontally but below those of level $i-1$. Finally, join elements s and t by a line segment if s covers t. This information can be read from the covering matrix.

A relatively simple way to determine the levels of the elements of a poset is by the following procedure. First determine the maximal elements (level 0). In other words, determine the elements that have no cover. The element p_j will have no cover if and only if $b_{ij} = 0$ for all $i \neq j$. Thus, if the jth column contains 1 in the jth row and 0 in all other rows, then p_j is a maximal element. Alternatively, if the rows of the matrix are summed, the maximal elements will correspond exactly to those components that contain a 1.

In the poset with covering matrix

$$M = \begin{bmatrix} 1 & 1 & 0 & 0 & 0 & 0 \\ 0 & 1 & 1 & 0 & 0 & 0 \\ 0 & 0 & 1 & 1 & 0 & 0 \\ 0 & 0 & 0 & 1 & 0 & 0 \\ 0 & 0 & 1 & 0 & 1 & 0 \\ 0 & 0 & 0 & 1 & 0 & 1 \end{bmatrix}$$

the sum of the rows is $(1 \quad 2 \quad 3 \quad 3 \quad 1 \quad 1)$ which indicates that the first, fifth, and sixth elements are the maximal elements. To find the elements of level 1, subtract rows 1, 5, and 6 from the row sum to obtain

$$(1 \quad 2 \quad 3 \quad 3 \quad 1 \quad 1) - (1 \quad 1 \quad 0 \quad 0 \quad 0 \quad 0) - (0 \quad 0 \quad 1 \quad 0 \quad 1 \quad 0)$$
$$- (0 \quad 0 \quad 0 \quad 1 \quad 0 \quad 1) = (0 \quad 1 \quad 2 \quad 2 \quad 0 \quad 0)$$

which indicates that the maximal element in the restriction to $\{p_2, p_3, p_4\}$ is p_2, the sole element in level 1. For level 2, subtract row 2 from

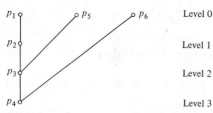

Figure 2.1

$(0 \quad 1 \quad 2 \quad 2 \quad 0 \quad 0)$ to obtain $(0 \quad 0 \quad 1 \quad 2 \quad 0 \quad 0)$ and level $2 = \{p_3\}$. Level 3 is determined from $(0 \quad 0 \quad 1 \quad 2 \quad 0 \quad 0) - (0 \quad 0 \quad 1 \quad 1 \quad 0 \quad 0) = (0 \quad 0 \quad 0 \quad 1 \quad 0 \quad 0)$ so that level $3 = \{p_4\}$. Thus the diagram is constructed in Figure 2.1.

In general, let R_0 be the row sum of the covering matrix. Level 0 equals the set of elements with a 1 in the corresponding component of R_0. If R_i has been computed, then R_{i+1} is R_i minus the rows of the covering matrix corresponding to elements in level i. Level $i + 1$ is now the set of elements corresponding to components in R_{i+1} which are 1.

Exercises

2-3   Draw the Hasse diagram of the posets given by the following covering matrices:

a
$$\begin{bmatrix} 1 & 0 & 1 & 1 & 0 & 0 \\ 0 & 1 & 1 & 1 & 0 & 0 \\ 0 & 0 & 1 & 0 & 0 & 1 \\ 0 & 0 & 0 & 1 & 0 & 1 \\ 1 & 1 & 0 & 0 & 1 & 0 \\ 0 & 0 & 0 & 0 & 0 & 1 \end{bmatrix}$$

b
$$\begin{bmatrix} 1 & 0 & 0 & 0 & 0 & 0 \\ 0 & 1 & 1 & 0 & 0 & 0 \\ 0 & 0 & 1 & 0 & 1 & 0 \\ 1 & 0 & 0 & 1 & 0 & 0 \\ 0 & 0 & 0 & 0 & 1 & 0 \\ 0 & 0 & 1 & 0 & 0 & 1 \end{bmatrix}.$$

2-4   Draw the Hasse diagram of the poset given by the following relation matrix:

$$\begin{bmatrix} 1 & 1 & 1 & 0 & 1 & 1 \\ 0 & 1 & 0 & 0 & 1 & 1 \\ 0 & 0 & 1 & 0 & 1 & 1 \\ 0 & 1 & 1 & 1 & 1 & 1 \\ 0 & 0 & 0 & 0 & 1 & 0 \\ 0 & 0 & 0 & 0 & 0 & 1 \end{bmatrix}.$$

2-5 Give the flowchart of an algorithm that determines the covering matrix from the relation matrix of a poset.

2-6 Give the flowchart of an algorithm that determines the levels from the relation matrix of a poset.

2-7 Give the flowchart of an algorithm that determines the relation matrix of a poset from the covering matrix.

2.3 SUBPOSETS, ISOMORPHISMS, AND ORDER-PRESERVING MAPS

The set of real numbers under the natural ordering is a totally ordered set. Any subset of the reals under this ordering is again a totally ordered set. This is the restriction of the ordering to the subset. We give the following formal definition of restriction.

Definition Let S be a nonempty set with partial order R and let T be a nonempty subset of S. The restriction of R to T is the set T with relation $R_T = R \cap (T \times T)$.

In other words, the restriction of the poset S to T is just the set T, with $(t_1, t_2) \in R_T$, if and only if $t_1 \in T$, $t_2 \in T$, and $(t_1, t_2) \in R$. It is not difficult to see that R_T is reflexive, antisymmetric, and transitive, so that T, with R_T, is again a poset. The set T with the restriction R_T is called a *subposet* of S. A totally ordered set can now be described as any poset that does not have a subposet of the form $s \;_{\circ} t$, that is, no pair s and t with $s \not\geq t$ and $t \not\geq s$. This is an example of a forbidden subposet, and we characterize the types of posets introduced and various types of lattices in terms of forbidden subposets.

In addition to using forbidden restrictions to characterize types of posets, various mappings from the poset to the real numbers can be used to characterize the poset. For example, a totally ordered set S containing n elements is essentially the same as $T_n = \{1, 2, 3, \ldots, n\}$ with the natural ordering of the integers. This is easily seen, since Exercise 1.14 shows that a maximal chain $s_n > s_{n-1} > \cdots > s_1$ exists and, since s is totally ordered, every element of s is in this maximal chain. If we relabel s_i as i, then we have $s_i \geq s_j$ if and only if $i \geq j$. Thus, as far as order is concerned, the two posets are the same. This idea is formalized in the concept of isomorphism of posets.

Definition A partially ordered set S is isomorphic to a partially ordered set T if there exists a one-to-one and onto function ϕ from S to T such that $s \leq u$ if and only if $\phi(s) \leq \phi(u)$ for any s and u in S.

The notion of isomorphism allows us to identify any finite totally ordered set S with the poset T_n, where n is the number of elements in S. However, this is still too restrictive. As an example, suppose the finals in the Olympic 400-meter dash has competitors, and suppose the race is run and the contestants totally ordered as to their finishing times (no ties allowed). The final awards in the race also form a totally ordered set, namely, gold medal > silver medal > bronze medal > no medal. Each person in the race is awarded one of the four alternatives and, if person A $\geq$ person B in terms of finishing times, then medal for person A $\geq$ medal for person B. Thus we have a mapping from the totally ordered set of b competitors to the totally ordered set of four medal awards. Such a mapping that preserves $\geq$ is called an order-preserving map.

Definition   A function f from the poset S to the poset T is called an *order-preserving map* from S to T if $x \geq y$ implies $f(x) \geq f(y)$ for all x, $y \in S$.

Theorem 2.2   Let S be a poset containing n elements. Then there is an order-preserving map f from S onto T_n.

Since S and T_n both contain n elements, if a function f from S to T_n is onto, f must be one-to-one. However, this shows that many order-preserving maps that are one-to-one and onto are not isomorphisms. In fact, we see in the exercises that an order-preserving map is an isomorphism if and only if an inverse order-preserving map exists.

Proof of Theorem 2.2   The proof proceeds by induction and in essence gives an algorithm which produces the function. Let $S = \{s_1, s_2, \ldots, s_n\}$. Define $f_1(s_1) = 1$. If f_i maps $S_i = \{s_1, s_2, \ldots, s_i\}$ onto T_i such that $s_j < s_l$ implies $f_i(s_j) < f_i(s_l)$, with s_j, $s_l \in S_i$, then f_{i+1} is constructed as follows. Let $B_i = \{s_j : s_j \in S_i \text{ and } s_j > s_{i+1}\}$. For all elements s in S_i not in B_i, we have either $s_{i+1} > s$ or s_{i+1} I s. Define $f_{i+1}(s) = f_i(s)$ for $s \in S_i \backslash B_i$, $f_{i+1}(s_{i+1}) =$ smallest integer in $\{f_i(b) : b \in B_i\}$ or $i + 1$ if this set is empty, and $f_{i+1}(b) = f_i(b) + 1$ for all b in B_i. The map f_{i+1} is a function from S_{i+1} onto T_{i+1} and, if $s_j < s_k$, with s_j, $s_k \in S_{i+1}$, and neither are equal to s_{i+1}, we have $f_i(s_j) < f_i(s_k)$, so that $f_{i+1}(s_j) < f_{i+1}(s_k)$. If s_j or s_k equals s_{i+1}, then by our construction we still have $f_{i+1}(s_j) < f_{i+1}(s_k)$. The function f_n is the desired map f from S onto T_n.

The function f in Theorem 2.2 is often called a consistent enumeration, because the map f labels the element s of S with the integer $f(s)$, where $s < t$ implies $f(s) < f(t)$, s and t in S.

As an example, suppose we have the poset in Figure 2.2. Following the procedure in the proof of Theorem 2.2, we obtain the functions f_i and the orderings of S_i induced by f_i as in Figure 2.3.

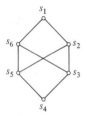

Figure 2.2

Function \ Image	1	2	3	4	5	6	
f_1	s_1						$B_1 = \{s_1\}$
f_2	s_2	s_1					$B_2 = \{s_1, s_2\}$
f_3	s_3	s_2	s_1				$B_3 = \{s_1, s_2, s_3\}$
f_4	s_4	s_3	s_2	s_1			$B_4 = \{s_1, s_2\}$
f_5	s_4	s_3	s_5	s_2	s_1		$B_5 = \{s_1\}$
f_6	s_4	s_3	s_5	s_2	s_6	s_1	

Figure 2.3

   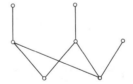

Figure 2.4   Poset P.   **Figure 2.5**   Transpose of P.

Two further important constructions in the theory of posets create new posets from old ones. The first construction is very simple and consists of turning the poset upside down. In other words, if P is a poset with relation R, then define R' (the *transpose* of R), to be $\{(y, x) : (x, y) \in R\}$. The relation R' is reflexive, antisymmetric, and transitive. The last property follows, since (a, b) and (b, c) in R' implies (b, a) and (c, b) in R, but R being transitive implies $(c, a) \in R$, so that $(a, c) \in R'$. The poset diagramed in Figure 2.4 has the transpose in Figure 2.5.

The term "transpose" comes from the fact that the relation matrix of the transpose of P is just the transpose of the relation matrix of P.

The second construction glues posets together to form new posets. The idea behind this is the total ordering of words in a dictionary. The English alphabet with blank as an additional letter is ordered: blank $<$ A $<$ B $<$ C $< \cdots <$ Z. A word is a string of the form $l_1 l_2 \cdots l_k$ with $l_1, l_2, \ldots, l_k$ in the alphabet. A word $l_1 l_2 \cdots l_k$ precedes $l'_1 l'_2 \cdots l'_k$ if either $l_1 < l'_1$ or $l_1 = l'_1$,

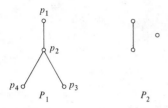

P_1 P_2

Figure 2.6

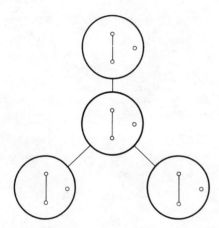

Figure 2.7

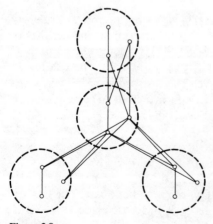

Figure 2.8

$l_2 = l'_2, \ldots, l_j = l'_j$ and $l_{j+1} < l'_{j+1}$ for some integer j, $2 \leq j < k$. Thus the word "homogeneous" comes before the word "homomorphism," since the first four letters are identical but the fifth letter, "g," of homogeneous comes before the fifth letter, "m," of homomorphism. Such an ordering is an example of a lexicographic ordering, which is defined as follows. Let $P_1, P_2, \ldots, P_k$ be posets. The *lexicographic product of* $P_1, P_2, \ldots, P_k$ is defined to be the set $P_1 \times P_2 \times \cdots \times P_k$, with $(a_1, a_2, \ldots, a_k) < (b_1, b_2, \ldots, b_k)$ if $a_1 < b_1$ or, if $a_i = b_i$, for $i = 1, \ldots, j$, but $a_{j+1} < b_{j+1}$, $j < k$. It is not difficult to see (and it is shown in the exercises) that the lexicographic product is indeed a poset.

As an example, suppose P_1 and P_2 are the posets diagramed in Figure 2.6. Since p_1 is the only maximal element in P_1, (p_1, x) is larger than (p_i, y) for all $i \neq 1$, $x, y \in P_2$. For $(p_1, y), (p_1, x) > (p_1, y)$ if and only if $x > y$, so that in the diagram for the lexicographic order of P_1 and P_2 the element p_1 is replaced by the poset P_2. Similarly, p_i in P_1 is replaced by the poset P_2. This yields Figure 2.7 which in turn gives rise to Figure 2.8.

As in the case in which the total order of the alphabet yields the total order of the dictionary, the lexicographic product of totally ordered sets is again totally ordered. The proof of this is left to the exercises.

Exercises

2-8   Find the restriction of the following posets to $\{x, y, z\}$:

a Poset with diagram

b Poset with diagram

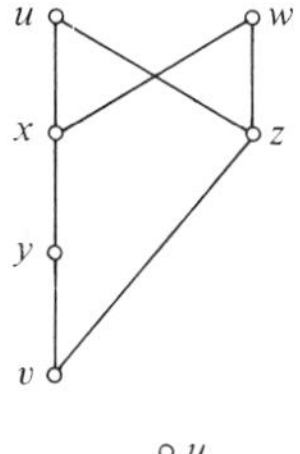

c Poset with diagram

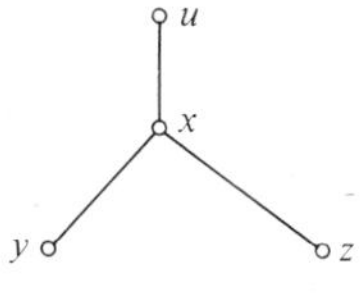

d Poset with diagram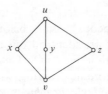

2-9 Find a restriction of the form ⚬⚬ / ⚬⚬ in the poset in Figure 2.9.

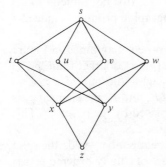

Figure 2.9

2-10 Find a restriction of the form ⚬⚬ / ⚬ in the poset in Figure 2.10.

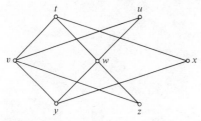

Figure 2.10

2-11 Let f be a function from the poset S to the poset T. Let e_S be the identity function on S and e_T be the identity function on T. Prove that f is an isomorphism of the posets if and only if f is an order-preserving map and there exists an order-preserving map g from T to S such that $f \circ g = e_T$ and $g \circ f = e_S$.

2-12 For the posets in Exercise 2.1c through g determine order-preserving maps satisfying the conclusion of Theorem 2.2.

2-13 Prove that composition of isomorphisms is again an isomorphism.

2-14 Prove that isomorphism between posets is an equivalence relation on any set of posets.

2-15 Prove that composition of order-preserving maps is again an order-preserving map.

2-16 Prove that the poset of all integers under the natural order is not isomorphic to the poset of all positive integers under the natural order.

2-17 Prove that the poset of all integers under the natural order is not isomorphic to the poset of all rational numbers under the natural order.

2-18 Prove that the poset of all real numbers without 0 is not isomorphic to the poset of all real numbers.

2-19 Prove that the poset of all integers larger than a fixed integer k is isomorphic to the poset of all positive integers.

2-20 Prove that the transpose of a total order is a total order.

2-21 Prove that the lexicographic product of the posets $P_1, P_2, \ldots, P_k$ is a poset.

2-22 Construct a Hasse diagram for the lexicographic products of the following posets.

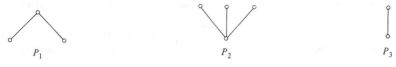

P_1 P_2 P_3

2-23 Prove that the lexicographic product of totally ordered sets is a totally ordered set.

2-24 Let P_1 and P_2 be posets, with a_1 and a_2 fixed elements in P_1 and P_2, respectively. Prove that the function $f_1(x, y) = x$ is an order-preserving map from the lexicographic product of P_1 and P_2 onto P_1 where $x \in P_1$ and $y \in P_2$. Show that the function $f_2(x, y) = y$ is *not* an order-preserving map from the lexicographic product onto P_2.

---

*2.4 WEAK ORDERS

The concept of weak order arose historically in an attempt to model preference, with regard to price only, in economics. The plethora of different brands of the same product is partially ordered by $x > y$ if the price of x is less than the price of y. This is an example of a weak order, which is defined in Section 2.1 to be a poset with transitive indifference. Recall that, in a poset, x is indifferent to y, written $x \, I \, y$, if $x \not> y$ and $y \not> x$. We characterize weak orders in terms of both forbidden subposets and order-preserving functions.

Theorem 2.3 A poset P is a weak order if and only if P contains no subposet of the form ⢁ ∘ (i.e., no subposet isomorphic to a poset with the diagram ⢁ ∘).

Proof   If P is a weak order and we also have $\begin{smallmatrix} x \\ y \end{smallmatrix}$ $\circ z$ as a subposet, then $x \not> z$, $z \not> x$, so that x I z. Likewise z I y. Since indifference is assumed to be transitive, x I y, which contradicts $x > y$. Thus there cannot be a subposet of the form $\begin{smallmatrix} x \\ y \end{smallmatrix}$ $z \circ$. Assume now that there is no subposet of the form $\begin{smallmatrix} \\ \end{smallmatrix}$ $\circ$ and suppose x I z and z I y. If it always happens that x I y, then indifference is transitive and P is a weak order. Thus suppose x is not indifferent to y. Hence we may assume $x > y$. However, x I z and z I y gives the subposet $\begin{smallmatrix} x \\ y \end{smallmatrix}$ $\circ z$, which contradicts the hypothesis. Hence indifference must be transitive, and P is a weak order.

The existence of a function f from a finite poset P to the integers such that $x > y$ if and only if $f(x) > f(y)$ for each x and y in P characterizes weak orders.

In order to show this, we first note that a restriction of a weak order is again a weak order. In fact, Theorem 2.4 contains a stronger statement.

Theorem 2.4   Let Q be a given poset. If P contains no subposet isomorphic to Q, then any restriction of P contains no subposet isomorphic to Q.

Proof   The proof consists of noting that a subposet T of a subposet S of the poset P is again a subposet of P, since $T \subseteq S \subseteq P$, and if R is the relation for P, then $R_S = R \cap (S \times S)$ and $(R_S)_T = R_S \cap (T \times T) = R \cap (S \times S) \cap (T \times T) = R \cap (T \times T) = R_T$.

Since a weak order is exactly a poset with no subposet isomorphic to $\begin{smallmatrix} x \\ y \end{smallmatrix}$ $\circ z$, then the restriction of a weak order is a weak order.

Theorem 2.5   A finite poset P with n elements is a weak order if and only if there is an order-preserving map f from P to $T_n = \{1, 2, 3, \ldots, n\}$, under the natural order, such that $x > y$ if and only if $f(x) > f(y)$ for all $x, y \in P$.

Proof   Suppose first that P is a weak order. If P contains only one element x, simply map x to 1. Suppose P contains m elements. Pick a maximal element y of P. The subposet $P \backslash \{y\}$ is a weak order by Theorem 2.4, and by induction there exists f' from $P \backslash \{y\}$ to T_{m-1} such that $u > v$ if and only if $f'(u) > f'(v)$ for u, v in $P \backslash \{y\}$. Either y is a unique maximal element, in which case $y > u$ for all u in $P \backslash \{y\}$ or there exists z in $P \backslash \{y\}$ such that z is a maximal element in P. In the first case define $f(u) = f'(u)$ for all $u \neq y$ and $f(y) = m$, and in the second case define $f(u) = f'(u)$ for all $u \neq y$ and $f(y) = f'(z)$. In each case we need only check that $y > w$ if and only if $f(y) > f(w)$. The first case is clear, and in the second case $f(z) = f(y) > f(w)$ implies $z > w$ and thus $y > w$.

Suppose now that P is a poset and that there is an order-preserving map f from P to T_n, with $x > y$, if and only if $f(x) > f(y)$. If P is not a weak order, then there exists a subposet $\begin{smallmatrix} u \\ v \end{smallmatrix} \begin{smallmatrix} \circ \\ \circ \end{smallmatrix} \circ w$ of P. However, $u > v$ implies $f(u) > f(v)$, but u I w implies $f(u) = f(w)$ and v I w implies $f(v) = f(w)$. This means $f(u) = f(w) = f(v)$, which is a contradiction. Thus a subposet of the form $\begin{smallmatrix} \circ \\ \circ \end{smallmatrix} \circ$ cannot exist in P, and P is a weak order.

To compute the function f given in Theorem 2.5 is an easy task. Let (a_{ij}) be the relation matrix for the weak order P (the covering matrix will do equally well). Determine the maximal elements (the elements of level 0) and map these to n, where n is the number of elements in P. In general, determine the ith level and map these elements to $n - i$. This yields a function satisfying the hypothesis of Theorem 2.5.

Exercises

2-25   Determine, if possible, a function f satisfying Theorem 2.4 for each of the posets given by the following diagrams:

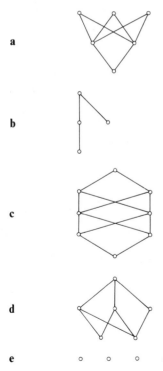

a

b

c

d

e

2-26   Prove that the function produced by the algorithm at the end of the section indeed satisfies Theorem 2.5.

2-27   Determine a flowchart for the algorithm at the end of the section.

2-28   Using a scale from 0 to 5, 0 being poor and 5 being excellent, give your ratings for eight different sports. Draw a diagram for the resulting weak order.

2-29   Determine an upper triangular relation matrix for the weak order in Exercise 2-28.

2-30   Prove that the relation matrix for a weak order can be put in upper triangular form and describe the types of resulting matrices.

---

*2.5   SEMIORDERS

Early in the development of a theory of preference for economics, it was realized that weak order was not the proper setting. In general, preference for a class of equal quality products is not based solely on price, since the buyer may be indifferent to small variations in the price. The difference in price between a car at \$4050.00 and a car at \$4050.01 is probably irrelevant to the buyer. The example in Section 2.1 involving discriminating between sweetnesses illustrates the fact that there may be some threshold of discriminating sweetness in coffee. The difference between 1 and 1.05 cubes of sugar is not noticed, but the difference between 1 and 2 cubes is. This section characterizes semiorders in terms of forbidden subposets and also in terms of an order-preserving map f to the reals, where $x > y$ in the poset if and only if $f(x) > f(y) + 1$, where 1 can be taken to be the length of the interval of nondiscrimination.

Recall that a semiorder is a poset P such that, if $a > b$, b I c, but $c > d$, then $a > d$; and if $a > b$, $b > c$, but b I d, then either $a > d$ or $d > c$.

Theorem 2.6   The poset P is a semiorder if and only if P contains no subposet of the form ⧺ ⧺ or ⧉ ∘.

Proof   First let P be a semiorder. A subposet of the form $\begin{smallmatrix} a & & c \\ & & \\ b & & d \end{smallmatrix}$ implies $a > b$, $c > d$, and b I c, but $a \not> d$, contradicting the first condition for a semiorder. A subposet of the form $\begin{smallmatrix} a \\ b \\ c \end{smallmatrix} d\circ$ implies $a > b$, $b > c$, b I d, $a \not> d$, $d \not> c$, which contradicts the second condition for a semiorder. Thus a semiorder contains no subposets of the form ⧺ ⧺ or ⧉ ∘.

Suppose now that P is a poset with no subposets of the form ⧺ ⧺ or ⧉ ∘. If $a > b$, $c > d$, b I c and, furthermore, a I d, then $\begin{smallmatrix} a & & c \\ b & & d \end{smallmatrix}$ is a subposet. Thus a is not indifferent to d, so that either $a > d$ or $d > b$, a contradiction. Hence

Figure 2.11

$a > d$, and the first condition for a semiorder is fulfilled. If $a > b, b > c, b$ I d, then $a \not> d, d \not> c$ yields a subposet $\begin{smallmatrix} a & \\ b & \circ \\ & c \end{smallmatrix} d\circ$, so that either $a > d$ or $d > c$, which is the second condition for a semiorder. Thus P is a semiorder, and the theorem is shown.

In order to characterize a semiorder in terms of a certain order-preserving map to the reals, we need to investigate the semiorder more thoroughly. If x is in the semiorder P, then define $lh(x) = \{y \in P : x > y\}$. This set is called the lower holdings of x and consists of the elements of P that are strictly smaller than x. Define $uh(x) = \{z \in P : z > x\}$. This set is called the upper holdings of x and consists of the elements of P that are strictly larger than x. For example, the poset T with the diagram given in Figure 2.11 is a semiorder (which is not a weak order), and we have $lh(p_5) = \emptyset$, $lh(p_3) = \{p_5\}$, $lh(p_4) = \{p_5\}$, $lh(p_2) = \{p_3, p_5\}$, and $lh(p_1) = \{p_2, p_3, p_4, p_5\}$. The sets $lh(t)$ for t in T themselves form a poset by set inclusion. In fact, these sets form a totally ordered set $lh(p_5) \subseteq lh(p_3) \subseteq lh(p_4) \subseteq lh(p_2) \subseteq lh(p_1)$. Likewise, the sets $uh(t)$ for t in T are again totally ordered by set inclusion, since $uh(p_1) = \emptyset \subseteq uh(p_2) = \{p_1\} \subseteq uh(p_4) = \{p_1\} \subseteq uh(p_3) = \{p_1, p_2\} \subseteq uh(p_5) = \{p_1, p_2, p_3, p_4\}$. This fact is an important property of semiorders and in fact characterizes posets that cannot have subposets of the form $\substack{\circ \\ \circ} \substack{\circ \\ \circ}$.

Theorem 2.7   The poset P has no subposet of the form $\substack{\circ \\ \circ} \substack{\circ \\ \circ}$ if and only if the set of lower holdings of elements of P is totally ordered by set inclusion and the set of upper holdings of elements of P is totally ordered by set inclusion.

Proof   Let P have no subposet of the form $\substack{\circ \\ \circ} \substack{\circ \\ \circ}$. Suppose x, y are in P and suppose $z \in lh(x)$ but $z \notin lh(y)$. We show that $lh(x) \supset lh(y)$. If $y \in lh(x)$, then $lh(x) \supset lh(y)$, so suppose $y \notin lh(x)$. Thus we have $\substack{x \circ y \\ \circ z}$ as a subposet. If $u \in lh(y)$ and $u \not< x$, then we have the subposet $\substack{\circ x \\ \circ z} \substack{\circ y \\ \circ u}$, contradicting the hypothesis. Thus $u \in lh(x)$ and $lh(x) \supset lh(y)$. A similar argument shows that the upper holdings are totally ordered by set inclusion.

Suppose now that P is a poset whose lower holdings of elements form a totally ordered set under set inclusion and whose upper holdings are also totally ordered. If $\substack{\circ a \\ \circ b} \substack{\circ c \\ \circ d}$ is a subposet, then $b \in lh(a)$, $b \notin lh(c)$, $d \in lh(c)$, but

$d \notin lh(a)$ thus $lh(a)$ is not contained in $lh(c)$ and $lh(c)$ is not in $lh(a)$, which is a contradiction. Thus the subposet ⦂ ⦂ is forbidden.

In a semiorder, not only are the lower holdings and upper holdings both totally ordered by set inclusion but also, if $lh(x) \subsetneqq lh(y)$, then $uh(y) \subseteq uh(x)$. In the example in Figure 2.11, $lh(p_5) \subsetneqq lh(p_3) \subsetneqq lh(p_2) \subsetneqq lh(p_1)$ and, for the reversed sequence p_1, p_2, p_3, p_5, $uh(p_1) \subseteq uh(p_2) \subseteq uh(p_3) \subseteq uh(p_5)$. This additional property follows for a general semiorder, since $lh(x) \subsetneqq lh(y)$ implies there exists z with $y > z$ but $x \not> z$. Suppose now that $v \in uh(y) \backslash uh(x)$, that is, $v > y$, $v \not> x$. Since $lh(x) \subsetneqq lh(y)$, $x \not> y$, and $x \not> v$. Thus we have the subposet ⦂ x ∘, which is forbidden in a semiorder. Similarly, if $uh(x) \subsetneqq uh(y)$, then $lh(y) \subset lh(x)$. These additional properties characterize semiorders.

Theorem 2.8   A poset P is a semiorder if and only if the upper holdings and the lower holdings of P are both totally ordered by set inclusion and, furthermore, (1) $lh(x) \subsetneqq lh(y)$ implies $uh(y) \subset uh(x)$, and (2) $uh(x) \subsetneqq uh(y)$ implies $lh(y) \subset lh(x)$.

Proof   Theorem 2.7 and the discussion preceding this theorem show that, if P is a semiorder, then the upper holdings and lower holdings are totally ordered and (1) and (2) hold. Suppose now that the upper holdings and lower holdings of P are totally ordered by set inclusion and that (1) and (2) hold. Theorem 2.7 guarantees that P contains no subposet of the form ⦂ ⦂. It remains only to show that P contains no subposet of the form ⦂ ⦂ ∘u with x, y, z, and u in P. Since the lower holdings are linearly ordered, either $lh(u) \supseteq lh(y)$ or $lh(y) \supsetneqq lh(u)$. The former is impossible, since $z \in lh(y)$, $z \notin lh(u)$. Thus $lh(y) \supsetneqq lh(u)$. By hypothesis $uh(u) \supseteq uh(y)$, so that $x \in uh(u)$ and $x > u$, a contradiction. Thus the existence of the subposet ⦂ ∘ contradicts the hypothesis, and P contains no subposet of this form. Theorem 2.6 now shows that P is a semiorder.

Theorem 2.8 is an important tool in constructing a function f from P into the reals, with $x > y$, if and only if $f(x) > f(y) + 1$. However, before we proceed with the proof, the problem can be simplified in the following manner. If P_1 and P_2 are posets and g is a function from P_1 onto P_2 such that $x > y$ if and only if $g(x) > g(y)$, then certain theorems about P_2 which involve only the concept of $>$ can be "lifted" to a corresponding theorem about P_1 and $>$. For example, if P_2 is a semiorder with the function f_2 from P_2 into the reals satisfying $u > v$, u and v in P_2, if and only if $f_2(u) > f_2(v) + 1$, then the function $f_1 = f_2 \circ g$ is such that $x > y$, x and y in P_1, if and only if $f_1(x) > f_1(y) + 1$. This is just a case of transitivity of if and only if, namely, $x > y$ if and only if $g(x) > g(y)$ if and only if $f_2(g(x)) > f_2(g(y)) + 1$. That is, $x > y$ if and only if $f_1(x) > f_1(y) + 1$.

This phenomenon can be used in limiting the discussion of semiorders

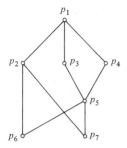

Figure 2.12

	Lower holdings	Upper holdings
p_1	$\{p_2, p_3, p_4, p_5, p_6, p_7\}$	$\varnothing$
p_2	$\{p_6, p_7\}$	$\{p_1\}$
p_3	$\{p_5, p_6, p_7\}$	$\{p_1\}$
p_4	$\{p_5, p_6, p_7\}$	$\{p_1\}$
p_5	$\{p_6, p_7\}$	$\{p_1, p_3, p_4\}$
p_6	$\varnothing$	$\{p_1, p_2, p_3, p_4, p_5\}$
p_7	$\varnothing$	$\{p_1, p_2, p_3, p_4, p_5\}$

Figure 2.13

to those semiorders P where $x \neq y$ in P implies either $lh(x) \neq lh(y)$ or $uh(x) \neq uh(y)$.

For example, the semiorder in Figure 2.12 has the lower holdings and upper holdings in Figure 2.13. Since $lh(p_3) = lh(p_4)$ and $uh(p_3) = uh(p_4)$, $p_3 \sim p_4$ and similarly $p_6 \sim p_7$. All other pairs of distinct elements are not equivalent. Thus the set of equivalence classes is $\{\{p_1\}, \{p_2\}, \{p_3, p_4\}, \{p_5\}, \{p_6, p_7\}\}$, which yields a poset isomorphic to the poset in Figure 2.11. Thus to find a function from the poset in Figure 2.12 to the reals such that $x > y$ if and only if $f(x) > f(y) + 1$, it is sufficient to do this for the poset in Figure 2.11.

We are now ready to prove Theorem 2.9.

Theorem 2.9 Let Q be any poset. There exist a poset P_Q, depending on Q, and an order-preserving map g from Q onto P_Q such that $x \neq y$ in P_Q implies either $lh(x) \neq lh(y)$ or $uh(x) \neq uh(y)$. Furthermore, $u > v$, u and v in Q, if and only if $g(u) > g(v)$ in P_Q.

Proof We define an equivalence relation on the elements of Q by $a \sim b$ if $lh(a) = lh(b)$ and $uh(a) = uh(b)$, a, b in Q. Let $\bar{a}$ be the equivalence class containing a. Define $\bar{a} > \bar{b}$ if $a > b$. If $\bar{a} > \bar{b}$, with $a > b$, then $a_1 > b_1$ for all $a_1 \in \bar{a}$ and $b_1 \in \bar{b}$. This holds, since $\bar{a} = \bar{a}_1$ and $\bar{b} = \bar{b}_1$ implies $lh(a) = lh(a_1)$

and $uh(b) = uh(b_1)$. Thus $b \in lh(a) = lh(a_1)$, so $b < a_1$ and $a_1 \in uh(b) = uh(b_1)$, so $a_1 > b_1$. The relation $\bar{a} > \bar{b}$ is also transitive, a fact which is relegated to the exercises. Since $\bar{a} > \bar{b}$ implies $x > y$ for any x in $\bar{a}$ and y in $\bar{b}$, we have $\bar{a} \geq \bar{b}$ and $\bar{b} \geq \bar{a}$ implies $\bar{a} = \bar{b}$. Thus the set of equivalence classes forms a poset. Call this poset P_Q. Define the function g from Q onto P_Q by $g(a) = \bar{a}$. For a and b in Q, we have $a > b$ if and only if $\bar{a} > \bar{b}$, so that $a > b$ if and only if $g(a) > g(b)$. Thus $a \geq b$ implies $g(a) \geq g(b)$. Thus P_Q is the desired poset, and g is the desired order-preserving map.

We may note here that Theorem 2.9 provides an alternate method of proving the existence of an order-preserving map g from a finite weak order W into T_n, where n is the number of elements in W. Since $\substack{\circ \\ \circ}$ is a prohibited subposet of a weak order, if a and b are indifferent, then $uh(a) = uh(b)$ and $lh(a) = lh(b)$, so that $\bar{a} = \{b : b \mathbin{I} a\}$. Since $a > b$, $b > a$, or $a \mathbin{I} b$, in a weak order $\bar{a} > \bar{b}$, $\bar{b} > \bar{a}$, or $\bar{a} = \bar{b}$. Thus the poset P_W obtained in Theorem 2.9 is a finite totally ordered set which is isomorphic to T_m with some $m \leq n$.

To characterize semiorders in terms of an order-preserving map, we first prove Theorem 2.10.

Theorem 2.10   Let P be a poset and f a function from P into the real numbers such that $x > y$, x and y in P, if and only if $f(x) > f(y) + 1$. Then P is a semiorder.

Proof   Suppose $\substack{a \\ b} \ \substack{c \\ d}$ is a subposet of P. Thus $f(a) > f(b) + 1$ and $f(c) > f(d) + 1$. Since the reals are totally ordered, either $f(c) \geq f(a)$ or $f(a) > f(c)$. In the first case $f(c) \geq f(a) > f(b) + 1$, so that $f(c) > f(b) + 1$ and $c > b$, a contradiction. In the second case $f(a) > f(c) \geq f(d) + 1$, so that $a > d$, again a contradiction. Thus $\substack{a \\ b} \ \substack{c \\ d}$ cannot be a subposet. Suppose now that $\substack{a \\ b \\ c} \ \circ d$ is a subposet of P. Thus $a > b$ and $b > c$ implies $f(a) > f(b) + 1$ and $f(b) > f(c) + 1$. Since the reals are totally ordered, either $f(d) \geq f(b)$ or $f(d) < f(b)$. The first case shows that $f(d) \geq f(b) > f(c) + 1$, so that $d > c$, a contradiction. The second case implies $f(a) > f(b) + 1 > f(d) + 1$, so $a > d$, again a contradiction. Thus $\substack{a \\ b \\ c} \ d \circ$ is a forbidden subposet, and P is indeed a semiorder.

The converse of Theorem 2.10 requires somewhat more labor to prove, since the function f is actually constructed. Let us illustrate with the semiorder T given in Figure 2.11. First list the elements of T in order of size of lower holdings, with elements of smaller lower holdings preceding elements of larger lower holdings. If the lower holdings of two elements are equal, then the one with larger upper holding will be listed first. Thus, for the semiorder T, we have the list p_5, p_3, p_4, p_2, p_1. The function f is constructed to satisfy $f(p_5) < f(p_3) < f(p_4) < f(p_2) < f(p_1)$. Define $f(p_5) = 1$. Since $p_3 > p_5$, we require $f(p_3) > f(p_5) + 1 = 2$, so let $f(p_3) = 2.5$. Since $p_4 > p_5$

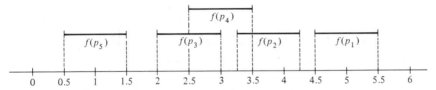

Figure 2.14 Representation of semiorder T.

but $p_4 \not> p_3$, we want $f(p_4) > f(p_5) + 1 = 2$ and $f(p_4) < f(p_3) + 1 = 3.5$. Thus define $f(p_4) = 3$. Since $p_2 > p_3$ and p_5, and $p_2 \not> p_4$, we want $f(p_2) > f(p_3) + 1 = 3.5$, but $f(p_2) < f(p_4) + 1 = 4$. Thus define $f(p_2) = 3.75$. Since P_1 is larger than all, define $f(p_1) = 5$. This function satisfies $f(x) > f(y)$ if $x > y$, and if we take one interval of width 1 with $f(x)$ as midpoint of the interval, we obtain T as represented in Figure 2.14.

The converse of Theorem 2.10 is now shown for the case where P is finite.

Theorem 2.11 Let P be a finite semiorder. Then there exists a function f from P into the reals such that $x > y$, x and y in P, if and only if $f(x) > f(y) + 1$.

Proof Because of Theorem 2.9, we may assume that, for $x \neq y$ in P, either $lh(x) \neq lh(y)$ or $uh(x) \neq uh(y)$. Now label the elements of P, $x_1, x_2, \ldots, x_n$, where if $i > j$ then $lh(x_i) \supseteq lh(x_j)$ and $uh(x_i) \subseteq uh(x_j)$. This can be accomplished, since the lower holdings are totally ordered by set inclusion and, if $lh(y) \supsetneq lh(x)$, then by Theorem 2.8 $uh(y) \subseteq uh(x)$. If the lower holdings of a set of elements are equal, since the upper holdings are totally ordered, and distinct for these elements, we can label the elements so that the index i increases as the upper holdings of x_i decrease. This labeling has the property that, if $x_i > x_j$, then $lh(x_i) \supsetneq lh(x_j)$ so $i > j$ and, furthermore, for any x_k, $k < j$, we have $uh(x_k) \supseteq uh(x_j) \supseteq uh(x_i)$. Since $x_i \in uh(x_j)$, then $x_i \in uh(x_k)$ and $x_i > x_k$. Similarly, if $e > i$, then $lh(x_e) \supseteq lh(x_i)$, so that $x_j \in lh(x_e)$ and $x_e > x_j$. To recapitulate, if $x_i > x_j$, then $i > j$ and for any $k > i$, $x_l > x_j$ and any $k < j$, $x_i > x_k$. We now define $f(x)$, by first defining $f(x_1) = 1$. Suppose $f(x_1), f(x_2), \ldots, f(x_i)$ have been defined and satisfy $x > y$ if $f(x) > f(y) + 1$ and $x \not> y$ if $f(x) < f(y) + 1$, with x, y in $\{x_1, x_2, \ldots, x_i\}$, and, furthermore, satisfy $f(x_1) < f(x_2) < \cdots < f(x_i)$. If $i < n$, $f(x_{i+1})$ is defined as follows. There are four cases to consider.

Case 1 If $x_{i+1} \not> x_j$ for any j, $1 \leq j < i + 1$, then $x_i \not> x_j$ for any j, $1 \leq j < i$. Thus $f(x_i) < f(x_1) + 1 = 2$ so define $f(x_{i+1}) = 1 + f(x_i)/2$. Thus $f(x_{i+1}) - f(x_1) = f(x_i)/2 < 1$, and $f(x_i) < f(x_{i+1}) < f(x_1) + 1$, as desired. For the remaining cases, $x_{i+1} > x_j$ for some j. Pick j to be the largest integer with $x_{i+1} > x_j$, $1 \leq j < i + 1$.

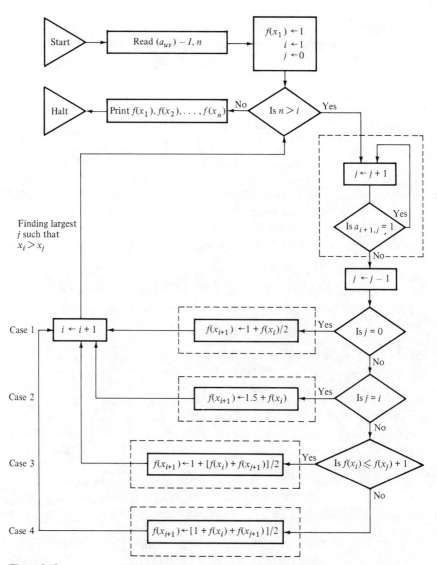

Figure 2.15

Case 2   If $j = i$, define $f(x_{i+1}) = f(x_i) + 1.5$.

Case 3   If $j < i$ and $f(x_i) \le f(x_j) + 1$, define $f(x_{i+1}) = f(x_j) + 1 + (f(x_{j+1}) - f(x_j))/2$. Thus $f(x_{i+1}) - f(x_j) > 1$ and $f(x_{i+1}) - f(x_{j+1}) = 1 - [f(x_{j+1}) - f(x_j)]/2 < 1$. Thus $f(x_{i+1}) > f(x_i)$, $f(x_{i+1}) > f(x_j) + 1$, $f(x_{i+1}) < f(x_{j+1}) + 1$, as desired.

Case 4 If $j < i$ and $f(x_i) > f(x_j) + 1$, define $f(x_{i+1}) = f(x_i) + \frac{1}{2} - [f(x_i) - f(x_{j+1})]/2$. Since $f(x_i) - f(x_{j+1}) < 1$, $f(x_{i+1}) > f(x_i)$. Furthermore, $f(x_{i+1}) - f(x_j) \geq 1.5 - [f(x_i) - f(x_{j+1})]/2 > 1$ and

$$f(x_{i+1}) - f(x_{j+1}) = \tfrac{1}{2} + [f(x_i) - f(x_{j+1})]/2 < 1$$

and $f(x_{i+1})$ is defined as desired.

Thus, when $i = n$, a function f has been constructed that satisfies the conclusion of the theorem.

Theorem 2.11 contains an algorithm which constructs f, once the elements of P have been labeled $x_1, x_2, \ldots, x_n$, with $lh(x_i) \subseteq lh(x_j)$ and $uh(x_i) \supseteq uh(x_j)$ for $i < j$, and assuming $lh(x_i) = lh(x_k)$ and $uh(x_i) = uh(x_k)$ implies $i = k$. Let (a_{uv}) be the relation matrix for the semiorder P with the elements of P ordered in the above manner. Figure 2.15 is a flowchart of the algorithm that constructs an f for Theorem 2.11. The input data is $(a_{uv}) - I$ and n, where I is the $n \times n$ identity matrix.

Theorems 2.10 and 2.11 combine to give a characterization for finite semiorders, namely, a finite poset P is a semiorder if and only if there exists a function f into the reals such that $x > y$ if and only if $f(x) > f(y) + 1$ for x and y in P.

Exercises

2-31 For the semiorder P construct the semiorder P_ϱ given by Theorem 2.9. Give the equivalence classes explicitly.

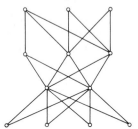

Figure 2.16 Semiorder P.

2-32 Prove that the relation $\bar{a} > \bar{b}$ given in Theorem 2.9, where $\bar{a}$ and $\bar{b}$ are equivalence classes of elements, is transitive.

2-33 Construct the function f from the semiorder P in Figure 2.16 into the reals that satisfies $x > y$ if and only if $f(x) > f(y) + 1$ for x, y in P.

2-34 Determine an algorithm which begins with the adjacency matrix of a semiorder and reorders the elements $x_1, x_2, \ldots, x_n$, with $lh(x_i) \supseteq lh(x_j)$ and $uh(x_i) \subseteq uh(x_j)$ for $i > j$. Draw the flowchart for this algorithm.

---

*2.6   INTERVAL ORDERS

Section 2.1 gave an example of an interval order which is a set of
intervals of the real line with one interval greater than another interval if and
only if the left end point of the first is greater than the right end point of the
second. We then defined an *interval order* to be a poset such that $a > b$, b I c,
$c > d$ implies $a > d$. This section shows that any finite interval order is
indeed isomorphic to a set of intervals of the real line with the partial order
as given above.

We first characterize interval orders in terms of forbidden posets.

Theorem 2.12   A poset is an interval order if and only if there is no
subposet of the form ⁝ ⁝.

The proof of this is straightforward and is left to the exercises.

Theorem 2.12 can now be used to restate Theorem 2.7 in terms of
interval orders.

Theorem 2.13   The poset P is an interval order if and only if the set of
lower holdings of elements of P is totally ordered by set inclusion and the set
of upper holdings of elements of P is totally ordered by set inclusion.

The poset in Figure 2.17 is an interval order, and Figure 2.18 shows the
upper and lower holdings of each element. The elements have been listed
with elements of larger lower holdings preceding elements of smaller lower
holdings. In this example, the upper holdings do not necessarily satisfy
$uh(x) \subseteq uh(y)$ when $lh(x) \supsetneq lh(y)$, as $x = p_6$ and $y = p_3$ show. This is not
surprising, since only semiorders have this property (by Theorem 2.8) and
the poset in Figure 2.17 contains the subposet

$$\begin{array}{l} {}^{\circ}p_1 \\ \mid \quad {}^{\circ}p_3 \\ {}^{\circ}p_6 \\ \mid \\ {}^{\circ}p_4 \end{array}$$

which is forbidden for semiorders.

In order to map an interval order to a set of intervals, we must find the
left end points of each interval and the right end points of each interval and
properly intersperse the right and left end points. Let $r(x)$ be the right end
point of x, and $l(x)$ the left end point. Thus the element x is mapped to the
interval $[l(x), r(x)]$. If the lower holdings of x strictly contain the lower
holdings of y, then $l(x) > l(y)$. Thus we must have $lh(x) \supsetneq lh(y)$ implies
$l(x) > l(y)$. Similarly, $uh(x) \subsetneq uh(y)$ implies $r(x) > r(y)$. The lower holdings
and upper holdings thus indicate the relative ordering of the left end points

Figure 2.17

	Lower holdings	Upper holdings
p_2	$\{p_6, p_4, p_5, p_3\}$	$\varnothing$
p_1	$\{p_6, p_5, p_4\}$	$\varnothing$
p_6	$\{p_5, p_4\}$	$\{p_1, p_2\}$
p_3	$\{p_5\}$	$\{p_2\}$
p_4	$\varnothing$	$\{p_1, p_2, p_6\}$
p_5	$\varnothing$	$\{p_1, p_2, p_3, p_6\}$

Figure 2.18

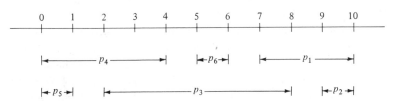

Figure 2.19

and the right end points, respectively. In the example in Figure 2.17, $l(p_2) > l(p_1) > l(p_6) > l(p_3) > l(p_4) = l(p_5)$, and

$$r(p_2) = r(p_1) > r(p_3) > r(p_6) > r(p_4) > r(p_5).$$

It remains to intersperse the left and right end points. We must have $r(p_2) > l(p_2)$, so that $r(p_2) = r(p_1) > l(p_2)$. However, p_3 is less than p_2, so $l(p_2) > r(p_3)$. Likewise, p_6 is less than p_2 and p_1, so $l(p_1) > r(p_6)$. Also, p_4 is less than p_6, p_1 and p_2, so $l(p_6) > r(p_4)$. Finally, p_5 is less than p_3, p_6, p_1, and p_2, so $l(p_3) > r(p_5)$. Thus we have

$$r(p_2) = r(p_1) > l(p_2) > r(p_3) > l(p_1) > r(p_6) > l(p_6) > r(p_4) > l(p_3) > r(p_5)$$

$$> l(p_4) = l(p_5).$$

Any map of these end points into the reals that preserves the strict ordering yields an appropriate interval order, so the above ordering can be represented by the set of intervals illustrated in Figure 2.19.

The ideas illustrated in this example are sufficient to enable us to characterize finite interval orders.

Theorem 2.14   Let P be a finite interval order. Then there exist functions l and r from P into the real line such that $l(x) < r(x)$ and $x > y$ if and only if $l(x) > r(y)$ for all x and y in P.

Proof   For each x in P, let l_x, r_x be symbols with the convention that, if $lh(x) = lh(y)$, then $l_x = l_y$, and if $uh(x) = uh(y)$, then $r_x = r_y$. If S is the set of such symbols, we order S by $l_x \geq l_y$ if $lh(x) \supseteq lh(y)$, and by $r_x \geq r_y$ if $uh(x) \subseteq uh(y)$. Finally, $l_x < r_x$, $r_x < l_y$ for all $y > x$, and $r_x > l_y$ for all $y \not> x$. This relation is reflexive, since $r_x \geq r_x$ and $l_x \geq l_x$. Since the set of lower holdings is totally ordered, as is the set of upper holdings, the relation is antisymmetric and transitive whenever all the elements are from $\{r_x\}$ or all the elements are from $\{l_y\}$. If $r_x \geq l_y$ and $l_y \geq r_x$, then (since equality is not possible) $y \not> x$ and yet $y > x$, a contradiction. Thus the relation is antisymmetric. To show transitivity suppose $r_x \geq r_y$ and $r_y > l_z$. This implies $uh(x) \subseteq uh(y)$ and $z \not> y$. Thus $z \notin uh(y)$, so *a fortiori*, $z \notin uh(x)$ and $z \not> x$, so that $r_x > l_z$. The remaining cases for transitivity are $r_x > l_y$, $l_y > r_z$ implies $r_x > r_z$; $r_x > l_y$, $l_y \geq l_z$ implies $r_x > l_z$; $l_x \geq l_y$, $l_y > r_z$ implies $l_x > r_z$; $l_x > r_y$, $r_y \geq r_z$ implies $l_x > r_z$; and $l_x > r_y$, $r_y > l_z$ implies $l_x > l_z$. If $r_x > l_y$ and $l_y > r_z$, then $y \not> x$ and $y > z$. Thus $z \not> x$, so that $uh(z) \supsetneq uh(x)$, so that $r_x > r_z$, as desired. The remaining cases for transitivity are similarly straightforward. It remains to make the observation that S is totally ordered and, if S has n elements, then S is isomorphic to T_n, the poset of positive integers $\leq n$ under the natural order. Let the isomorphism take r_x to $r(x)$ in the reals and l_x to $l(x)$. We then have $r(x) > l(x)$ for all x, and $u > v$ if and only if $l_u > r_v$ if and only if $l(u) > r(v)$, proving the theorem.

Once the functions $l(x)$ and $r(x)$ are obtained using Theorem 2.14 and the algorithm embodied in its proof, then there is an order-preserving map from P onto a set of intervals of the real line such that $x > y$ in P if the left end point of the image of x is greater than the right end point of the image of y. An element z of P is simply mapped to the interval $[l(z), r(z)]$.

Since Section 2.1 shows that any set of intervals of the real line with partial order $[l(x), r(x)] > [l(y), r(y)]$, when $l(x) > r(y)$, is indeed an interval order, we have the following theorem.

Theorem 2.15   Let P be a finite poset. P is an interval order if and only if there exists an order-preserving map from P to a set of intervals of the real line such that $x > y$ if and only if $[l(x), r(x)] > [l(y), r(y)]$.

Exercises

2-35   Determine a function from the interval order in Figure 2.20 to a poset of intervals of the real line such that the function satisfies Theorem 2.15.

Figure 2.20

2-36 Determine the flowchart for an algorithm that determines whether a given partial order is an interval order. (*Hint:* Use Theorem 2.13.) Assume that the relation matrix is the input.

2-37 Determine the flowchart for an algorithm that yields for an interval order P the functions $l(x)$ and $r(x)$ which satisfy Theorem 2.14, $x \in P$. Assume that, in addition to the relation matrix, the ordering of lower holdings and upper holdings is known.

---

*2.7 SOCIAL CHOICE

A poset is an exact formulation corresponding to the intuitive idea of preference. Each individual in a society has a preference for certain things, and the preferences of the individuals in the society often determine decisions or actions taken by the society as a whole. The preference of society as a whole reflects the individual preferences of its members, and this preference can be thought of as social choice. This section defines abstractly the meaning of social choice and examines various properties of social choice commonly thought to be desirable in a democratic society. Furthermore, we prove that all these desirable properties cannot hold simultaneously. This fact is called the voting paradox.

Let S be a fixed nonempty set. The set S may represent anything for which the individuals of the society have notions of preference. The set S is called the set of alternatives. For example, S can be the set of candidates for a particular office in an election, S can represent the different types of breakfast cereal available in a store, or S may represent several available alternatives for the use of a piece of land. We define $\mathscr{P}$ to be the set of all possible partial orders on S. For example, if $S = \{a, b\}$ and the partial orders in $\mathscr{P}$ are represented by their diagrams, then $\mathscr{P} = \{ {}^a_b, {}^b_a, a\ b\}$. If S has 3 elements, then $\mathscr{P}$ contains 19 elements composed of 6 with diagram ${}^\circ_\circ$, 6 with diagram ${}^\circ\ \circ$, 3 each with diagrams $\wedge$ and $\vee$, respectively, and one with diagram $\circ\ \circ\ \circ$. We define $\mathscr{L}$ to be the set of all possible weak orders on S. Thus, if $|S| = 2$, $\mathscr{P} = \mathscr{L}$, but for $|S| = 3$, $\mathscr{L}$ contains 13 orders composed of 6 with diagrams ${}^\circ_\circ$, 3 each with diagrams $\wedge$ and $\vee$, respectively, and one with diagram ∘ ∘ ∘. We wish to investigate the possible ways society can partially order S when each of its individual members partially orders S. Thus we assume that a social decision about S is a function of the individual decisions. Explicitly, let X and Y be subsets of $\mathscr{P}$. We think of X as the set of partial orders the individuals of the society are allowed to express, and Y as the set of partial orders allowed to society as a whole.

Suppose also that n individuals are involved with the decision process. A *social decision function* is a function from $X \times X \times \cdots \times X$ (taken n times) to Y. The ith component of the domain of the function can be thought of as the poset chosen by the ith individual.

For example, consider the process involved in a federal election. S is the set of candidates running for office. The integer n is the number of eligible voters, and the set X is the allowable partial ordering. Since in a federal election an allowable partial ordering consists of indicating a preference for one candidate over all others or else not voting at all, the set X consists of partial orders of type $\underset{\circ \ \circ \ \cdots \ \circ}{\overset{\circ}{\diagup}}$ (with one candidate indicated over all others) or ∘ ∘ ∘ ⋯ ∘ (with no vote cast). The social decision function for this voting procedure then picks a partial order of the type $\underset{\circ \ \circ \ \cdots \ \circ}{\overset{\circ}{\diagup}}$, where the maximum element is the individual with the most votes. If there are several individuals with the same number of votes, the returning officer casts a ballot to break the tie.

In our analysis, however, there is no restriction on the type of social decision function nor on the set X, and in practice there are many types of such decision functions. For example, preferential voting has been used by the student's union at the University of Alberta and by the province of Alberta in provincial elections. In this case X is the set of all total orders on S, and the voter orders the slate of candidates from 1 (most preferred) down to $k = |S|$ (least preferred). The social decision function now totally orders the candidates by tabulating the number of first-place votes for each candidate and determining the candidate with the least number of first-place votes (with the returning officer breaking ties). This candidate is ranked last by the social decision function. The ballots favoring this candidate are then taken and distributed according to the second preference expressed on each ballot. The number of ballots now held by each of the remaining candidates is counted. The candidate with the smallest number of ballots is then ranked second last, and these ballots are used in the next step. In general, if the last $= k, k - 1, \ldots, i$ spots have been determined by the social decision function, the ballots of the ith-ranked candidate are then distributed among the remaining $i - 1$ candidates by giving each ballot to the unranked candidate highest in the listing of that ballot. The ballots are then counted, and the candidate with the least number is given the $i - 1$ place in the total order. The process is repeated until the total order is completed.

Weighted voting is also a common social decision process. For example, in a corporation, the power of each shareholder is weighted by the number of shares that person holds. In a yes-no vote situation, if shareholders $i_1, i_2, \ldots, i_p$ vote yes, while shareholders $j_1, \ldots, j_s$ vote no, with shareholder i_t having n_{i_t} shares, then the decision is yes if $n_{i_1} + \cdots + n_{i_p} > n_{j_1} + \cdots + n_{j_s}$ and no if $n_{j_1} + \cdots + n_{j_s} > n_{i_1} + \cdots + n_{i_p}$, and ties are broken by the chairperson.

We are not concerned with any particular social decision function but wish to investigate the general properties of social decision functions. In fact, we formulate the following conditions which seem desirable in a social decision function. We first fix the notation. Let S be the set of alternatives. Let X be some subset of $\mathscr{P}$, the set of all partial orders on S. The social decision function is

$$\mathscr{F} : \underbrace{X \times \cdots \times X}_{n \text{ times}} \to X.$$

For $P_1, \ldots, P_n$ in X, we denote $(x, y) \in P_i$ by $x \geq_i y$, and $(x, y) \in \mathscr{F}(P_1, \ldots, P_n)$ by $x \geq y$. Similarly, for $P'_1, \ldots, P'_n$ in X, we denote $(x, y) \in P'_i$ by $x \geq'_i y$, and $(x, y) \in \mathscr{F}(P'_1, \ldots, P'_n)$ by $x \geq' y$.

In our analysis we take X to be $\mathscr{L}$, the set of all weak orders on S. Thus $\mathscr{F} : \mathscr{L} \times \cdots \times \mathscr{L} \to \mathscr{L}$. Furthermore, we assume that there are more than two alternatives, so that for x, y, z in S each individual can indicate best, second best, and third best. Thus we have $|S| \geq 3$.

Suppose each individual has ordered the alternatives. Now suppose that each individual may increase the ranking of a particular alternative x but must leave all other alternatives fixed. The first condition then asserts that, if x is socially preferred to y under the first set of orderings, x will be socially preferred to y under the second set of orderings.

Condition 1   Let $x, y \in S$. Suppose $u \geq_i v$ if and only if $u \geq'_i v$ for all u and v in S, $u \neq x$, $v \neq x$, and for $i = 1, 2, \ldots, n$, and suppose for $z \in S$, $x \geq_i z$ implies $x \geq'_i z$, $i = 1, \ldots, n$. If $x \geq y$, then $x \geq' y$.

The second condition is by far the strongest and states that for any pair of alternatives the social decision function depends only on the individual preferences regarding the pair. Thus all other choices are considered irrelevant as far as deciding which of the two alternatives is preferred, as stated explicitly in Condition 2.

Condition 2   Suppose $x \geq_i y$ exactly when $x \geq'_i y$ and $y \geq_i x$ exactly when $y \geq'_i x$ for each i. Then $x \geq y$ if and only if $x \geq' y$.

It is not difficult to see that the following plausible procedure cannot satisfy Conditions 1 and 2. Suppose the individuals of the society partial-order the elements of S, and if more individuals prefer x to y than prefer y to

x, the social decision function makes x preferred to y overall. This seems a reasonable procedure but in fact does not result in a final partial order. As an example, suppose three individuals, 1, 2, and 3, partial-order three alternatives, A, B, and C, and suppose person 1 has the order $\genfrac{}{}{0pt}{}{\circ\,A}{\circ\,B}$, person 2 chooses $\genfrac{}{}{0pt}{}{\circ\,C}{\genfrac{}{}{0pt}{}{\circ\,A}{\circ\,B}}$, and person 3 chooses $\genfrac{}{}{0pt}{}{\circ\,B}{\genfrac{}{}{0pt}{}{\circ\,C}{\circ\,A}}$. Thus A is preferred to B in two out of three cases, B is preferred to C in two out of three cases, and C is preferred to A in two out of three cases. Thus our function does not yield a final partial order, since the resulting relation is not transitive. We may remedy this situation by imposing the social decision function from outside, as is the case with taboos, religious dogma, and sometimes law. Alternatively, some individual may be a taste leader or, in harsher terms, a dictator, in which case a social decision function could give the partial order selected by the taste leader. There exist numerous social decision functions incorporating aspects of outside-imposed ordering, which satisfy Conditions 1 and 2. However, a democratic society generally dislikes outside-imposed ordering or a dictatorship. Thus we make two more assumptions concerning the social decision function.

Condition 3   For any x and y in S, $x \neq y$, there exist $P_1, \ldots, P_n$ in X with $(x, y) \in \mathscr{F}(P_1, \ldots, P_n)$.

Condition 4   For any integer i_0, if $x \geq_{i_0} y$, with x and y in S, $x \neq y$, then there exist $P_1, P_2, \ldots, P_{i_0-1}, P_{i_0+1}, \ldots, P_n$ such that $x \not\geq y$.

Thus Condition 3 says that ordering cannot be imposed from the outside, and Condition 4 says that there is no dictator who determines the ordering of all the alternatives.

We are now in a position to state and prove the impossibility theorem, which shows that no social decision function can exist that satisfies Conditions 1 through 4. In order to do this we need the notion of a decisive set of individuals. We can label the individuals of the society with the set $\{1, 2, 3, \ldots, n\}$. If x and y are two alternatives in S, then a *decisive set* for x over y is a subset J of $\{1, 2, \ldots, n\}$ such that for any partial orders $P_1, \ldots, P_n$ with $x \geq_k y$ for all k in J, then $x \geq y$. We have not specified the ordering of alternatives outside x and y or outside J. The first result shows that a set of individuals is decisive for x over y if that set's support of x over y dominates the opposition, united in upholding y over x.

Recall that $\mathscr{L}$ denotes the set of all weak orders on the set S. Let J denote a set of individuals and let K be the individuals not in J.

Theorem 2.16   Let x and y be distinct in S and $\mathscr{F}: \mathscr{L} \times \cdots \times \mathscr{L} \to \mathscr{L}$ be a social decision function satisfying Conditions 1 and 2. Let $P_1, P_2, \ldots, P_n$ be partial orders such that $x >_j y$ for all $j \in J$ and $y >_k x$ for all $k \in K$. If $x > y$, then J is decisive for x over y.

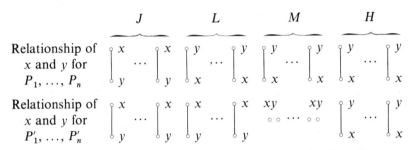

Figure 2.21 Types of relations between x and y under the weak orders $P_1, \ldots, P_n$ and $P'_1, \ldots, P'_n$.

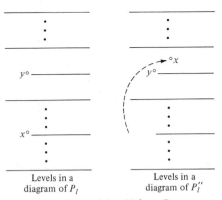

Levels in a   Levels in a
diagram of P_l diagram of P''_l

Figure 2.22 Determining P''_l from P_l.

Proof Let $P'_1, P'_2, \ldots, P'_n$ be partial orders such that, for $j \in J$, $x >'_j y$. We must show that $x >'y$, thus proving that J is decisive for x over y. What we do is to change the weak orders $P_1, P_2, \ldots, P_n$ slightly to obtain new weak orders $P''_1, P''_2, \ldots, P''_n$ such that Condition 1 holds (implying $x >''y$) and yet, on x and y, $P''_i = P'_i$ for all i so that Condition 2 then implies $x >'y$. The set of all individuals is partitioned into the following sets: $J, L = \{l : y >_l x$ and $x >'_l y\}$, $M = \{m : y >_m x$ and x is indifferent to y under $>'_m\}$, and $H = \{h : y >_h x$ and $y >'_h x\}$. Note that $L \cup M \cup H = K$. Figure 2.21 illustrates the orderings of x and y for the weak orders $P_1, P_2, \ldots, P_n$, and $P'_1, P'_2, \ldots, P'_n$ in relationship to J, L, M, and H.

We now define $P''_1, \ldots, P''_n$. For j in J and h in H, define $P''_j = P_j$, $P''_h = P_h$. For l in L, we change the position of x in the diagram of P_l so that x is just above y in the diagram of P''_l, without changing the position of any other element, as in Figure 2.22. Thus, for $u \neq x$, $v \neq x$ define $u >''_l v$ exactly when $u >_l v$, define $x >''_l z$ exactly when $y >_l z$, or $z = y$, or z is indifferent to y under P, and finally define $z >''_l x$ exactly when $z >_l y$. For l in L, P''_l is a weak order, and P_l and P''_l satisfy Condition 1. For m in M, we define P''_m according to Figure 2.23. Thus, for $u \neq x$, $v \neq x$, define $u >''_m v$ if $u >_m v$, define $x >''_m z$ if $y >_m z$, and finally define $z >''_m x$ if $z >_m y$. For m in M, P''_m is

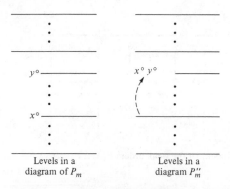

Figure 2.23   Determining P''_m from P_m.

a weak order, and P_m and P''_m satisfy Condition 1. Thus the hypotheses of Condition 1 are satisfied by $P_1, \ldots, P_n, P''_1, \ldots, P''_n$, and x and y. Thus $x > ''y$. Proof of the theorem is almost finished now, since $x > ''y$ and by construction $x > '_t y$ exactly when $x > '_t y$ and $y > ''_t x$ exactly when $y > '_t x$ for all individuals t. Thus Condition 2 implies that $x > 'y$, so that J is indeed decisive for x over y.

Theorem 2.16 gives a sufficient condition in order for a decisive set for x over y to exist, and Condition 3 now shows that the hypotheses of Theorem 2.16 can be satisfied.

Theorem 2.17   Let x and y be distinct in S and $\mathscr{F} : \mathscr{L} \times \cdots \times \mathscr{L} \to \mathscr{L}$ be a social decision function satisfying Conditions 1 through 3. Then there exists a decisive set for x over y.

Proof   By Condition 3 there exists some set $P_1, P_2, \ldots, P_n$ of weak orders such that $x > y$. Let $K = \{k : y >_k x\}$ and $J = \{j : x >_j y$ or x is indifferent to y under $P_j\}$. We claim that J is a decisive set. To see this, note that we need only change those P_g with $g \in G = \{g : x$ is indifferent to y under $P_g\}$. Thus define P^*_g for $g \in G$ as in Figure 2.24 and define $P^*_i = P_i$ for $i \notin G$.

The weak orders $P_1, \ldots, P_n$, and $P^*_1, \ldots, P^*_n$ and x and y satisfy the hypothesis of Condition 1, so that $x > *y$. Hence $P^*_1, \ldots, P^*_n$ satisfy the hypothesis of Theorem 2.16, so that J is a decisive set for x over y.

We note that a decisive set is not empty unless Condition 3 is violated, since an empty decisive set implies $x > y$ regardless of $P_1, \ldots, P_n$, which contradicts the fact that there exist weak orders that yield $y > x$.

Although a decisive set exists for x over y, we do not as yet know the effect these decisive sets have on the remaining alternatives. What we now show is that, if a set is decisive for x over y, then it is decisive for any alternative over any other alternative. This is accomplished in two steps.

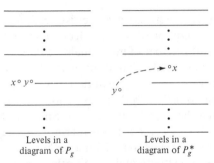

| Levels in a | Levels in a |
| diagram of P_g | diagram of P_g^* |

Figure 2.24 Determining P_g^* from P_g.

Theorem 2.18 Let $\mathcal{F} : \mathcal{L} \times \cdots \times \mathcal{L} \to \mathcal{L}$ be a social decision function satisfying Conditions 1 through 3. Let x, y, and z be distinct alternatives. If J is decisive for x over y, then J is decisive for x over z and z over y.

Proof Let $P_1, \ldots, P_n$ be weak orders such that $x >_j y$ and $y >_j z$ for all j in J, and $y >_k z$, $z >_k x$ for all k not in J. Since J is decisive for x over y, we have $x > y$. Since $y >_i z$ for all individuals i and Theorem 2.17 guarantees that there is some decisive set for y over z, then $y > z$. Thus, by transitivity, $x > z$. Since $x >_j z$ for all j in J and $z >_k x$ for all k not in J, Theorem 2.16 shows that J is decisive for x over z. To show that J is decisive for z over y, simply choose weak orders with $x >_j y$ and $z >_j x$ for j in J, and $y >_k z$, $z >_k x$ for k not in J. As in the first part of the proof, $x > y$ and $z > x$, so that $z > y$. Theorem 2.16 again shows that J is decisive for z over y.

Corollary With $\mathcal{F}$ as in Theorem 2.18, and $x \neq y$, $u \neq v$ in S, if J is decisive for x over y, then J is decisive for u over v.

Proof If $v \neq x$, then Theorem 2.18 shows that J is decisive for x over v and a further application shows that J is decisive for u over v. Thus we need only consider the case in which $v = x$. By hypothesis, there exists a third alternative z in S with $x \neq z$, $y \neq z$. Theorem 2.18 shows that J is decisive for z over y. Thus J is decisive for z over x, that is, z over v. Hence Theorem 2.18 shows that J is decisive for u over v.

We are now ready to prove the impossibility theorem, which says that a social decision function $\mathcal{F} : \mathcal{L} \times \cdots \times \mathcal{L} \to \mathcal{L}$ satisfying Conditions 1 through 3 must be a dictatorship.

Theorem 2.19 Let $\mathcal{F} : \mathcal{L} \times \cdots \times \mathcal{L} \to \mathcal{L}$ be a social decision function satisfying Conditions 1 through 3. Then there exists an individual i_0 such that $u >_{i_0} v$ implies $u > v$ for arbitrary u and v, regardless of the weak orders $P_1, \ldots, P_{i_0-1}, P_{i_0+1}, \ldots, P_n$.

Proof   Let $x \neq y$ be in S. By Theorem 2.17 there exists a decisive set J for x over y. Furthermore, J cannot be empty. Out of all possible decisive sets for x over y, pick one that contains the least number of individuals—call it I_0. We show that I_0 contains exactly one individual and that this individual is a dictator. Since I_0 is not empty, let $i_0 \in I_0$. Choose P_{i_0} such that $x >_{i_0} y$ and $y >_{i_0} z$, and for the remaining i in I_0 choose P_i such that $z >_i x$ and $x >_i y$. Finally, for k not in I_0, choose P_k such that $y >_k z$ and $z >_k x$. Since I_0 is decisive for x over y and $x >_i y$ for all i in I_0, $x > y$. Furthermore, since $\mathscr{F}(P_1, P_2, \ldots, P_n)$ is a weak order, we have by Theorem 2.3 that either $x > z$ or else $z > y$. In case $x > z$, $x >_{i_0} z$ by transitivity and for all other individuals j, $z >_j x$ so that Theorem 2.16 implies $\{i_0\}$ is decisive for x over z and Theorem 2.18 implies $\{i_0\}$ is decisive for x over y. Thus $I_0 = \{i_0\}$. In case $z > y$, we have $z >_i y$ for all i in I_0, $i \neq i_0$ but $y >_j z$ for all $j \notin I_0$ and $j = i_0$. Thus the set of all i in I_0, $i \neq i_0$, is a decisive set for z over y by Theorem 2.16 and for x over y by Theorem 2.18. This new set, however, contains fewer elements than I_0 (namely, it does not contain i_0) so that we have a set, decisive for x over y, with fewer elements than I_0, which is a contradiction. Hence z is not greater than y, and we are in the first case, namely, $I = \{i_0\}$. Theorem 2.18 now guarantees that $\{i_0\}$ is decisive for every pair of elements in S, so that i_0 is a dictator.

Corollary   There does not exist a social decision function $\mathscr{F} : \mathscr{L} \times \cdots \times \mathscr{L} \to \mathscr{L}$, with $|S| \geq 3$, that satisfies Conditions 1 through 4.

All is not lost with the proof of Theorem 2.19, however. The problems with determining a social choice function come up not because we wish Conditions 1 through 4 to hold, but because, first, the domain X of possibilities for an individual's partial order is to be as large as the set of all weak orders on S and, second, the range Y of the final social choice must be as small as the set of all weak orders.

There are several time-honored social choice functions that satisfy Conditions 1 through 4. The system of voting for a single candidate or issue, where the winner is the candidate or issue with the most votes, is a common method of social choice in Western democracies. In this method the partial orders available to the voter are simply of the form ⟋⟍⋯∘, whereby one candidate is indicated over all others, or ∘ ∘ ∘ ⋯ ∘, whereby no candidate is indicated. The final social choice is again of the form ⟋⟍⋯∘, and the winner is indicated over all others. Thus, if $X = \{⟋⟍⋯∘, ∘ ∘ ∘ \cdots ∘\}$, then this is a social decision function from $X \times X \times \cdots \times X$ to X. This decision function satisfies Conditions 1 through 4, is easy to implement, and, most important in our political system, always yields a unique maximal element (if ties are broken by the returning officer). However, this function has the disadvantage that it severely limits an individual's expression of his or her preference. This decision procedure also does not necessarily indicate the wishes of society as a whole. For example, if there are candidates A, B, and C and seven voters whose true preferences for A, B, and C are given by the total orders

$$
\begin{array}{ccccccc}
A & A & A & B & B & C & C \\
\downarrow & \downarrow & \downarrow & \downarrow & \downarrow & \downarrow & \downarrow \\
B, & B, & B, & A, & A, & B, & B, \\
\downarrow & \downarrow & \downarrow & \downarrow & \downarrow & \downarrow & \downarrow \\
C & C & C & C & C & A & A
\end{array}
$$

respectively, and if only "most preferred" can be expressed on a ballot, candidate A will be the victor, whereas in actuality candidate B is preferred to candidate A by four out of seven individuals. However, Theorem 2.19 indicates that there is no decision function on the set of all weak orders that satisfies Conditions 1 through 4.

The second naturally occurring decision function is the method of choice by consensus of a council of elders. In this method, the council members are the individuals $1, 2, \ldots, n$ who are involved in the choice function, and $x > y$ if and only if $x >_i y$ for all $i = 1, 2, \ldots, n$. This decision procedure satisfies Conditions 1 through 4 and allows each individual to select an arbitrary partial order. Furthermore, the council can be arbitrarily large so as to include all the individuals in the society. The essential drawback in this choice function is that it is difficult to obtain a unique maximal element. Since obtaining a unique maximal element is necessary in many of our choice procedures, this failure is of great importance. Several American Indian tribes used this method as their choice function, and it was effective in choosing a winner. If consensus was not achieved, then discussion followed and, after allowing members to change their preference, the choice function was again applied. Since council members were "responsible," a consensus was ordinarily obtained. This method of consensus of a council of elders is impractical if the council is large or if the council members are adamant in holding to widely differing views.

Chapter 3

Graphs

3.1 INTRODUCTION

The theory of graphs originated from several sources. In 1736 the mathematician Euler generalized and solved the Konigsberg bridges problem. This problem consisted of finding a walking route across the seven bridges connecting the mainland and two islands in the Pregel River so that each bridge was crossed once and only once (Figure 3.1). In 1847 the physicist Kirchhoff studied the flow of electric current in a set of arbitrarily joined wires. This was the first important application of graphs and led to a fruitful area of investigation called networks. Next the mathematician Cayley considered special graphs called trees in a series of papers beginning in 1857. He first analyzed equations of differential operators and later applied the theory of trees to determining the number of possible carbon compounds of the form C_nH_{2n+2}.

These problems seemed quite disjoint at first, but gradually a theory arose which encompassed all of them. The theory is called graph theory, and this chapter discusses its basic ideas.

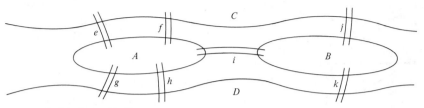

Figure 3.1 Konigsberg bridges.

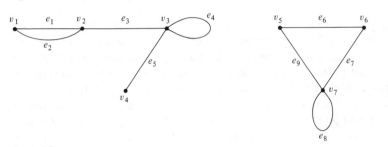

Figure 3.2

Definition A *graph G* consists of a nonempty set V of elements called *vertices*, a set E of elements called *edges*, and a function ε from E to the set of unordered pairs of elements of V.

The two vertices in $\varepsilon(e)$ for an edge e of a graph are called the *end points* of e. To emphasize the fact that a graph depends on V, E, and ε, we write $G = (V, E, \varepsilon)$. If there is only one edge with end points x and y, this edge is sometimes denoted $\overline{xy}$, and in this case we denote G by (V, E).

If V and E are both finite sets, then G is called a *finite graph*. A finite graph can be represented by a diagram in the plane by representing a vertex by a point, and an edge by a line segment joining the points representing the end points of the edge. Figure 3.2 is a diagram of a graph. Edge e_4 has end points v_3 and v_3 and is thus called a loop. Edges e_1 and e_2 have the same end points, namely, v_1 and v_2. The graph is split into two parts (called components) which are not connected.

In Euler's bridge problem, interpret the land areas as vertices and the bridges as edges. A solution then consists of traversing the graph using each edge exactly once. The graph of the Konigsberg bridges is given in Figure 3.3. Kirchhoff's electrical network has an easy interpretation as a graph if the vertices are just the joining points for the wires and the wire segments between joints are just the edges. Even the structure of a molecule can be represented as a graph in which the atoms are vertices and the bonds between atoms are edges. All these graphs have only a finite number of edges and a finite number of vertices.

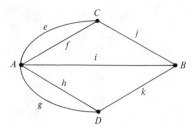

Figure 3.3

A graph can be represented in several ways. One way is to label the vertices 1, 2, ..., n and represent the edges by unordered pairs $\{i, j\}$ if the edge has end points vertex i and vertex j. Another method is to represent the graph as a matrix. As before, label the vertices of the graph 1, 2, ..., n. The matrix (a_{ij}) is a $n \times n$ matrix with the i, j entry equal to the number of edges with end points i and j. This matrix is called an *adjacency matrix* of the graph G, and G can be constructed from the information contained in the matrix. For example, the adjacency matrix of the graph in Figure 3.3, with vertices A, B, C, and D labeled 1, 2, 3, and 4, respectively, is

$$\begin{bmatrix} 0 & 1 & 2 & 2 \\ 1 & 0 & 1 & 1 \\ 2 & 1 & 0 & 0 \\ 2 & 1 & 0 & 0 \end{bmatrix}.$$

Note that the adjacency matrix is symmetric; that is, $a_{ij} = a_{ji}$, $1 \le i \le n$, $1 \le j \le n$.

3.2   CHAINS, CYCLES, AND COVERINGS

This section introduces the notions of chains and cycles and gives the solution to a generalization of the bridges problem.

Definition   An *edge sequence* is a sequence e_1, e_2, ..., e_n of edges (repetitions allowed) such that there is a sequence of vertices $v_0, v_1, ..., v_n$, the end points of e_j being v_{j-1} and v_j. The edge sequence is said to extend from v_0 to v_n and to have *length n*.

A *chain sequence* is an edge sequence in which there is no repetition of edges. A *cycle sequence* is a chain sequence that extends from v_0 to v_n, $v_0 = v_n$. If we disregard the order in a chain (cycle) sequence—for example, whether it extends from v_0 to v_n or v_n to v_0—then the chain (cycle) sequence is called a *chain (cycle)*.

The Konigsberg bridges problem is equivalent to there being a chain in graph G in Figure 3.3 that contains all the edges of G. If there is such a walking route over the bridges, then each time a person comes to an island, he or she has to leave it, unless it is a starting or ending point. Thus the number of bridges touching that land area has to be even unless that area is possibly the starting or ending point of the walk. Hence we see at once that the Konigsberg bridges problem has no solution. However, there is a general formulation and solution to this problem.

Definition   A graph is *connected* if there exists a chain between any two vertices of the graph, or else if the graph contains only a single vertex.

Definition   The *degree* $\delta(v)$ of a vertex v of a graph G is the number of edges with end point v, with the convention that a loop with end points v and v contributes two to the degree of v.

In the example in Figure 3.3, $\delta(A) = 5$, $\delta(B) = 3$, $\delta(C) = 3$, and $\delta(D) = 3$.

Theorem 3.1   If G is a finite graph, the number of vertices of odd degree is even.

Proof   Each edge has two end points and thus contributes two to the sum of the degrees of the vertices. Hence $\sum_{v \in V} \delta(v)$ is even. Let V_0 be the set of vertices of even degree and V_1 the set of vertices of odd degree. Thus $\sum_{v \in V} \delta(v) = \sum_{v \in V_0} \delta(v) + \sum_{v \in V_1} \delta(v)$. Since $\delta(v)$ is even for each $v \in V_0$, $\sum_{v \in V_0} \delta(v)$ is even. Thus $\sum_{v \in V_1} \delta(v)$ is even. But $\delta(v)$ is odd for each $v \in V_1$, and the sum of an odd number of odd numbers is odd. Therefore there is an even number of vertices of odd degree.

Theorem 3.2   Let $G = (V, E, \varepsilon)$ be a connected finite graph with no vertices of odd degree, $|V| \geq 2$. Then the edges of G can be arranged to form a cycle.

Proof   Since G is finite, among the chains there is one (not necessarily unique) $e_1, \ldots, e_n$ of maximal length n. We first show that this chain is a cycle. Let $v_0, v_1, \ldots, v_n$ be the sequence of edges with v_{i-1}, v_i the end points of e_i, $i = 1, \ldots, n$. If an edge e' has an end point v_0 and $e' \notin \{e_1, \ldots, e_n\}$, then $e', e_1, \ldots, e_n$ is a chain of length $n + 1$, which contradicts the maximality of n. Thus each edge with v_0 an end point is in $\{e_1, \ldots, e_n\}$. The number of occurrences of v_0 in the sequence of end points $v_0, v_1; v_1, v_2; v_2, v_3; \ldots; v_{n-1}, v_n$ of the chain $e_1, e_2, \ldots, e_n$ is the degree of v_0. If $v_0 \neq v_n$, this number is $1 + 2k$, since after the initial occurrence in the sequence of end points, v_0 always

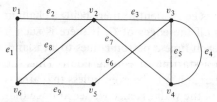

Figure 3.4

appears in pairs. However, v_0 has even degree, so we must have $v_0 = v_n$, and the longest chain is a cycle. Suppose e is an arbitrary edge with end points x and y. We now show that $e \in \{e_1, \ldots, e_n\}$. Since G is connected, there exists a chain $f_1, \ldots, f_l$ with edge f_i having end points w_{i-1} and w_i; $w_0 = v_0, w_1 = x$. If $\{e_1, \ldots, e_n\}$ contains $f_1, f_2, \ldots, f_t$ but not f_{t+1}, then $w_t = v_m$, some m, and e_{m+1}, $e_{m+2}, \ldots, e_n, e_1, e_2, \ldots, e_m, f_{t+1}$ is a chain of longer length. Thus $f_i \in \{e_1, \ldots, e_n\}$, $i = 1, \ldots, l$, and $x = w_l = v_p$ for some p. If $e \notin \{e_1, \ldots, e_n\}$, then e_{p+1}, $e_{p+2}, \ldots, e_n, e_1, \ldots, e_p, e$ is a chain of length greater than n. This is a contradiction, so that $e \in \{e_1, \ldots, e_n\}$ and all edges of G are in the cycle $e_1, \ldots, e_n$.

Definition   A *covering* of a graph is a partition of the set of edges into subsets, each of which can be arranged to form a chain or cycle.

The graph in Figure 3 has a covering $\{e_1, e_2, e_8\}$, $\{e_9, e_6, e_3, e_7, e_4, e_5\}$, which consists of one chain and one cycle.

By Theorem 3.2, a connected finite graph can be covered by a single cycle. Any graph has a trivial covering by chains; that is, each edge is a chain by itself. This is unsatisfactory, since it is often desirable to cover a graph with the least number of chains possible. This is called a *minimal covering*. The next theorem indicates the number of chains in a minimal covering of a finite graph. Theorem 3.2 has already shown us that a finite connected graph with each vertex having even degree has a minimal covering of one cycle. Hence we need only examine finite graphs with at least one vertex of odd degree and, because of Theorem 3.1, the number of vertices of odd degree is $2n, n \geq 1$.

Theorem 3.3   Let G be a finite connected graph with $2n$ vertices of odd degree, $n \geq 1$. Then every minimal covering consists of n chains, each of which joins two vertices of odd degree.

Proof   Let $\{v_1, v_2, v_3, \ldots, v_{2n-1}, v_{2n}\}$ be the vertices of odd degree. Add edges e_k with end points v_{2k-1}, v_{2k} to $G, k = 1, \ldots, n$. Since each vertex v_i has an additional edge with end point v_i, v_i has even degree. Thus all vertices now have even degree and, by Theorem 3.2, there is a cycle covering the new graph. From this cycle, delete the edges $e_1, \ldots, e_n$. This gives n chains, since no two e_i's have a vertex in common. Thus we have a covering of G with n chains, each of which joins two vertices of odd degree.

There cannot be a covering of G by less than n chains, since this implies that there are less than 2n vertices of odd degree.

Exercises

3-1 Determine the degree of each vertex of the graph in Figure 3.5.

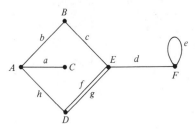

Figure 3.5

3-2 Determine a minimal covering of the graph in Figure 3.5.

3-3 Let G be a graph. A vertex v_0 is said to be connected to v_1 if there is an edge sequence from v_0 to v_1 or $v_0 = v_1$. Prove that connectedness is an equivalence relation on the set of vertices of G, hence partitions the set of vertices into equivalence classes of connected vertices. An equivalence class, along with any edges joined to a vertex of the class, forms a *connected component* of the graph.

3-4 Let G be the graph consisting of vertices {integers n: $2 < n < 13$} and edges $e_{i,j}$ joining the vertices i and j if i divides j. Draw a diagram of the graph and determine the connected components of the graph.

3-5 Write the adjacency matrix of the graph in Figure 3.5.

3-6 Show that the number of people who dance (at a dance where the dancing is done in couples) an odd number of times is even.

3-7 Prove that, if at a party, any pair of people shake hands at most once with each other, then there are two people at the party who shake hands the same number of times.

3.3   SUBGRAPHS AND SPANNING SUBGRAPHS

In many applications of graph theory nonessential edges and vertices can be eliminated. This section defines concepts related to this problem and gives a method of solving the puzzle Instant Insanity.

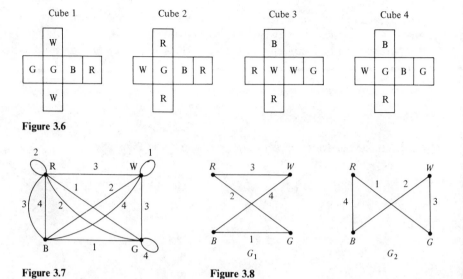

Figure 3.6

Figure 3.7   Figure 3.8

Definition   A *subgraph* of a graph G consists of a subset U of the set of vertices of G and a subset F of the set of edges of G such that the end points of the edges of F are in U.

Definition   A *spanning subgraph* of C is a subgraph of G that contains all the vertices of G.

Definition   A graph is *regular of degree n* if each vertex has degree n.

The equipment for Instant Insanity consists of four cubes whose faces are four colors. The object of the puzzle is to stack the cubes in a rectangular prism so that each color appears once and only once on each face of the prism.

A typical set is represented in Figure 3.6 and colored red (R), white (W), green (G), and blue (B).

To solve the puzzle, construct a graph with four vertices, one corresponding to each of the four colors. An edge connecting two vertices belongs to the graph if the colors are on the opposite side of a cube. Label the edges according to which cube determines them. Thus the graph of the above four cubes is given in Figure 3.7. Two spanning regular subgraphs G_1 and G_2 of degree 2 must be found such that the edges of G_1 are disjoint from the edges of G_2 and each edge of G_1 (or G_2) is obtained from a different cube. Thus for Figure 3.7 two such subgraphs are shown in Figure 3.8. Stack the cubes according to G_1 so that each color appears once on the front and once on the back of the stack. The edges of G_1 are $\overline{RW}$, $\overline{WB}$, $\overline{BG}$, and $\overline{GR}$, so we have the

	Edge	Front	Back
Cube 3	$\overline{RW}$	R	W
Cube 4	$\overline{WB}$	W	B
Cube 1	$\overline{BG}$	B	G
Cube 2	$\overline{GR}$	G	R

Figure 3.9

	Edge	Left side	Right side
Cube 3	$\overline{WG}$	W	G
Cube 4	$\overline{RB}$	R	B
Cube 1	$\overline{GR}$	G	R
Cube 2	$\overline{BW}$	B	W

Figure 3.10

stack given in Figure 3.9. G_2 now determines the colors on the sides of the stack.

Since each cube can be rotated about an axis through the front and back, there is no problem in arranging the colors so the left and right sides correspond with Figure 3.10.

The existence of two regular subgraphs of degree 2 with disjoint sets of edges is thus sufficient to solve the puzzle. It is also a necessary condition, since if a solution exists, then the set of four edges of the graph corresponding to the front and back of the stack will be disjoint from the set of edges corresponding to the left and right sides of the stack. These two sets form the edges of the two subgraphs. Since a face of the stack must have every color represented, then every vertex of the graph must be included in each of the two subgraphs. Thus the subgraphs are spanning. Furthermore, each vertex of the spanning subgraph has degree 2, since a color occurs exactly once on one face of the prism and exactly once on the opposite face. Thus the existence of two regular subgraphs of degree 2 with disjoint sets of edges is necessary.

Exercises

3-8   Construct a connected spanning subgraph of the graph in Figure 3.11 with a minimum number of edges. Is this subgraph regular?

3-9   Construct a nonconnected regular spanning subgraph of degree 2 for the graph in Figure 3.11.

3-10   Solve the Instant Insanity puzzle in Figure 3.12.

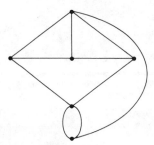

Figure 3.11

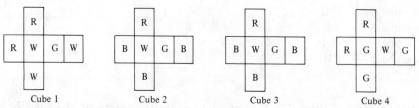

	R		
R	W	G	W
	W		

Cube 1

	R		
B	W	G	B
	B		

Cube 2

	R		
B	W	G	B
	B		

Cube 3

	R		
R	G	W	G
	G		

Cube 4

Figure 3.12   Instant Insanity.

3-11   Given four cubes with faces colored red, white, green, or blue such that each cube has a face of each color, does there necessarily exist an Instant Insanity stacking?

3.4   TREES

Graphs that have no cycles are important in many search procedures. A graph with no cycles is called a *forest*. A connected forest is called a *tree*. These graphs have a simple structure. A molecule of a chemical compound can be represented as a graph with vertices representing the atoms and edges representing the bonds between the atoms. One of the simplest organic molecules is a hydrocarbon of the form C_nH_{2n+2}, and the graph of this molecule must be a tree. The structure of a sentence in English forms a tree. The preceding sentence is decomposed as shown in Figure 3.13.

Denote the number of vertices of a finite graph $G = (V, E)$ by $|V|$ and the number of edges by $|E|$. Figure 3.14 diagrams some trees with n vertices, $n = 1, 2, \ldots, 6$. We claim that these are essentially all trees with n vertices, $n = 1, 2, \ldots, 6$. In making this claim, we must decide what we mean for two graphs to be essentially the same. The graphs $G_1 = (\{a, b, c\}, \{\overline{ab}, \overline{bc}\})$ and $G_2 = (\{u, v, w\}, \{\overline{uv}, \overline{vw}\})$ are distinct, and yet if we change the vertices of G_1 from a to u, b to v, c to w, we obtain G_2. Thus G_1 and G_2 are essentially the same.

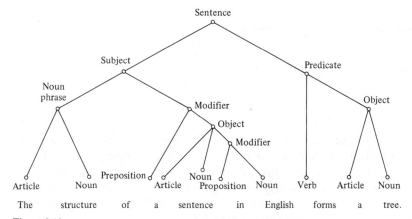

Figure 3.13

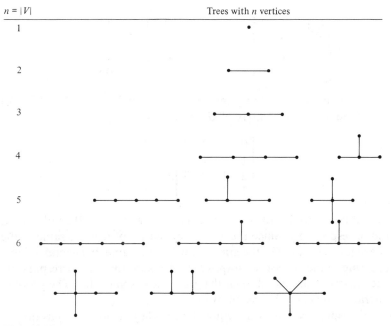

Figure 3.14

Definition The graph $G = (V, E)$ is *isomorphic* to the graph $G_1 = (V_1, E_1)$ if there is a one-to-one map v from V onto V_1 and a one-to-one map ϕ from E onto E_1 satisfying $\phi(\overline{uv}) = \overline{v(u)v(v)}$. We write $G \cong G_1$ and call the mappings an *isomorphism*.

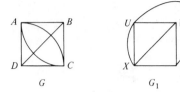

Figure 3.15

As a simple example, consider the graphs G and G_1 in Figure 3.15. Superficially they may appear different, but the mapping $A \to U$, $B \to V$, $C \to X$, and $D \to W$ and the mapping $\overline{AC} \to \overline{UX}$, $\overline{AB} \to \overline{UV}$, $\overline{BC} \to \overline{VX}$, $\overline{BD} \to \overline{VW}$, $\overline{CD} \to \overline{XW}$, and $\overline{AD} \to \overline{UW}$ form an isomorphism from G to G_1. It is laborious to check whether or not two graphs are isomorphic. In the previous example the adjacency matrix for G, where A, B, C, and D are 1, 2, 3, and 4, respectively, and the adjacency matrix for G_1, where U, V, W, and X are 1, 2, 3, and 4 are

$$\begin{bmatrix} 0 & 1 & 2 & 1 \\ 1 & 0 & 1 & 1 \\ 2 & 1 & 0 & 1 \\ 1 & 1 & 1 & 0 \end{bmatrix} \quad \text{and} \quad \begin{bmatrix} 0 & 1 & 1 & 2 \\ 1 & 0 & 1 & 1 \\ 1 & 1 & 0 & 1 \\ 2 & 1 & 1 & 0 \end{bmatrix},$$

respectively. Switching the third and fourth rows and the third and fourth columns of the adjacency matrix of G_1 produces

$$\begin{bmatrix} 0 & 1 & 2 & 1 \\ 1 & 0 & 1 & 1 \\ 2 & 1 & 0 & 1 \\ 1 & 1 & 1 & 0 \end{bmatrix},$$

which corresponds to the adjacency matrix of G_1 with U, V, W, and X as 1, 2, 4, and 3, respectively. Since the adjacency matrix of G is the same as the new adjacency matrix of G_1, the graphs must be the same. In general, if there is an ordering of the vertices of graphs H and K such that the corresponding adjacency matrices are equal, then the graphs are isomorphic. The proof of this general statement is left as an exercise.

Clearly isomorphism is an equivalence relation on the collection of graphs. One representative from each isomorphism class of trees with n vertices, $1 \le n \le 6$, is listed in Figure 3.14.

The trees in Figure 3.14 all have the property that $|E| = |V| - 1$. This fact almost characterizes trees.

Theorem 3.4   The following properties are equivalent. For a finite graph $G = (V, E)$,

i G is a tree.

ii G is connected and $|E| = |V| - 1$.

iii G has no cycles and $|E| = |V| - 1$.

Proof That (i) implies (ii) will be shown by induction on $|E|$. The statement is true for $|E| = 0$. Since a tree has no cycles, there must be a vertex $v \in V$ with degree 1. Otherwise we could construct a cycle. Delete v, and the edge with v as an end point, from G. The new graph $G_1 = (V_1, E_1)$ is still connected and has no cycles, so that, by the induction hypothesis, $|E_1| = |V_1| - 1$. Hence adding the deleted vertex and edge, $|E| = |V| - 1$.

That (ii) implies (iii) will similarly be shown by induction on $|E|$. We must show that if G is connected with $|E| = |V| - 1$ then G has no cycles. Again this is true for $|E| = 0$. Connectedness ensures that, except for the case $|E| = 0$, there are no vertices of degree 0. If each vertex has degree ≥ 2, then $2|E| = \sum_{v \in V} \delta(v) \geq \sum_{v \in V} 2 = 2|V|$, which by hypothesis cannot happen. Hence G must have a vertex w of degree 1. Delete this vertex and the edge with w as end point to obtain a new graph $G_1 = (V_1, E_1)$. The hypothesis of (ii) is still satisfied, hence by induction G_1 has no cycles. Since w cannot belong to any cycle in G, then G has no cycles.

(iii) implies (i). It remains to be proven that G is connected if it has no cycles and $|V| = |E| - 1$. By Exercise 3-3, G is partitioned into connected components, each of which must be a tree. Hence for each component (V_c, E_c), $|E_c| = |V_c| - 1$. Thus

$$|V| - 1 = |E| = \sum_c |E_c| = \sum_c \left(|V_c| - \sum 1 \right) = |V| - \sum_c 1.$$

This happens only when there is one component. Thus G is connected.

Exercises

3-12 Determine the distinct trees with seven vertices.

3-13 Determine whether the following pairs of connected graphs are isomorphic.

 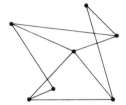

Figure 3.16

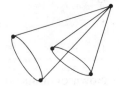

Figure 3.17

3-14   Prove that, if G_1 is isomorphic to G_2, then $\delta(v) = \delta(v(v))$ for each vertex v of G_1.

3-15   Prove that G is a tree if and only if every two vertices of G are connected by a unique chain.

3-16   Prove that a connected graph has a subgraph that is a spanning tree and describe a method for determining such a spanning tree.

3-17   Prove that a graph G is isomorphic to a graph H if and only if there is an ordering of the vertices of G and H such that the resulting adjacency matrices are equal.

3.5 MAXIMAL SPANNING SUBTREES

A finite connected graph in general has many connected spanning sub-graphs. One of the simplest types is a spanning subgraph that is a tree—a *spanning subtree* for short. It is not difficult to determine a spanning subtree of a finite connected graph $G = (V, E)$. Let $G_0 = G$. If $G_i = (V, E_i)$ is a connected subgraph of G, and G_i is not a tree, then G_i contains a cycle. Choose an edge e of this cycle and define $E_{i+1} = E_i \setminus \{e\}$. The subgraph $G_{i+1} = (V, E_{i+1})$ of G is still connected, and $|E_{i+1}| = |E_i| - 1$. Since $|E|$ is finite, we must eventually have an integer j such that $G_j = (V, E_j)$ is a connected subgraph of G containing no cycles. Thus G_j is a spanning subtree.

In many applications each edge e of G has a real number $\lambda(e)$ associated with it. This may represent cost, time, profit, capacity, or numerous other variables denoting a relationship between the vertices. A fundamental prob-lem is to find a spanning subtree T of G that maximizes $\sum_{e \in E(T)} \lambda(e)$, where $T = (V(T), E(T))$. Such a tree is called a *maximal spanning subtree*. It is not difficult to imagine a procedure for determining such a subtree. Just follow the process described for constructing a spanning subtree but at each step choose an edge e with $\lambda(e)$ minimal for any e in any cycle. A graph may have many maximal spanning subtrees, and the following theorem characterizes them.

Theorem 3.5 Let G be a finite connected graph with a real number $\lambda(e)$ associated with each edge. A spanning subtree T of G is maximal if and only if $\lambda(f) \leq \min\{\lambda(e_1), \ldots, \lambda(e_k)\}$, where f is any edge of G and $e_1, \ldots, e_k$ is the unique tree chain between the end points of f.

Proof If there exists an edge f in G with $\lambda(f) > \min\{\lambda(e_1), \ldots, \lambda(e_k)\}$, say $\lambda(f) > \lambda(e_j)$, where $e_1, \ldots, e_n$ is the tree chain between the end points of f, then define $E' = (E\backslash\{e_j\}) \cup \{f\}$ and $T' = (V, E')$, where $T = (V, E)$. T' is still connected and since $|E'| = |E| = |V| - 1$, T' is a spanning subtree. The fact that $\sum_{e \in E(T')} \lambda(e) > \sum_{e \in E(T)} \lambda(e)$ contradicts the maximality of T. Thus $\lambda(f) \leq \min\{\lambda(e_1), \ldots, \lambda(e_n)\}$.

To show the reverse implication we show that, for any spanning subtrees T_1 and T_2 satisfying $\lambda(f) \leq \min\{\lambda(e_1), \ldots, \lambda(e_k)\}$, $\sum_{e \in E(T_1)} \lambda(e) = \sum_{e \in E(T_2)} \lambda(e)$. Thus, since maximal spanning subtrees satisfy $\lambda(f) \leq \min\{\lambda(e_1), \ldots, \lambda(e_k)\}$, then any spanning subtree satisfying this inequality is maximal. Let $\overline{vw}$ be an edge of $E(T_1)\backslash E(T_2)$. Thus $\lambda(\overline{vw}) \leq \min\{\lambda(\overline{vv_1}), \lambda(\overline{v_1 v_2}), \ldots, \lambda(\overline{v_{k-1} w})\}$, where $\overline{vv_1}, \ldots, \overline{v_{k-1} w}$ is the unique chain in T_2 connecting $v_0 = v$ and $v_k = w$. Now there is some edge $\overline{v_i v_{i+1}} \notin E(T_1)$ with $\lambda(\overline{vw}) = \lambda(\overline{v_i v_{i+1}})$. Otherwise, for each $\overline{v_i v_{i+1}} \notin E(T_1)$, there is a unique chain $\overline{u_0 u_1}, \ldots, \overline{u_{e-1} u_e}$ in T_1 connecting v_i and v_{i+1} with $\lambda(\overline{vw}) < \lambda(\overline{v_i v_{i+1}}) \leq \min\{\lambda(\overline{u_0 u_1}), \ldots, \lambda(\overline{u_{e-1} u_e})\}$. Thus, for each $\overline{v_i v_{i+1}} \notin E(T_1)$, these chains are disjoint from $\overline{vw}$. All other $\overline{v_i v_{i+1}}$ are in $E(T_1) \cap E(T_2)$, hence disjoint from $\overline{vw}$. Gluing the $\overline{v_i v_{i+1}} \in E(T_1) \cap E(T_2)$ and these chains together results in a cycle in T_1, which is a contradiction. Thus, for some v_i, $\lambda(\overline{vw}) = \lambda(\overline{v_i v_{i+1}})$. Hence delete $\overline{v_i v_{i+1}}$ from $E(T_2)$ and add $\overline{vw}$ to $E(T_2)$. This gives a new spanning subtree $T_2(1)$ which has $\sum_{e \in E(T_2)} \lambda(e) = \sum_{e \in E(T_2(1))} \lambda(e)$ and satisfies $\lambda(f) \leq \min\{\lambda(e_1), \ldots, \lambda(e_k)\}$. It has one more edge in common with T_1. Continuing this procedure we obtain a sequence $T_2(j)$ of spanning subtrees satisfying the inequality, with $\sum_{e \in E(T_2(j))} \lambda(e) = \sum_{e \in E(T_2)} \lambda(e)$, which eventually must be T_1. Thus $\sum_{e \in E(T_2)} \lambda(e) = \sum_{e \in E(T_1)} \lambda(e)$, and the theorem is proved.

Exercises

3-18 Determine a maximal spanning subtree of the graph in Figure 3.18 by using the procedure outlined in the text.

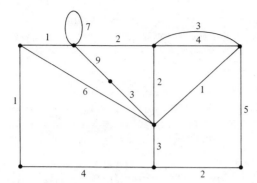

Figure 3.18

3-19   Prove that the result of the procedure given to construct a spanning subtree actually yields a spanning subtree.

3-20   Prove that the result of the procedure given to construct a maximal spanning subtree actually yields a maximal spanning subtree.

3-21   Let $G = (V, E)$ be a connected finite graph with $\lambda(e)$ a real number associated with each edge. Define $T_0 = (V, \phi)$. If $T_i = (V, F_i)$ is a subgraph of G without cycles, choose $e \in E\backslash F_i$ such that $T_{i+1} = (V, F_i \cup \{e\})$ contains no cycles and $\lambda(e)$ is maximal for such e. Prove that $T_{|V|-1}$ is a maximal spanning subtree.

3.6 DIRECTED GRAPHS

Graphs in which the edges are oriented in a specific direction occur naturally in the study of the flow of electric current, the flow of commodities in an economy, and the scheduling of jobs at a construction project. Graphs in which the edges are given a direction are called directed graphs. To distinguish directed graphs from graphs, vertices are called nodes and edges are called arcs. To be precise, a *directed graph* $G = (N, A, \varepsilon)$ consists of a nonempty set N of nodes, a set A of arcs, and a function ε from A to $N \times N$. The pair of nodes $\varepsilon(a) = (u, v)$ is sometimes written $\overrightarrow{uv} = a$ and directs the arc from u to v. The arc is said to originate at u and terminate at v. We in general write $G = (N, A)$ for a directed graph.

As with graphs, a directed graph can be represented by an *adjacency matrix*. Label the nodes $1, 2, \ldots, n$ and define $a_{i,j}$ to be the number of arcs originating at i and terminating at j. Note that the adjacency matrix for a directed graph need not be symmetric.

The notion of degree of a vertex v can be broken into the *out-degree* $\theta(v)$ of the vertex, which is the number of arcs that originate at v, and the *in-degree* $\iota(v)$ of the vertex, which is the number of arcs that terminate at v. The degree of a vertex v is $\delta(v) = \theta(v) + \iota(v)$.

Although a distinction has been made between graphs and directed graphs, the two concepts are closely related. If $G = (V, E)$ is a graph, then a directed graph is obtained from G by taking the nodes to be the set V and the arcs to be $\{\overrightarrow{xy}, \overrightarrow{yx} : \overline{xy} \in E\}$. Thus each edge is replaced by two arcs, one going in each direction. If $D = (N, A)$ is a directed graph, then by forgetting the direction of the arcs a graph is obtained. This graph has N as the set of vertices and edges $= \{\overline{xy} : \overrightarrow{xy} \in A\}$. Thus any definition made for some facet of graph theory can apply to directed graphs by forgetting the direction of the arcs and considering the directed graph as a graph. For example, in Figure 3.19, the sequence of arcs $\overleftarrow{fe}, \overrightarrow{eg}, \overleftarrow{gb}, \overrightarrow{ba}$ becomes the chain $\overline{fe}, \overline{eg}, \overline{gb}, \overline{ba}$ when the direction is forgotten. Thus $\overleftarrow{fe}, \overrightarrow{eg}, \overleftarrow{gb}, \overrightarrow{ba}$ is called a chain in a directed graph. This convention is used to define *chain*, *cycle*, *length*, and *tree* in directed graphs. There are, however, special types of chains and cycles which are singled out. A *path* is a chain of the form $\overrightarrow{v_0 v_1}, \overrightarrow{v_1 v_2}, \ldots, \overrightarrow{v_{n-1} v_n}$. This path extends from v_0 to v_n, and v_n is said to be *accessible* from v_0. A *circuit* is a path with $v_0 = v_n$. Section 3.2 gives criteria for determining a minimal covering of a graph by chains and cycles. A directed graph can be covered by paths and circuits, and we can ask for a minimal covering by paths and circuits. Let $P = \{v \in V : \theta(v) > \iota(v)\}$, the set of nodes with net positive out-degree, and $N = \{v \in V : \theta(v) < \iota(v)\}$, the set of nodes with net negative out-degree. Since the total out-degree of the graph equals the total in-degree, $\sum_{v \in P} (\theta(v) - \iota(v)) = \sum_{v \in N} [\iota(v) - \theta(v)]$. This number characterizes minimal coverings and in fact we have the following theorem.

Theorem 3.6 Let G be a connected directed graph. If P is empty, then a minimal covering of G consists of one circuit. If P is not empty, then a minimal covering consists of $k = \sum_{v \in P} [\theta(v) - \iota(v)]$ paths. In the latter case, each path in a minimal covering extends from a node of P to a node of N.

The proof is analogous to the procedure in Section 3.2, hence is left as an exercise.

Finally, $G_1 = (N_1, A_1, \varepsilon_1)$ is a *subgraph* of a directed graph $G = (N, A, \varepsilon)$ if $N_1 \subset N$, $A_1 \subset A$, and $\varepsilon_1(a) = \varepsilon(a)$ for all $a \in A_1$. A *subtree* of a directed graph is a subgraph that is also a tree.

Exercises

3-22 Determine $\iota(v)$ and $\theta(v)$ for each node in Figure 3.19.

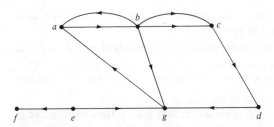

Figure 3.19

3-23 Determine a chain that includes all the nodes in Figure 3.19. Is there a path that includes all the nodes?

3-24 Draw a connected subgraph of the graph in Figure 3.19, which includes exactly the nodes accessible from c.

3-25 Prove Theorem 3.6.

3-26 Determine a minimal covering of the graph in Figure 3.19 by paths and circuits.

3-27 Write the adjacency matrix for the directed graph in Figure 3.19.

3-28 Let (a_{ij}) be the adjacency matrix of a directed graph with no loops. Let r be the row vector with components $\sum_{i=1}^{n} a_{ij}$ and c be the column vector with components $\sum_{j=1}^{n} a_{ij}$. Give interpretations of r and c. Referring only to r and c, determine the number of paths in a minimal covering of the directed graph whose adjacency matrix is

$$\begin{bmatrix} 0 & 1 & 2 & 0 & 1 & 1 \\ 1 & 0 & 1 & 1 & 2 & 0 \\ 0 & 1 & 0 & 1 & 0 & 0 \\ 1 & 2 & 0 & 0 & 1 & 3 \\ 1 & 0 & 2 & 0 & 0 & 1 \\ 2 & 0 & 0 & 1 & 1 & 0 \end{bmatrix}.$$

3.7 ROOTED TREES

A *rooted tree* is a directed graph T with a distinguished node v_0 such that all nodes of T are accessible from v_0 and that T considered as an undirected graph is a tree. The node v_0 is called the *root* of the rooted tree T, and T is often called a *tree rooted at* v_0. Rooted trees play an important role in context-free languages and in maximization problems.

The graph in Figure 3.20 is an example of a rooted tree. Here we assume that all arcs are directed downward, hence the direction need not be indicated on the diagram.

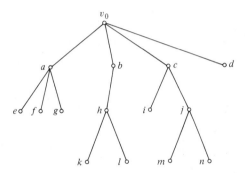

Figure 3.20 Rooted tree.

Let λ be a function from the set of arcs of a directed graph G to the real numbers.

Definition A *longest-distance tree* T rooted at v_0 is a tree T rooted at v_0, which is a subgraph of G containing all nodes of G accessible from v_0, such that for each node v in T, $\sum_{e \in P} \lambda(e) = \max\{\sum_{e \in P'} \lambda(e) : P'$ is a path in G from v_0 to $v\}$, where P is the unique tree path from v_0 to v.

It is not difficult to see that there is always a subgraph of G that is a tree rooted at v_0 and contains all vertices of G accessible from v_0. In general, the last condition in the definition of a longest-distance tree is impossible to fulfill, since there could be a circuit C with $\sum_{e \in C} \lambda(e) > 0$. This may imply that the longest distance to a node necessarily includes a circuit. Thus a longest-distance tree is not possible. To eliminate this consideration, only directed graphs with $\sum_{e \in C} \lambda(e) \le 0$ for any circuit C are considered. In order to facilitate the notation, for any path P, define $\lambda(P) = \sum_{e \in P} \lambda(e)$. If w is a node in a tree T rooted at v_0, define $L(w) = \lambda(P)$, where P is the unique tree path from v_0 to w.

As an example, all nodes in graph H in Figure 3.21 are accessible from a. Each arc is labeled with $\lambda(\text{arc})$. The paths originating at a are exactly $P_1 = (\overrightarrow{ab})$, $P_2 = (\overrightarrow{ab}, \overrightarrow{bc})$, $P_3 = (\overrightarrow{ab}, \overrightarrow{be})$, $P_4 = (\overrightarrow{ad})$, $P_5 = (\overrightarrow{ad}, \overrightarrow{de})$, and $P_6 = (\overrightarrow{ad}, \overrightarrow{df})$. The subtrees of H rooted at a are exactly those in Figure 3.22. The path lengths are $\lambda(P_1) = 1$, $\lambda(P_2) = 1 + 2 = 3$, $\lambda(P_3) = 1 + 5 = 6$, $\lambda(P_4) = 3$, $\lambda(P_5) = 3 + 4 = 7$, and $\lambda(P_6) = 3 + 2 = 5$. Thus T_1 is a longest-distance subtree of H rooted at a, since the tree path length from a to a node of H is indeed the longest path. Only node e has more than one path to it from a, so we only need to note that $6 = \lambda(P_3) < \lambda(P_5) = 7$ to ensure that T_1 is indeed the longest-distance tree.

The following theorem gives a criterion for longest-distance trees.

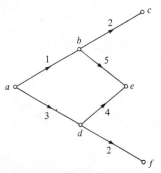

Figure 3.21   *H*.

Theorem 3.7   Let G be a directed graph with $\lambda(C) \leq 0$ for any circuit C in G. The subtree T is a longest-distance tree rooted at v_0 if and only if T is a tree rooted at v_0, which includes all nodes accessible from v_0 and satisfies $L(v) \geq L(u) + \lambda(\overrightarrow{uv})$, where $\overrightarrow{uv}$ is any arc with end points in T.

Proof   If T is a longest-distance tree rooted at v_0, then T is certainly a tree rooted at v_0 that contains all nodes accessible from v_0. If $\overrightarrow{uv}$ is an arc of the graph with $L(v) < L(u) + \lambda(\overrightarrow{uv})$, then the tree length is not the longest route to v. The tree path to u, and then the arc from u to v, give a longer path. Hence the inequality is satisfied.

Suppose T is a tree rooted at v_0, which includes all nodes accessible from v_0 and satisfies $L(v) \geq L(u) + \lambda(\overrightarrow{uv})$, where $\overrightarrow{uv}$ is any arc with an end point in T. If T is not a longest-distance tree, then T contains a node w, and the graph contains a path $P = \overrightarrow{v_0 v_1}, \overrightarrow{v_1 v_2}, \ldots, \overrightarrow{v_k w}$, with $w = v_{k+1}$, such that $L(w) < \lambda(P)$. There is a first node v_j in P such that $L(v_j) < \lambda(\overrightarrow{v_0 v_1}, \ldots, \overrightarrow{v_{j-1} v_j})$. But then $L(v_{j-1}) \geq \lambda(\overrightarrow{v_0 v_1}, \ldots, \overrightarrow{v_{j-2} v_{j-1}})$ and $L(v_{j-1}) + \lambda(\overrightarrow{v_{j-1} v_j}) \geq \lambda(\overrightarrow{v_0 v_1}, \ldots, \overrightarrow{v_{j-2} v_{j-1}}) + \lambda(\overrightarrow{v_{j-1} v_j}) = \lambda(\overrightarrow{v_0 v_1}, \ldots, \overrightarrow{v_{j-1} v_j}) > L(v_j)$. This contradicts $L(v_j) \geq L(v_{j-1}) + \lambda(\overrightarrow{v_{j-1} v_j})$, hence for every path P from v_0 to w, $L(w) \geq \lambda(P)$ and T is a longest-distance tree.

Theorem 3.7 suggests an algorithm to determine a longest-distance tree. Let T be any tree rooted at v_0 and containing all vertices accessible from v_0. If T satisfies $L(v) \geq L(u) + \lambda(\overrightarrow{uv})$ for any u, v in T, then T is a longest-distance tree. If not, then there is an arc $\overrightarrow{uv}$ with $u, v \in T$ and $L(v) < L(u) + \lambda(\overrightarrow{uv})$. Form a new tree by deleting the last arc from the tree path to v and adjoining the arc $\overrightarrow{uv}$. This gives a new tree T_1 with the distance along a tree path in T_1 being greater than or equal to the distance of the tree paths in T. If

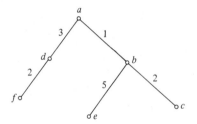

Figure 3.22 Subtrees of H rooted at a.

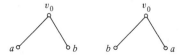

Figure 3.23 Diagrams for rooted tree T.

the graph is finite this procedure must terminate, and the resulting tree will satisfy $L(v) \geq L(u) + \lambda(\overrightarrow{uv})$ for all u, v in the tree.

The concept of longest path is often used in the special context where $\lambda(\overrightarrow{uv}) = 1$ for all arcs $\overrightarrow{uv}$. Thus the path $\overrightarrow{v_0 v_1}$, $\overrightarrow{v_1 v_2}$, ..., $\overrightarrow{v_{n-1} v_n}$ has length $\sum_{i=0}^{n-1} \lambda(\overrightarrow{v_i v_{i+1}}) = \sum_{i=0}^{n-1} 1 = n$, just the number of arcs in the path from v_0 to v_n. By convention, if the function λ is not explicit, the distance from v_0 to w on the path $\overrightarrow{v_0 v_1}$, $\overrightarrow{v_1 v_2}$, ..., $\overrightarrow{v_{n-1} w}$ is simply n, the number of arcs in that path.

The rooted tree $T = (\{v_0, a, b\}, \{\overrightarrow{v_0 a}, \overrightarrow{v_0 b}\}$ is represented by each of the diagrams in Figure 3.23. The diagrams are quite distinct since, in one, a occurs to the left of b and, in the other, b occurs to the left of a. This distinction is important if the tree is used to represent a sentence or an expression. For example, if a and b are distinct positive integers, the first diagram for T could represent a/b and the second could represent b/a, which are not equal in this case.

Let v be a node in a directed graph. The node w is an *immediate successor* of v if $\overrightarrow{vw}$ is an arc of the graph.

Definition A *labeled tree* is a finite rooted tree such that for each node v the set S_v of immediate successors of v is totally ordered, say $S_v = \{v_1, v_2, ..., v_k\}$, $v_1 > v_2 > \cdots > v_k$.

The nodes of a labeled tree can be totally ordered in a way that reflects the tree structure. Let N be the set of positive integers under the ordering $1 > 2 > 3 > \cdots$. Define N^* to be the set of all finite sequences of positive integers with $n_1 n_2 \cdots n_l \geq m_1 m_2 \cdots m_l$ if (i) $n_1 > m_1$ or (ii) $n_i = m_i$, $i = 1, 2, ..., k$ and $n_{k+1} > m_{k+1}$ or $k = l$. This ordering is very much like the lexicographic product introduced in Section 2.3 and can be checked to be a total

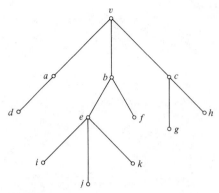

Figure 3.24

Node	Immediate successors	Address
v	a, b, c	1
a	d	1.1
b	e, f	1.2
c	g, h	1.3
d		1.1.1
e	i, j, k	1.2.1
f		1.2.2
g		1.3.1
h		1.3.2
i		1.2.1.1
j		1.2.1.2
k		1.2.1.3

Figure 3.25

ordering of N^*. We now define a function α (the *addressing function*) from the nodes of a labeled tree to N^*.

1 For the root v, define $\alpha(v) = 1$.

2 If $\alpha(w)$ has been defined and the immediate successors of $\alpha(w)$ are $v_1, v_2, \ldots, v_k$, define $\alpha(v_i)$ to be $\alpha(w)i$.

For example, the labeled tree in Figure 3.24 is addressed by the table in Figure 3.25. The element $\alpha(w)$ for a node w is called the *address* of w. In Figure 3.25, the addresses $\alpha(w)$ are written in the form $n_1 n_2 n_3 \cdots n_l$ to distinguish them from integers in base 10.

The addressing function for a labeled tree describes the unique tree path from the root to the addressed node. Let w be a node and $\alpha(w) = n_1 n_2 \cdots n_m$. The tree path from the root v to w is given by $\overrightarrow{vv_1}, \overrightarrow{v_1 v_2}, \ldots,$ $\overrightarrow{v_{m-2} w}$ when $\alpha(v_i) = n_1 n_2 \cdots n_{i+1}$ for $i = 1, \ldots, m-2$, and $\alpha(v) = n_1$. Thus in

Figure 3.25 the address $\alpha(k) = 1.2.1.3$ indicates that the path from v to k runs successively through the nodes addressed 1, 1.2, 1.2.1, 1.2.1.3, that is, the nodes v, b, e, k, so that the path is $\overrightarrow{vb}, \overrightarrow{be}, \overrightarrow{ek}$.

Exercises

3-29   Determine a longest-distance tree rooted at v_0 in the graph in Figure 3.26.

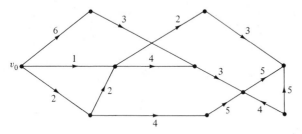

Figure 3.26

3-30   Give a plausible definition for a shortest-distance tree rooted at v_0 in a graph G. What condition must be placed on the circuits of G in order for a shortest-distance tree to exist?

3-31   State and prove a theorem similar to Theorem 3.7 that characterizes shortest-distance trees. [There is an easy proof using Theorem 3.7 and defining $\gamma(e) = -\lambda(e)$.]

3-32   Determine a longest-distance tree rooted at s for the following graph.

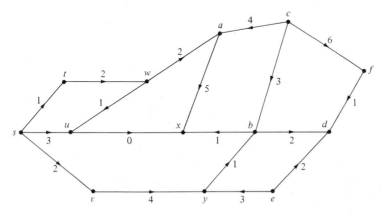

3-33   The solitaire game "Clock" is played as follows. A deck of 52 playing cards is dealt face down in 13 piles of 4 cards each. Twelve piles are arranged in a circle corresponding to the hour markings on a clock, and the thirteenth pile is placed in the center. The player begins by turning up the top card of the center pile and, if the face value of this card is k (ace is 1, jack is 11, queen is 12, and king is 13), then the card is laid face up beside the kth pile. The process begins again by turning up the top card of the kth pile and laying this card next to the corresponding pile. The process continues until a card is laid beside an empty pile. The player wins if and only if all cards are turned over. Suppose G is a graph with 13 vertices $v_1, v_2, \ldots, v_{13}$ and 12 arcs $\overrightarrow{v_i v_j}$, $i = 1, \ldots, 12$, where the bottom card in the ith pile is j (at the start of the game). Prove that the player wins the game if and only if G is a tree.

3-34 Give necessary and sufficient algebraic conditions for a matrix to be the adjacency matrix of a rooted tree.

3-35 Prove that the addressing for a labeled tree indicates the tree path from the root to the given node.

3.8 CRITICAL-PATH METHOD

The critical-path method is an important application of longest-distance trees to the planning and scheduling of operations comprising a project. Developers and builders are vitally concerned with the time span of a construction project. The longer the project takes, the longer the investment is unproductive, hence the costlier the project will be. Thus it is essential to determine a schedule of individual operations that minimizes the total time spent on the project. The critical-path method does this, and further-more outlines the activities in the project essential in the minimization of time spent. This feature allows the builder flexibility in scheduling activities that are not critical, so that the use of the labor force and expenditures for materials can be optimized.

The activities comprising a project form the basis for constructing a directed graph. This graph illustrates the dependencies among the activities of a project. It essentially shows which activities must precede and which activities must follow a given activity. There are two different methods for constructing a graph. One method uses arcs to represent activities and nodes to represent points in time, called events, such as the completion of a certain activity or a cohesive set of activities, or possibly the beginning of a certain set of activities. Since there is only one arc for each activity, dummy arcs must sometimes be added to show some essential dependencies. For exam-ple, if activities a and b end at event v and activities c and d begin at event v, but activity d actually depends only on activity b, then an additional event w and a dummy arc e must be added to the graph. Figure 3.27 illustrates this. Each arc a is labeled with the time $\lambda(a)$ needed to complete that particular

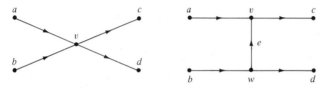

Figure 3.27

activity. The time needed to complete a dummy arc (nonexistent activity) is 0. Since each activity must be completed in order for the project to be completed, each arc in the graph must be completed. Hence each arc in any path from the starting node to the finishing node must be completed. The time taken for the whole project is at least $\sum_{e \in P} \lambda(e)$, where P is any path from the starting node to the finishing node.

In particular a longest such path must be completed. A longest path from start to finish is called a *critical path* and, if any activity on this path is delayed, then the whole project will be delayed. The time that must elapse before a certain event takes place is similarly the longest (in terms of time) path between the start and that event. Hence, with each event v, there is a minimum time $t(v)$ that must elapse before v can take place. The time $t(v)$ is calculated for each node v by determining a longest-distance tree T rooted at the starting node s. Thus $t(v)$ is the tree length from s to v in a longest-distance tree rooted at s. Define $t(v, z)$ to be the length of a longest path from v to z and define $t^*(v) = t(z) - t(v, z)$. Since $t(v) + t(v, z) \le t(z)$, $t(v) \le t^*(v)$, and equality holds if and only if v is a node on a longest path. The time $t^*(v)$ is the maximal time that can elapse before event v is reached without affecting the final completion date of the whole project. The interval $[t(v), t^*(v)]$ is called the *floating time* for the event v and indicates the earliest time and the latest time that v can occur. With each arc $\overrightarrow{uv}$ is associated the *free margin* for that activity, $t(v) - t(u) - \lambda(\overrightarrow{uv})$. This is the extra time available for completion of that activity before any other activity is affected. The *total margin* is $t^*(v) - t(u) - \lambda(\overrightarrow{uv})$, which represents the extra time available for that activity before the completion date for the whole project is affected.

Suppose the directed graph G in Figure 3.28 represents the activities comprising a project. A longest-distance tree for G is given in Figure 3.29. The longest paths from the various nodes to z are given in Figure 3.30. Figure 3.31 shows the values of t, t^*, the floating time, and the free margin for G. As a sample calculation, $t(x)$ is the length of the tree path from s to x, so that $t(x) = 3 + 5 = 8$. Also, $t(p) = 2$ and $t(z) = 3 + 4 + 4 + 1 = 12$. The number $t(x, z)$ is the length of the longest path from x to z, so that $t(x, z) = 1 + 2 = 3$. Thus $t^*(x) = t(z) - t(x, z) = 12 - 3 = 9$, the free margin of $\overrightarrow{px}$ is $t(x) - t(p) - \lambda(\overrightarrow{px}) = 8 - 2 - 4 = 2$, and the total margin of $\overrightarrow{px}$ is $t^*(x) - t(p) - \lambda(\overrightarrow{px}) = 9 - 2 - 4 = 3$.

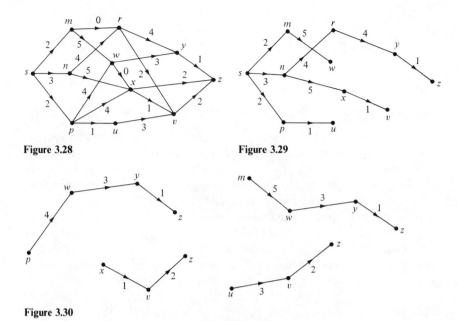

Figure 3.28

Figure 3.29

Figure 3.30

The data in Figure 3.31 can be illustrated on a bar chart with time as the horizontal scale and the horizontal bars representing activities and their durations and the free margin and total margins (Figure 3.32). The bar corresponding to an activity $\overrightarrow{ab}$ begins at $t(a)$ and ends at $t^*(b)$, where the first (solid) part of the bar represents $\lambda(\overrightarrow{ab})$, the second (clear) part of the bar represents the free margin, and the third (hatched) part of the bar represents the *interfering margin*, which is the difference between the total margin and the free margin.

The second type of graph constructed to represent the activities forming a project has the activities as the nodes of the graph. The arcs of the graph represent the dependencies among the various activities. Thus $\overrightarrow{uv}$ will be an arc if activity u must be completed before activity v begins. Since dependency in projects is transitive, only the essential arcs need be put in. That is, if there is a path from u to v already, then the arc $\overrightarrow{uv}$ does not need to be added, since the existence of the path implies that v already depends on u. The logic in constructing this type of graph is simpler than in the activity arc type of graph, since dummy events and dummy activities do not have to be considered; but the latter is still the most popular method in actual use, since it readily illustrates the time and margins for an activity.

One can easily change from a graph in which the arcs represent certain things to a graph in which the nodes represent those things. If G is a graph, then first construct G' by adding nodes w_0 and w_1 to G along with arcs $\overrightarrow{w_0 v}$ if

Node	t	t^*	Arc	Free margin	Total margin
s	0	0	$\overrightarrow{sm}$	0	1
m	2	3	$\overrightarrow{sn}$	0	0
n	3	3	$\overrightarrow{sp}$	0	2
p	2	4	$\overrightarrow{mw}$	0	1
r	7	7	$\overrightarrow{pw}$	1	2
w	7	8	$\overrightarrow{nr}$	0	0
x	8	9	$\overrightarrow{nx}$	0	1
u	3	7	$\overrightarrow{px}$	2	3
y	11	11	$\overrightarrow{pu}$	0	4
v	9	10	$\overrightarrow{ry}$	0	0
z	12	12	$\overrightarrow{rv}$	0	1
			$\overrightarrow{wy}$	1	1
			$\overrightarrow{xz}$	2	2
			$\overrightarrow{xv}$	0	1
			$\overrightarrow{uv}$	3	4
			$\overrightarrow{yz}$	0	0
			$\overrightarrow{vz}$	1	1

Figure 3.31

no arc in G terminates at v and $\overrightarrow{uw_1}$ and if no arc in G begins at u. Construct the graph $\mu(G)$ by letting a node of $\mu(G)$ correspond to each arc of G'. An arc of G extends from u to v if u corresponds to an arc $\overrightarrow{st}$ of G' and v corresponds to an arc $\overrightarrow{tz}$ of G'. Figure 3.33 illustrates this procedure.

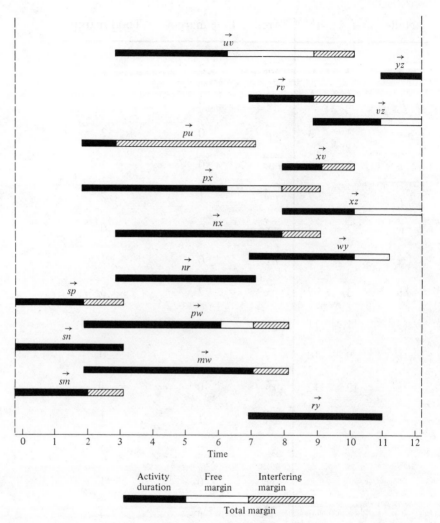

Figure 3.32

The original graph G can be obtained from $\mu(G)$ by defining nodes corresponding to each of the sets

$$m = \{\overrightarrow{ab},\ \overrightarrow{ac},\ \overrightarrow{ad},\ \overrightarrow{ae}\}, \qquad n = \{\overrightarrow{bf}\}, \qquad p = \{\overrightarrow{fg},\ \overrightarrow{cg},\ \overrightarrow{hg}\},$$
$$q = \{\overrightarrow{ei}\}, \qquad r = \{\overrightarrow{dh},\ \overrightarrow{ih}\},$$

and an arc will extend from node x to node y if there is a node of G' that is the end point of an arc in x and the beginning point of an arc in y. Hence we obtain Figure 3.34.

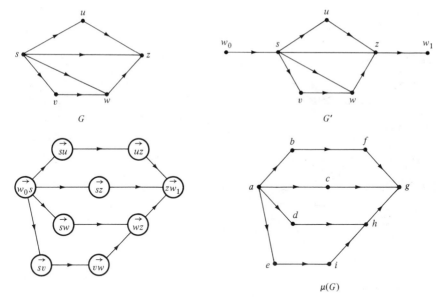

Figure 3.33

A directed graph that represents a project made up of activities does not have a circuit. Otherwise an activity in that circuit would depend on its being completed before it could begin, which is an absurdity. Hence the graph is a finite directed graph without circuits. Such a graph can be diagramed according to levels, similarly to diagraming a finite poset. Level 0 consists of the nodes that have no arcs terminating at that node. Level k consists of nodes of maximal distance k from any element of level 0. That is, there exists a path of length k from a node of level 0, but no path of longer length from an element of level 0. The different levels can be determined arithmetically by using the adjacency matrix to represent the graph. The u, v component will contain a 1 if $\overrightarrow{uv} \in G$, and a 0 otherwise. The matrix of the graph in Figure 3.34 with m, n, p, q, and r as 1, 2, 3, 4, and 5, respectively, is

$$M = \begin{bmatrix} 0 & 1 & 1 & 1 & 1 \\ 0 & 0 & 1 & 0 & 0 \\ 0 & 0 & 0 & 0 & 0 \\ 0 & 0 & 0 & 0 & 1 \\ 0 & 0 & 1 & 0 & 0 \end{bmatrix}.$$

Define $V_0 = \sum_{v \in N} R_v$, where R_v is the row corresponding to the node v. The components of V_0 with a 0 entry correspond to nodes with no arcs terminating at the node. They are the nodes of level 0. We can omit the arcs starting at nodes at level 0 by subtracting the rows R_v with v at level 0. Denote the nodes of level 0 by $L(0)$. Hence define $V_1 = V_0 - \sum_{v \in L(0)} R_v$, and the nodes

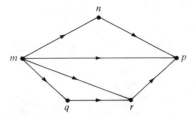

Figure 3.34

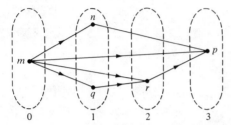

Figure 3.35

at level 1 are the new nodes represented by the 0's in V_1. Denote the nodes at level i by $L(i)$. Continuing we see that

$$V_i = V_{i-1} - \sum_{v \in L(i-1)} R_v$$

determines the nodes at level i.

For the example, $V_0 = (0 \quad 1 \quad 3 \quad 1 \quad 2)$

$$V_1 = (0 \quad 1 \quad 3 \quad 1 \quad 2) - (0 \quad 1 \quad 1 \quad 1 \quad 1) = (0 \quad 0 \quad 2 \quad 0 \quad 1)$$

$$V_2 = (0 \quad 0 \quad 2 \quad 0 \quad 1) - (0 \quad 0 \quad 1 \quad 0 \quad 0) - (0 \quad 0 \quad 0 \quad 0 \quad 1)$$

$$= (0 \quad 0 \quad 1 \quad 0 \quad 0)$$

$$V_3 = (0 \quad 0 \quad 1 \quad 0 \quad 0) - (0 \quad 0 \quad 1 \quad 0 \quad 0) = (0 \quad 0 \quad 0 \quad 0 \quad 0).$$

Hence level $0 = \{m\}$, level $1 = \{n, q\}$, level $2 = \{r\}$, level $3 = \{p\}$, and the graph is drawn as in Figure 3.35.

If the nodes of the graph are numbered by first numbering the nodes of level 0, then the nodes of level 1, then the nodes of level 2, and continuing in this manner until all the nodes are numbered, then the adjacency matrix will be strictly triangular, since there is no arc from a node of level i to a node of level j with $i \geq j$.

If v_1 is a node at level 1,

$$t(v_1) = \max\{\lambda(\overrightarrow{v_0 v_1}) : v_0 \text{ is any node at level } 0\}.$$

$$\vdots$$

If v_i is a node at level i,

$$t(v_i) = \max\{t(u) + \lambda(\overrightarrow{uv_i}) : \overrightarrow{uv_i} \text{ is any arc terminating at } v_i\}.$$

It is not difficult to describe a method for determining $t^*(v)$ for a graph described by levels.

Exercises

3-36 Determine a graph representing the construction of a reinforced-concrete foundation, consisting of the following activities. Measure foundations (1), dig foundations (4), erect forms (6), obtain reinforcing steel (2), assemble reinforcing steel (3), place steel in forms (2), order concrete (1), pour concrete (8). Calculate the free margin and total margin for each activity.

3-37 Using the matrix method determine the levels of the graph in Figure 3.36.

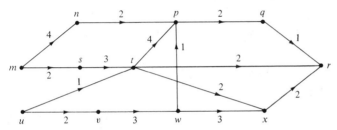

Figure 3.36   *G*.

3-38 Using Exercise 3-37 determine $t(v)$ for each node v of the graph in Figure 3.36.

3-39 Construct a method for a graph drawn in levels to determine $t^*(v)$.

3-40 Use the method of Exercise 3-39 to determine $t^*(v)$ for each $v \in G$.

3-41 Determine the critical paths in the following graph.

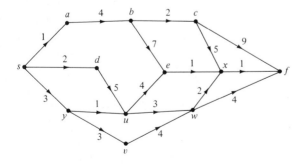

3-42 Determine $\mu(H)$ for the graph in Figure 3.37.

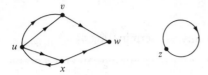

Figure 3.37   *H.*

3-43   Prove that the vertices of a directed graph without circuits can be ordered so that the resulting adjacency matrix is strictly upper triangular.

3-44   Let G be a directed graph. Define $\overrightarrow{xy} \sim \overrightarrow{uv}$ if either $y = v$ or $x = u$. For arcs a and b, define $a \approx b$ if there exists some sequence of arcs $a_1, \ldots, a_k$ such that $a \sim a_1$, $a_i \sim a_{i+1}$ for $i = 1, \ldots, k - 1$ and $a_k \sim b$. Prove that $\approx$ is an equivalence relation on the set of arcs of G.

3-45   Let G be a directed graph. Define a graph $\psi(G)$ by letting the set of nodes be the equivalence classes of arcs determined by the relation in Exercise 3-44. For each node s of G define an arc $\overrightarrow{uv}$ in $\psi(G)$ if the equivalence class of u contains $\overrightarrow{s_0 s}$ and the equivalence class of v contains $\overrightarrow{ss_1}$. Prove that each node determines at most one arc.

3-46   Determine $\psi(\mu(H))$ for the graph in Figure 3.37.

3-47   Prove $\psi(\mu(G)) \cong G$ for any directed graph G.

3.9   FLOWS IN NETWORKS

A *network* is a finite connected directed graph with no loops and at most one arc extending from a node u to a node v. Hence an arc is represented uniquely by $\overrightarrow{uv}$. These restrictions are not always essential in the analysis, but in practice parallel arcs are often combined into one arc. Networks are used to model traffic flow on a highway system, commodity flows through pipelines or transportation systems, communication flow in a communication system, and many other situations concerned with movement in a system. With each arc $\overrightarrow{uv}$ of a network is associated a non-negative real number $c(\overrightarrow{uv})$, called the capacity of $\overrightarrow{uv}$. A flow in a network from a source s to a sink t is a non-negative function f on the arcs of the graph, with $f(\overrightarrow{uv}) \leq c(\overrightarrow{uv})$ for all arcs $\overrightarrow{uv}$, such that the net flow out of the source s equals the net flow into the sink t and for any other node w the flow into w equals the flow out of w. More specifically, define $A(u)$, the nodes immediately after u, to be $\{v : \overrightarrow{uv}$ is an arc$\}$, and define $B(u)$, the nodes immediately before u, to

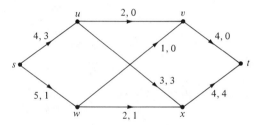

Figure 3.38 f.

be $\{v : \overrightarrow{vu} \text{ is an arc}\}$. A *flow* from source s to sink t is a non-negative real function on the arcs satisfying

$$f(\overrightarrow{uv}) \le c(\overrightarrow{uv}),$$

$$d = \sum_{u \in A(s)} f(\overrightarrow{su}) - \sum_{v \in B(s)} f(\overrightarrow{vs}) = \sum_{u \in B(t)} f(\overrightarrow{ut}) - \sum_{v \in A(t)} f(\overrightarrow{tv})$$

and

$$\sum_{u \in A(w)} f(\overrightarrow{wu}) - \sum_{v \in B(w)} f(\overrightarrow{vw}) = 0 \qquad \text{for all } w \ne s, t.$$

The number d is called the *value* of the flow and is the net flow out of s.

As an example, Figure 3.38 shows a network with the arcs labeled first with the capacity c, and second with the flow f. For each of the nodes u, v, w, and x there is exactly as much going into the node as going out. Furthermore, the net flow out of s is 4, and the net flow into t is 4, so that the value of the flow is 4.

If a network $G = (N, A)$ has a flow on it and if X is a set of nodes with $s \in X$ and $t \notin X$, then intuitively we would expect the net flow from the nodes in X into the nodes in $\bar{X} = N \backslash X$ to be d. Furthermore, the flow from X into $\bar{X}$ should not exceed the capacity of the arcs from X to $\bar{X}$. In the previous example, if $X = \{s, u, x\}$, then $\bar{X} = \{v, w, t\}$. The arcs from nodes in X to nodes in $\bar{X}$ are $\{\overrightarrow{uv}, \overrightarrow{sw}, \overrightarrow{xt}\}$, and the arcs from nodes in $\bar{X}$ to nodes in X are $\{\overrightarrow{wx}\}$. Thus the net flow from X to $\bar{X}$ is $f(\overrightarrow{uv}) + f(\overrightarrow{sw}) + f(\overrightarrow{xt}) - f(\overrightarrow{wx}) = 0 + 1 + 4 - 1 = 4$. The capacity of the arcs from X to $\bar{X}$ is $c(\overrightarrow{uv}) + c(\overrightarrow{sw}) + c(\overrightarrow{xt}) = 2 + 5 + 4 = 11$, which is certainly larger than 4.

The ideas in the preceding paragraph are generalized in Lemma 3.1. We first, however, fix some notation. If X and Y are two sets of nodes, define $(X, Y) = \{\overrightarrow{xy} : x \in X, y \in Y\}$. If g is any function on the arcs, $g(X, Y) = \sum_{\overrightarrow{xy} \in (X, Y)} g(\overrightarrow{xy})$. A *cut* is a set of arcs $(X, \bar{X})$ with $s \in X$ and $t \in \bar{X}$.

Lemma 3.1 Let f be a flow on a network (N, A), and let f have value d. If $(X, \bar{X})$ is a cut, then $d = f(X, \bar{X}) - f(\bar{X}, X)$ and $d \le c(X, \bar{X})$.

Proof By definition of a flow,

$$f(s, N) - f(N, s) = d$$

and

$$f(u, N) - f(N, u) = 0 \qquad \text{(for } u \neq s, t\text{)}.$$

Hence

$$\sum_{v \in X} [f(v, N) - f(N, v)] = d$$

$$= f(X, N) - f(N, X) = f(X, X \cup \bar{X}) - f(X \cup \bar{X}, X)$$

$$= f(X, X) + f(X, \bar{X}) - f(X, X) - f(\bar{X}, X),$$

since $X \cap \bar{X} = \phi$. Therefore $f(X, \bar{X}) - f(\bar{X}, X) = d$ and, since $f(X, \bar{X}) \leq c(X, \bar{X})$, the lemma is proven.

The lemma says that the value of the flow is less than or equal to the arc capacity $c(X, \bar{X})$ for any cut $(X, \bar{X})$. In particular, the value of the flow $\leq \min\{c(X, \bar{X}) : (X, \bar{X}) \text{ is any cut}\}$. In the example in Figure 3.38, the set X defining a cut contains s, along with any of the possibilities u, v, w, and x. Thus there are $2^4 = 16$ cuts. If these cuts are examined, the cut $(\{s, u, w, x\}, \{v, t\})$ has capacity $c(\overrightarrow{uv}) + c(\overrightarrow{wv}) + c(\overrightarrow{xt}) = 2 + 1 + 4 = 7$. This is the smallest capacity of any of the possible cuts, hence any flow on the network must have a value of at most 7.

Suppose we attempt to construct a flow on the network in Figure 3.38, which takes the value 7. One possibility is to increase the given flow by steps. For example, the flow on the path $\overrightarrow{su}, \overrightarrow{uv}, \overrightarrow{vt}$ is not at maximum value, since the flows on each of these arcs can be increased 1 unit and still remain within the capacity of each arc. Thus a new flow f_1 is obtained, which is shown in Figure 3.39. This flow likewise can be increased, since the flow on the path $\overrightarrow{sw}, \overrightarrow{wv}, \overrightarrow{vt}$ is not at maximum value but can be increased by 1 unit. Thus a new flow f_2 is obtained, as in Figure 3.40. The value of f_2 is 6, and each of the four paths from s to t has at least one arc with a flow equal to a capacity. Thus one may suspect that f_2 is a flow of maximal value. However, the possibility that the flow can be increased along a chain (which may not be a path), by increasing the flow in arcs oriented in the direction of s to t and decreasing the flow in arcs oriented in the direction of t to s, must be investigated. This in fact is the case, since the flow on the chain $\overrightarrow{sw}, \overrightarrow{wx}, \overleftarrow{xu}, \overrightarrow{uv}, \overrightarrow{vt}$ can be increased by 1 on the $\rightarrow$ arcs and can be decreased by 1 on the $\leftarrow$ arcs. Thus a new flow f_3 is obtained, given in Figure 3.41. Thus a flow has been found that has value 7 and, since there is a cut with capacity 7, this flow

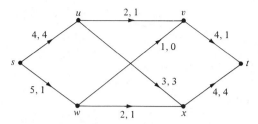

Figure 3.39 f_1.

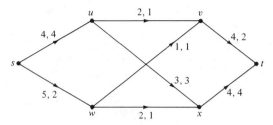

Figure 3.40 f_2.

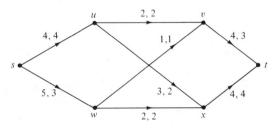

Figure 3.41 f_3.

has the maximum possible value. A flow with a value equal to $\min\{c(X, \bar{X}) : X$ is a cut$\}$ is called a *maximal flow*.

Theorem 3.8 says that there is always a maximal flow. Furthermore, the proof of this theorem yields an algorithm to construct such a maximal flow.

Theorem 3.8 Let G be a network with arc capacity $c(\overrightarrow{xy})$ associated with each arc. There exists a flow from source s to sink t with the value $\min\{c(X, \bar{X}) : (X, \bar{X})$ is any cut of $G\}$.

Proof Lemma 3.1 already guarantees that the value d satisfies

$$d \leq \min\{c(X, \bar{X}) : (X, \bar{X}) \text{ is a cut}\}.$$

Suppose that f is a flow. Let X be the set of nodes z such that either

$z = s$ or there exists a chain $a'_1, a'_2, \ldots, a'_k$ connecting s and z (i.e., the end points of a'_i are s'_{i-1}, s'_i, $i = 0, 1, \ldots, k$ with $s'_0 = s$ and $s'_k = z$) such that (1) if $a'_i = \overrightarrow{s'_{i-1}s'_i}$, $f(a'_i) < c(a'_i)$, and if $a'_i = \overleftarrow{s'_{i-1}s'_i}$, $f(a_i) > 0$, $i = 1, \ldots, k$. The set of arcs $(X, \bar{X})$ will be a cut if $t \notin X$. Suppose $t \in X$. Then there is a chain $a_1, a_2, \ldots, a_n$ between s and t, the end points of a_i being s_{i-1}, s_i, where $s = s_0$ and $s_n = t$, satisfying condition (1).

Let $\varepsilon = \min\{\{c(a_i) - f(a_i) : a_i = \overrightarrow{s_{i-1}s_i}\} \cup \{f(a_i) : a_i = \overleftarrow{s_{i-1}s_i}\}\}$. Define a function f' by $f'(a_i) = f(a_i) + \varepsilon$ if $a_i = \overrightarrow{s_{i-1}s_i}$, $f'(a_i) = f(a_i) - \varepsilon$ if $a_i = \overleftarrow{s_{i-1}s_i}$, and on the other arcs of the network $f' = f$. The function f' is still a flow, but the value of f' is $d + \varepsilon$. Thus the flow can be increased until finally a maximum value is obtained. At this point, $t \notin X$ and $(X, \bar{X})$ is a cut. For x in X, there is a chain $b_1, b_2, \ldots, b_m$, the end points of b_i being u_{i-1} and u_i with $u_0 = s$ and $u_m = x$, satisfying condition (1). If $y \in \bar{X}$ and there is an arc $\overrightarrow{xy}$ with $f(\overrightarrow{xy}) < c(\overrightarrow{xy})$, then $b_1, b_2, \ldots, b_m, \overrightarrow{xy}$ is a chain between s and y satisfying (1). This contradicts $y \in \bar{X}$, so $f(\overrightarrow{xy}) = c(\overrightarrow{xy})$. If there is an arc $\overleftarrow{xy}$ with $f(\overleftarrow{xy}) > 0$, we again have a chain between s and y satisfying (1). Thus $f(\overleftarrow{xy}) = 0$. Hence $f(X, \bar{X}) = c(X, \bar{X})$ and $f(\bar{X}, X) = 0$, proving the theorem.

Theorem 3.8 actually shows how to construct a maximal-flow function. A flow of zero on each arc is certainly possible, so there is a starting point. If a flow is not maximal, then there exists a sequence $s = s_0, s_1, \ldots, s_n = t$, and the flow can be augmented by $\varepsilon = \min\{c - f, f\}$, where min is taken over the appropriate arcs. This process is actually one of determining possible chains from s to t on which the flow can be increased. The previous example illustrates the fact that it is not sufficient to consider only paths in the algorithm, since the flow f_2 cannot be increased by finding a path from s to t with some spare capacity on each arc. Hence chains must be examined and, if there is a chain from s to t with spare capacity on each arc going in the s-to-t direction and some flow which could be diminished on each arc going in the t-to-s direction, then the flow can be increased, as was done to obtain f_3.

The procedure given above for increasing a flow f can be described in terms of finding a path in the associated incremental graph $G(f)$. The *associated incremental graph* has the same nodes as G. The arcs are determined as follows. If $\overrightarrow{uv}$ is an arc of G satisfying $f(\overrightarrow{uv}) < c(\overrightarrow{uv})$, then $\overrightarrow{uv}$ is an arc of $G(f)$. If $\overrightarrow{uv}$ is an arc of G satisfying $f(\overrightarrow{uv}) > 0$, then $\overrightarrow{vu}$ is an arc of $G(f)$. If there is a path from a source to a sink in the incremental graph, then there is a chain from a source to a sink in the original graph, which can be used to increase the flow. Label each arc $\overrightarrow{uv}$ of $G(f)$ with $c(\overrightarrow{uv}) - f(\overrightarrow{uv})$ if $\overrightarrow{uv} \in G$ and $f(uv)$ if $\overrightarrow{vu} \in G$. Hence the incremental graphs of the previous example are given in Figure 3.42.

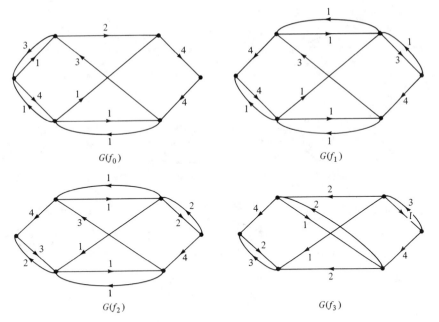

Figure 3.42

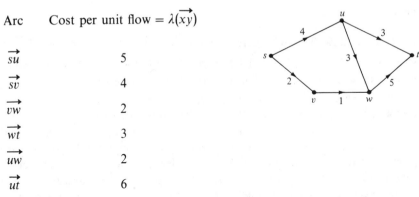

Figure 3.43   *H.*

It is clear in the diagram of $G(f_3)$ that there is no path from a source to a sink. In $G(f_2)$, there is a path, and thus the flow f_2 can be increased by min{values indicated on the arcs of the path}.

In many applications the arcs of the network not only have a capacity associated with each arc but also have a cost associated with each unit of flow on the arc. The problem is not just to find a maximal flow but to find such a flow with a minimum cost. This can be done quite simply by finding a least-cost tree in the associated incremental graph and using the tree path to

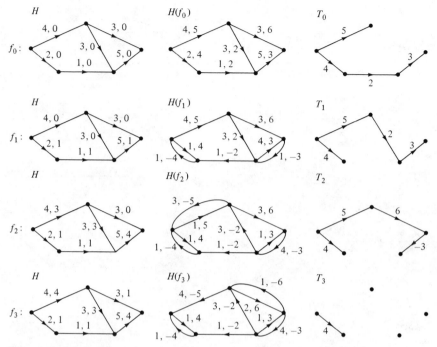

Figure 3.44

increase the flow. This will increase the flow with a minimum cost. If $\overrightarrow{uv}$ in $G(f)$ is obtained because $f(\overrightarrow{vu}) > 0$, then the cost associated with $\overrightarrow{uv}$ in $G(f)$ is minus the cost of $\overrightarrow{vu}$ in G. This is natural, since using $\overrightarrow{uv}$ in a path of $G(f)$ would decrease the flow on $\overrightarrow{vu}$ in G, hence decrease the cost of the flow on that arc. For example, suppose the graph H has the arc capacity and cost per unit flow given in Figure 3.43. The procedure yields the flows, incremental graphs, and least-cost trees given in Figure 3.44. The first number of each arc of H refers to arc capacity and the second refers to flow. The first number on each arc of $H(f_i)$ refers to spare capacity or positive flow, and the second refers to cost per unit flow. Each arc of the least-cost tree T_i is labeled with the cost per unit flow.

The procedure terminates when the tree T_i no longer contains the sink. The procedure is also suited for finding a flow of specified value of minimum cost. The procedure terminates in this case when the value of the flow is reached.

Exercises

3-48 Determine a maximal flow from s to t in Figure 3.45. Demonstrate a cut with a capacity equal to this flow.

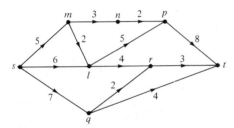

Figure 3.45

3-49 Determine a flow with a value of $10\frac{1}{2}$ from source v_0 to sink v_1 on the following network. Each arc is labeled with the arc capacity.

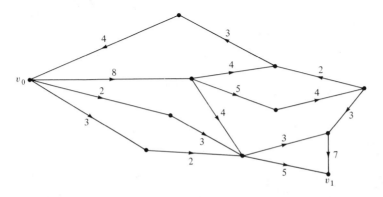

3-50 Determine a least-cost flow of value 5 for Figure 3.46, where the cost per unit flow is given by

$$\lambda(\overrightarrow{su}) = 2 \qquad \lambda(\overrightarrow{sw}) = 3 \qquad \lambda(\overrightarrow{uv}) = 1$$

$$\lambda(\overrightarrow{ux}) = 5 \qquad \lambda(\overrightarrow{wv}) = 1 \qquad \lambda(\overrightarrow{wx}) = 6$$

$$\lambda(\overrightarrow{vt}) = 3 \qquad \lambda(\overrightarrow{xt}) = 4$$

Show a step-by-step procedure with associated incremental graphs and least-cost trees.

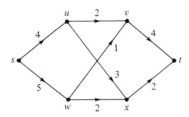

Figure 3.46

3-51 A *minimal cut* $(Z, \bar{Z})$ is a cut such that $c(Z, \bar{Z}) = \min\{c(W, \bar{W}) : (W, \bar{W})$ is any cut$\}$. If $(X, \bar{X})$ and $(Y, \bar{Y})$ are minimal cuts, prove that $(X \cup Y, \overline{X \cup Y})$ and $(X \cap Y, \overline{X \cap Y})$ are minimal cuts.

3-52 Let $(Y, \bar{Y})$ be a minimal cut and f a maximal flow. If $(X, \bar{X})$ is the minimal cut defined by the flow f in Theorem 3.8, prove that $X \subseteq Y$.

3-53 Define a reasonable concept of flow on a network where there may be several sources and several sinks. Prove that this can be reduced to considering a flow on a network with one source and one sink. (*Hint:* Add two extra nodes and appropriate arcs.)

3-54 Determine a flow from s to t on the network G that yields a profit of \$35 and has the minimum value of all flows that yield a profit of \$35. Each arc is labeled with the arc capacity and the profit per unit flow for that arc.

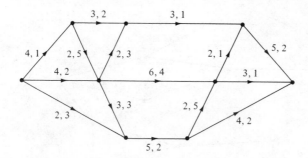

3-55 State the general problem illustrated in Exercise 3-54 and give an algorithm that yields a solution.

3-56 The network shown has arcs labeled with the arc capacity. The cost of increasing the capacity for an arc is given in the table.

Arc	Cost per unit of increased capacity
$\overrightarrow{su}$	20
$\overrightarrow{sw}$	60
$\overrightarrow{uv}$	30
$\overrightarrow{ux}$	35
$\overrightarrow{wx}$	30
$\overrightarrow{vt}$	40
$\overrightarrow{xt}$	45
$\overrightarrow{wv}$	28

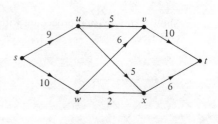

Determine the minimal cost of increasing the capacity of the network so that a flow of value 20 is possible.

3-57   Let G be a network with arc capacity $c(\overrightarrow{xy})$, $\overrightarrow{xy}$ an arc. Let $\lambda(\overrightarrow{xy})$ be the cost per unit of increased capacity on arc $\overrightarrow{xy}$. State a general algorithm which yields the minimal cost of increasing the capacity of the network so that a flow of specified value is possible. Prove that this algorithm actually does this.

Chapter

4

Boolean Algebra

4.1 INTRODUCTION

Boolean algebra is named after George Boole (1815–1864), who first analyzed some of the fundamental structures of logic in his book *The Laws of Thought*. Previously both DeMorgan and Leibniz had thought that logic should be mathematizable, but it remained to Boole actually to complete the task. Boolean algebra continued to develop as a mathematical subject, one of the outstanding achievements being Stone's representation theorem developed in the 1930s. At the end of the 1930s, Shannon published two papers which show that Boolean algebra provides an excellent tool for analyzing electrical switching circuits. Since then switching theory has motivated many of the studies in Boolean algebra.

Although applications of Boolean algebra to logic and switching circuits provide excellent motivation for its study, one of the easiest examples to study is the set of subsets of a set U. We are interested in the operations of union, intersection, and complementation on the set of all subsets of a set. In the exercises in Section 1.1 some of the properties of this algebra are examined. Using this as a guide, Boolean algebra is now defined.

Definition A *Boolean algebra* is a set B with two binary operations, intersection $\wedge$ and union $\vee$, and one unary operation, complementation $\bar{}$, satisfying the following axioms for any $x, y, z \in B$.

1 $x \wedge y = y \wedge x, \qquad x \vee y = y \vee x$ (commutativity).

2 $(x \wedge y) \wedge z = x \wedge (y \wedge z),$ (associativity).
$\qquad x \vee (y \vee z) = (x \vee y) \vee z$

3 $x \wedge (x \vee y) = x, \qquad x \vee (x \wedge y) = x$ (absorption).

4 $x \vee (y \wedge z) = (x \vee y) \wedge (x \vee z)$
(distributivity).

$\qquad x \wedge (y \vee z) = (x \wedge y) \vee (x \wedge z)$

5 There exist elements 0 and 1 satisfying
$\qquad x \vee 0 = x, \qquad x \wedge 0 = 0$
$\qquad x \vee 1 = 1, \qquad x \wedge 1 = x$ (univeral bound).

6 $x \wedge \bar{x} = 0, \qquad x \vee \bar{x} = 1$ (complementation).

7 $\bar{\bar{x}} = x$ (involution).

8 $\overline{x \wedge y} = \bar{x} \vee \bar{y}$
(DeMorgan's laws).

$\overline{x \vee y} = \bar{x} \wedge \bar{y}$

The elements 0 and 1 in the definition correspond to the empty set and the whole set, respectively, in the algebra of all subsets of a set.

Even though the algebra of all subsets of a set forms a Boolean algebra, a priori there may be many other systems that satisfy these axioms. One may hope that there is a unique 0 and 1 for a Boolean algebra, since this is what happens for the algebra of subsets of a set. If 0^* and 1^* also satisfy axiom (5), then $0 = 0 \vee 0^* = 0^* \vee 0 = 0^*$ and, similarly, $1^* = 1 \vee 1^* = 1^* \vee 1 = 1$. Furthermore, one may suspect that $x \wedge x = x$ and $x \vee x = x$. This is called the *idempotent law* and follows from the absorption and universal bound laws by $x \wedge x = x \wedge (x \vee 0) = x$ and $x \vee x = x \vee (x \wedge 1) = x$. In fact, even without universal bounds the law still follows just from the absorption law by

$$x = x \wedge (x \vee (x \wedge x)) = x \wedge x \qquad \text{and} \qquad x = x \vee (x \wedge (x \vee x)) = x \vee x.$$

In the above cases, the second identity is proven in the same manner as the first simply by interchanging $\vee$ and $\wedge$.

In the proof using both the absorption and universal bound laws, the second identity follows by interchanging $\vee$ and $\wedge$, and with 0 and 1 interchanged as well. If the axioms are examined, whenever $\vee$ and $\wedge$ are interchanged, and 0 and 1 are interchanged, the result is still an axiom. Hence in any proof of a statement, if $\vee$ and $\wedge$ and 0 and 1 are interchanged, we obtain a proof of a new statement, namely, one in which $\vee$ and $\wedge$ and 0 and 1 are interchanged. This leads to the principle of duality.

Principle of Duality Any theorem about Boolean algebras involving only $\vee$, $\wedge$, $^-$, 0, and 1 remains true if $\vee$ and $\wedge$ and 0 and 1 are interchanged.

Any set with binary operations $\wedge$ and $\vee$ and unary operation $^-$ that satisfies axioms (1) through (8) is a Boolean algebra. The algebra of subsets of a set U is easily found to be a Boolean algebra, where 0 is the empty set $\varnothing$ and 1 is the whole set U.

Another example of a Boolean algebra is the set of all functions from a set U to a two-element set, say $\{0, 1\}$, with $(f \wedge g)(u) = \min\{f(u), g(u)\}$, $(f \vee g)(u) = \max\{f(u), g(u)\}$, and $\bar{f}(u) = 1 - f(u)$, where u is any element of U. It need not be a tedious job to check that all the axioms are satisfied. If the function f is interpreted as corresponding uniquely to a subset S_f of U by putting u in S_f if and only if $f(u) = 1$, then it follows that the definition for intersection, union, and complementation of functions corresponds to the definition for intersection, union, and complementation of subsets. Hence the algebra of functions defined above is really a Boolean algebra. Because of the correspondence, the two algebras are essentially the same in the sense of Boolean algebra.

The set $\{0, 1\}$, with $a \wedge b = \min\{a, b\}$, $a \vee b = \max\{a, b\}$, and $\bar{a} = 1 - a$, a and b in $\{0, 1\}$, is a simple Boolean algebra. Thus in the previous paragraph, the algebra of all functions of a set U to a two-element set $\{0, 1\}$ is just the algebra of all functions from the set U to the simplest Boolean algebra. The set of all functions from a set U to an arbitrary Boolean algebra B, with $(f \wedge g)(u)$ defined to be $f(u) \wedge g(u)$, $(f \vee g)(u)$ defined to be $f(u) \vee g(u)$, and $\bar{f}(u)$ defined to be $\overline{f(u)}$, satisfies the axioms for a Boolean algebra.

A special but important case of the algebra of all functions from a set U to $\{0, 1\}$ is the algebra of Boolean functions. A *Boolean function* on n variables is a function from $\{(x_1, \ldots, x_n) : x_i \text{ is } 0 \text{ or } 1 \text{ for each } i = 1, \ldots, n\}$ to $\{0, 1\}$. The Boolean functions on two variables x_1 and x_2 are given in the following table.

x_1	x_2	f_0	f_1	f_2	f_3	f_4	f_5	f_6	f_7	f_8	f_9	f_{10}	f_{11}	f_{12}	f_{13}	f_{14}	f_{15}
0	0	0	0	0	0	0	0	0	0	1	1	1	1	1	1	1	1
0	1	0	0	0	0	1	1	1	1	0	0	0	0	1	1	1	1
1	0	0	0	1	1	0	0	1	1	0	0	1	1	0	0	1	1
1	1	0	1	0	1	0	1	0	1	0	1	0	1	0	1	0	1

Since $f_i \vee f_j = \max\{f_i, f_j\}$, $f_i \wedge f_j = \min\{f_i, f_j\}$, and $\bar{f}_i = 1 - f_i$, we have, for example, the following table.

x_1	x_2	f_4	f_9	$f_4 \vee f_9$	$f_4 \wedge f_9$	$\bar{f}_4$	$\bar{f}_9$
0	0	0	1	1	0	1	0
0	1	1	0	1	0	0	1
1	0	0	0	0	0	1	1
1	1	0	1	1	0	1	0

Functions from a Boolean algebra to the simplest Boolean algebra $\{0, 1\}$ assign to each element the value 0 or 1. Analogously, many statements in a language can be assigned the value true or false. If we restrict ourselves only to statements that are unambiguous and can be assigned the notion true or false, then there is a function from this set of statements to the two-element set. Statements that are unambiguous and can be assigned the notion true or false are called *propositions*.

To be precise, let $\{p, q, r, \ldots\}$ be an infinite set. The elements $p, q, r, \ldots$ are called *variables*. We can build up formal statements called *well-formed formulas* using the variables and the symbols $\vee$, $\wedge$, and $^-$ by the rule that, if s and t are formal statements, then $(s) \vee (t)$, $(s) \wedge (t)$, and $(\bar{s})$ are formal statements. Furthermore, each variable is a formal statement. Formal statements can be mapped to statements in English simply by mapping the variables to statements in English: $\vee$ to "or," where "or" means either one of the statements or both of the statements, $\wedge$ to "and," and $^-$ to "it is not true that." Thus, if p is mapped to the statement, "Rain is wet," and q is mapped to the statement, "Burning wood provides most of our energy," then the formal statement $(p) \wedge (\bar{q})$ is mapped to "Rain is wet and it is not true that burning wood provides most of our energy." The parentheses have been omitted, since the omission introduces no ambiguity. This convention will be used hereafter. If p and q are mapped to propositions, then the formal statements $(\bar{p})$, $(p) \vee (q)$, and $(p) \wedge (q)$ are mapped to propositions. The truth or falsity of each of the images of the three formal statements depends on the truth or falsity of the image of p and the image of q. The following table (called a truth table) illustrates this dependency, where 1 is interpreted as meaning true and 0 is interpreted as meaning false.

p	q	$(p) \wedge (q)$	$(p) \vee (q)$	$(\bar{p})$
0	0	0	0	1
0	1	0	1	1
1	0	0	1	0
1	1	1	1	0

The truth table is obtained by examining the ideas of truth or falsity of statements in the natural language, English. The resulting truth tables yield the same functional values as $\vee$, $\wedge$, and $^-$ in the Boolean algebra of Boolean functions in two variables.

Propositions built up by means of the connectives "and," "or . . . or both," and "it is not true that" from simpler propositions are called composite propositions. There are numerous other ways of building propositions in English from simpler propositions. For example, "if . . . then . . ." and "if and only if" can be used as connectives. In the construction of formal statements, symbols representing these connectives can be incorporated. In addition to $\vee$, $\wedge$, and $^-$ the symbols $\rightarrow$ and $\leftrightarrow$ can be used in building formal statements and in mapping the resulting formal statements to statements in English, $\rightarrow$ can be mapped to "if . . . then . . . ," and $\leftrightarrow$ can be mapped to "if and only if." With the usual understanding of truth or falsity in English, the following is the resulting truth table, again with 0 meaning false and 1 meaning true.

p	q	$(p) \rightarrow (q)$	$(p) \leftrightarrow (q)$
0	0	1	1
0	1	1	0
1	0	0	0
1	1	1	1

The truth table for the formal statement $((\bar{p})) \vee (q)$ is:

p	q	$(\bar{p})$	$((\bar{p})) \vee (q)$
0	0	1	1
0	1	1	1
1	0	0	0
1	1	0	1

This shows that as a function $((\bar{p})) \vee (q)$ takes the same values as $(p) \rightarrow (q)$. Thus, if p and q are mapped to propositions, the truth values of the propositions that are images of $((\bar{p})) \vee (q)$ and $(p) \rightarrow (q)$ will be identical.

Exercises

4-1 Determine the number of elements in the Boolean algebra of all functions from a set containing n elements to a two-element set.

4-2 Determine the number of Boolean functions in n variables.

4-3 Write the truth table for $(\overline{(p \vee q)} \wedge r) \vee (p \wedge \bar{r})$.

4-4 Determine formal statements with variables p, q and connectives $\vee$, $\wedge$, and $^-$ that yield truth tables identical to those of the formal statements $p \leftrightarrow q$ and "p but not q," respectively.

4-5 If x is an element of the Boolean algebra B, and z in B satisfies $z \vee x = 1$, $z \wedge x = 0$, prove that $z = \bar{x}$.

4.2 FINITE BOOLEAN ALGEBRAS

Several Boolean algebras given as examples in Section 4.1 are only disguises for one Boolean algebra. In fact, for finite Boolean algebras, there is essentially at most one Boolean algebra of any given size. The term "essentially" is made precise by the following definition.

Definition A Boolean algebra B_1 is said to be *isomorphic* to a Boolean algebra B_2 if there is a one-to-one mapping f from B_1 onto B_2 satisfying $f(x \vee y) = f(x) \vee f(y)$, $f(x \wedge y) = f(x) \wedge f(y)$, and $\overline{f(x)} = f(\overline{x})$ for all x and y in B_1.

In other words, except for changing the name of the element x to $f(x)$, the Boolean algebras B_1 and B_2 are exactly the same under the operations of $\vee$, $\wedge$, and $^-$. We show that a finite Boolean algebra is isomorphic to the Boolean algebra of all subsets of a finite set. Hence the order of any finite Boolean algebra is 2^n, where n is a positive integer. In the Boolean algebra of all subsets of a set S, each subset is determined exactly by the elements of S contained in the subset; thus in an arbitrary finite Boolean algebra B, we must identify which elements correspond to the singleton subsets of S. If in addition a notion of containment (a partial order), which corresponds to the containment of subsets, is determined, then we have the natural identification of an element z of a Boolean algebra with a set, namely, the set of all singletons contained in z. This we proceed to do.

For x and y in a Boolean algebra B, define $x \geq y$ whenever $x \wedge y = y$. This corresponds to containment in the Boolean algebra of subsets of a set, and in fact is shown in the exercises to be a partial order for any Boolean algebra. A singleton subset of a set S is simply a nonempty subset containing only the empty set and itself. The element 0 of B corresponds to the empty set, since for any x in B, $x \wedge 0 = 0$, so that 0 is contained in every element of B. Thus an element $x \neq 0$ of B corresponds to a singleton if $x > y \geq 0$ implies $y = 0$. The set of these singleton elements (called atoms) is denoted by A. Thus an element z of B can be mapped to a subset of a set, namely, the subset of A consisting of atoms smaller than z. Explicitly for z in B, define $\phi(z) = \{a \in A : z \wedge a \neq 0\}$. For a finite Boolean algebra B, the mapping ϕ will be shown to be an isomorphism from B onto the set of all subsets of A. First, note that $\phi(u \wedge z) = \phi(u) \cap \phi(z)$ for all u and z in B, since

$$\{a \in A : (u \wedge z) \wedge a \neq 0\} = \{a \in A : u \wedge a = a = z \wedge a \neq 0\}$$
$$= \{a \in A : u \wedge a = a\} \cap \{a \in A : z \wedge a = a\}.$$

It is likewise straightforward to show that $\phi(u \vee z) = \phi(u) \cup \phi(z)$ and $\phi(\bar{u}) = \overline{\phi(u)}$. It only remains to show that ϕ is onto and one-to-one. This is the most challenging part of the proof and is not necessarily true if the Boolean algebra is infinite. The fact that the function is one-to-one and onto is left to the exercises.

Exercises

4-6   For x and y in a Boolean algebra B, define $x \geq y$ when $x \wedge y = y$. Prove that $\geq$ defines a partial order on the elements of B.

4-7   Draw a diagram of the partial ordering of the Boolean algebra of all functions from a four-element set to a two-element set.

4-8   Prove that, if x and y are in a Boolean algebra B, $x \wedge y = y$ if and only if $x \vee y = x$.

4-9   Let B be the Boolean algebra of all functions from $\{a, b, c\}$ to $\{0, 1\}$. Determine the set of atoms of B. For each function f, determine the subset of atoms contained in f.

4-10   Which of the following can be the diagram for a Boolean algebra under the partial order $x \geq y$, when $x \wedge y = y$? Give reasons.

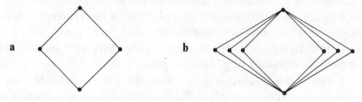

a   b

(All arrows point downward.)

4-11   Determine whether the following is the diagram of a Boolean algebra. Give reasons.

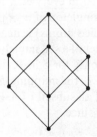

For the following questions let u and z be elements in a finite Boolean algebra B and $\phi(u) = \{a$ an atom of $B : u \wedge a = a\}$.

4-12   If $u > z$, prove that $\bar{z} \wedge u$ contains an atom.

4-13 Prove that the map ϕ from B to the set of subsets of atoms is one-to-one.

4-14 Prove that $a_1 \vee a_2 \vee \cdots \vee a_n \geq u$, with $u, a_1, a_2, \ldots, a_n$ atoms of B, implies that $u = a_i$ for some i, $1 \leq i \leq n$.

4-15 Prove that the map ϕ from B to the set of all subsets of atoms is onto.

4.3 SWITCHING CIRCUITS

In the first two sections, we investigate the Boolean algebra of all subsets of a given set, the Boolean algebra of all functions from a set to a two-element set, and the Boolean algebra of propositions. These three algebras are essentially the same and are very important in theoretical considerations. However, by far the most important practical application of Boolean algebras lies in the realm of electrical engineering. This is not surprising, since devices such as mechanical switches, diodes, magnetic dipoles, and transistors are all two-state devices. The two states may be realized as current or no current, magnetized or not magnetized, high potential or low potential, and closed or open.

These devices may be used to construct various new devices. Some very simple examples of this are illustrated in Figures 4.1 through 4.3. In each example the electromagnets labeled x and y determine whether the corresponding switch is open or closed. In Figures 4.1 and 4.2 the switches are normally held open by a spring. When current flows through the electromagnet, the switch is pulled closed. In Figure 4.3 the switch is normally held closed by a spring and, when current flows through the electromagnet, the switch is forced open. The flow of current through the main circuit thus depends on whether the electromagnets x and y are on or off. If on is denoted by 1 and off is denoted by 0, and current flowing through the main circuit is denoted by 1, while no current is denoted by 0, then this dependency is shown in Figure 4.4.

These dependencies are given by Boolean functions in the variables x and y. Thus the figures are labeled with the corresponding functions $x \wedge y$, $x \vee y$, and $\bar{x}$. In general, if two two-terminal switching circuits f_1 and f_2 depend on the switches $x_1, x_2, \ldots, x_n$, then $f_1 \wedge f_2$ will denote the switching circuit determined by f_1 and f_2 in series, $f_1 \vee f_2$ will denote the switching circuit determined by f_1 and f_2 in parallel, and $\bar{f_1}$, the inversion of f_1, will denote the switching circuit (as in Figure 4.3) that takes the value 1 when f_1 takes the value 0 and takes the value 0 when f_1 takes the value 1. These circuits are illustrated diagramatically in Figure 4.5. It is thus clear that any two-terminal switching circuit built up from simple switches using series and

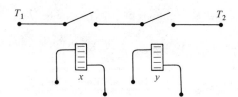

Figure 4.1 $x \wedge y$.

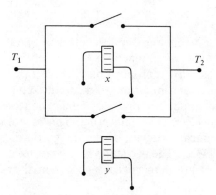

Figure 4.2 $x \vee y$.

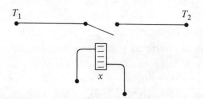

Figure 4.3 $\bar{x}$.

x	y	$x \wedge y$	$x \vee y$	$\bar{x}$
0	0	0	0	1
0	1	0	1	1
1	0	0	1	0
1	1	1	1	0

Figure 4.4

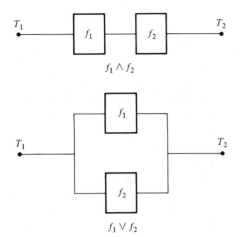

Figure 4.5

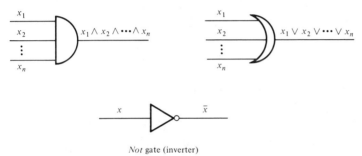

Figure 4.6

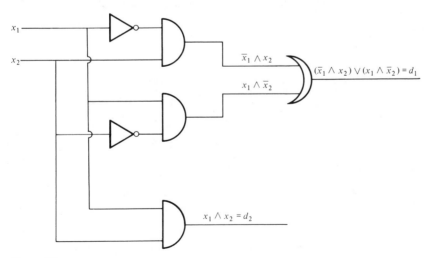

Figure 4.7

parallel construction with various inversions can be represented by a Boolean function with variables $x_1, x_2, \ldots, x_n$, which represent the various switches. Similarly, if an expression is formed in the intuitive way, using the variables $x_1, x_2, \ldots, x_n$ and the symbols $\vee$, $\wedge$, and $^-$, then this expression determines a two-terminal switching circuit formed by various series and parallel constructions with inversions. This procedure is made precise in Section 4.4, and we will see that the notion of expression is equivalent to the notion of function.

An alternative method of diagraming a two-state electronic device composed of parallel and series connections and inversion is by a gating network. Figure 4.6 shows a representation of these gates, and Figure 4.7 illustrates a device built up from these gates (such devices are called *gating networks*) which adds two single-digit binary integers and expresses the result as a two-digit binary integer. Note that d_1 represents the unit's digit and d_2 represents the two's digit.

Exercises

4-16 Draw two switching circuits representing the expressions $x_1 \wedge (x_2 \vee x_3)$ and $(x_1 \wedge x_2) \vee (x_1 \wedge x_3)$, respectively, and give a table indicating the functional dependency of these expressions on the values of x_1, x_2, and x_3.

4-17 Determine a Boolean expression that represents the switching circuit given in Figure 4.8. In this figure the switches are simply denoted by the letters x_i and inversion is denoted by a $^-$ over the appropriate switches.

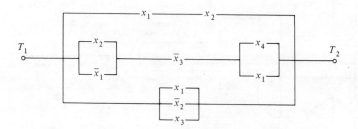

Figure 4.8

4-18 Draw a switching circuit which represents the Boolean expression $((x_1 \vee x_2) \wedge \bar{x}_3) \vee (x_1 \wedge x_2)$.

4-19 Draw a gating network representing the Boolean expression given in Exercise 4-18.

4-20   Design a circuit that adds two three-digit binary integers.

4-21   Determine a simpler switching circuit that gives the same effect as the circuit in Figure 4.8.

4.4   BOOLEAN POLYNOMIALS AND DISJUNCTIVE NORMAL FORM

The set of Boolean expressions in the variables $x_1, \ldots, x_n$, with coefficients from a Boolean algebra B, is defined inductively in the following manner. The symbols $x_1, \ldots, x_n$ and the elements of B are Boolean expressions. If Boolean expressions p_1 and p_2 have been defined, then $(p_1) \wedge (p_2)$, $(p_1) \vee (p_2)$, and $\overline{p_1}$ are Boolean expressions. For example, $((x_1) \wedge (x_2)) \vee ((x_3) \vee (x_5))$ is a Boolean expression, since x_1, x_2, x_5 being Boolean expressions implies that $(x_1) \wedge (x_2)$ and $(x_3) \vee (x_5)$ are Boolean expressions. Hence $\overline{(x_1) \wedge (x_2)}$ and finally $((x_1) \wedge (x_2)) \vee ((x_3) \vee (x_5))$ are Boolean expressions. We operate on these expressions using axioms (1) through (8) of a Boolean algebra. For example, using De Morgan's law, the expression $(\overline{(x_1)} \vee \overline{(x_2)}) \vee ((x_3) \vee (x_5))$ can be obtained from $\overline{((x_1) \wedge (x_2))} \vee ((x_3) \vee (x_5))$.

The expression $(x_1) \wedge (x_2)$ is called a subexpression of $((x_1) \wedge (x_2)) \vee ((x_3) \vee (x_5))$. To make this precise, suppose p_1 and p_2 are Boolean expressions. Subexpressions are now defined inductively. The subexpressions of $(p_1) \wedge (p_2)$ are the expression itself and subexpressions of p_1 and p_2. The subexpressions of $(p_1) \vee (p_2)$ are the expression itself and the subexpressions of p_1 and p_2. The subexpressions of $\overline{p_1}$ are the expression itself and the subexpressions of p_1. Subexpressions of x_1 and $b \in B$, respectively, are x_1 and b, respectively. Thus the subexpressions of $((x_1) \wedge (x_2)) \vee ((x_3) \vee (x_5))$ are $((x_1) \wedge (x_2)) \vee (x_3 \vee (x_5))$, $(x_1) \wedge (x_2)$, $(x_3) \vee (x_5)$, $(x_1) \wedge (x_2)$, x_1, x_2, x_3, and x_5. It is easy to show by induction that each Boolean expression represents a two-terminal switching circuit built up by series and parallel constructions with inversion. Also, any two-terminal switching circuit constructed from simpler circuits in series or parallel, or inversion of simpler circuits, can be represented by a Boolean expression.

It is clear that the set of Boolean expressions in the variables $x_1, \ldots, x_n$ with coefficients from B does not satisfy the axioms of a Boolean algebra. However, if we are to use these expressions as tools for analyzing Boolean algebra, then they should satisfy the axioms for a Boolean algebra. This situation can be remedied by placing an equivalence relation on the set of Boolean expressions. The expression p_1 is said to be equivalent to the expression p_2 if there is a sequence $p_1 = q_1, q_2, \ldots, q_k = p_2$ of Boolean expressions such that the Boolean expression q_{i+1} is obtained from the Boolean expression q_i by using one of the rules (1) through (8) listed in the definition of Boolean algebra to change some subexpression of q_i. If $\sim$ denotes a change in the expression using rules (1) through (8) and, as is customary, the parentheses around a variable x_i are omitted, we have

$$
\begin{aligned}
p_1 &= (x_1 \wedge \overline{(x_1 \vee x_2)}) \vee ((x_1 \wedge x_2) \vee (x_1 \wedge x_3)) \\
&\sim (x_1 \wedge (\overline{x_1} \wedge \overline{x_2})) \vee ((x_1 \wedge x_2) \vee (x_1 \wedge x_3)) && \text{by (8)} \\
&\sim ((x_1 \wedge \overline{x_1}) \wedge \overline{x_2}) \vee ((x_1 \wedge x_2) \vee (x_1 \wedge x_3)) && \text{by (2)} \\
&\sim (0 \wedge \overline{x_2}) \vee ((x_1 \wedge x_2) \vee (x_1 \wedge x_3)) && \text{by (6)} \\
&\sim (\overline{x_2} \wedge 0) \vee ((x_1 \wedge x_2) \vee (x_1 \wedge x_3)) && \text{by (1)} \\
&\sim 0 \vee ((x_1 \wedge x_2) \vee (x_1 \wedge x_3)) && \text{by (5)} \\
&\sim ((x_1 \wedge x_2) \vee (x_1 \wedge x_3)) \vee 0 && \text{by (1)} \\
&\sim ((x_1 \wedge x_2) \vee (x_1 \wedge x_3)) && \text{by (5)} \\
&\sim x_1 \wedge (x_2 \vee x_3) = p_2 && \text{by (4).}
\end{aligned}
$$

It is left for the exercises to show that the notion of equivalence defined above is actually an equivalence relation. An equivalence class is called a Boolean polynomial, and a Boolean expression in this class is said to represent that polynomial. When no confusion is possible, a polynomial is designated by some representative.

Each Boolean expression in the variables $x_1, \ldots, x_n$ with coefficients from a Boolean algebra B determines a function by substituting the value 1 or 0 for each variable x_i. The domain of the function is $\{(x_1, x_2, \ldots, x_n) : x_i$ is 0 or 1$\}$, and the range of the function is contained in B.

It is easy to check that using one of the laws (1) through (8) of Boolean algebra to change a subexpression does not change the functional value of the Boolean expression. Thus the functional value is not only defined for a Boolean expression, it is also defined for the corresponding Boolean polynomial. In fact, we show that each Boolean function in n variables corresponds to a unique Boolean polynomial in n variables and, furthermore, that each Boolean polynomial with n variables has a unique canonical representative, called its *disjunctive normal form*. With no cause for confusion, we write $=$ for $\sim$.

Lemma 4.1 Let $f(x)$ be a Boolean polynomial in one variable x with coefficients from the Boolean algebra B. Then $f(x) = (f(1) \wedge x) \vee (f(0) \wedge \bar{x})$.

Proof If the polynomial $f(x)$ is just the element b in B, then $f(1) = b$ and $f(0) = b$. Thus $(f(1) \wedge x) \vee (f(0) \wedge \bar{x}) = (b \wedge x) \vee (b \wedge \bar{x})$ which by distributivity is $b \wedge (x \vee \bar{x}) = b \wedge 1 = b$. If the polynomial is $f(x) = x$, then $f(1) = 1$

and $f(0) = 0$. Therefore $(f(1) \wedge x) \vee (f(0) \wedge \bar{x}) = (1 \wedge x) \vee (0 \wedge \bar{x}) = x \vee 0 = x$. Suppose that Lemma 4.1 has been proven true for polynomials $f(x)$ and $g(x)$. Thus

$$
\begin{aligned}
(f(x)) \vee (g(x)) &= ((f(1) \wedge x) \vee (f(0) \wedge \bar{x})) \vee ((g(1) \wedge x) \vee (g(0) \wedge \bar{x})) \\
&= ((f(1) \wedge x) \vee (g(1) \wedge x)) \vee ((f(0) \wedge \bar{x}) \vee (g(0) \wedge \bar{x})) \\
&= ((f(1) \vee g(1)) \wedge x) \vee ((f(0) \vee g(0)) \wedge \bar{x}) \\
&= (((f \vee g)(1)) \wedge x) \vee (((f \vee g)(0)) \wedge \bar{x}).
\end{aligned}
$$

Also,

$$
\begin{aligned}
(f(x)) \wedge (g(x)) &= ((f(1) \wedge x) \vee (f(0) \wedge \bar{x})) \\
&\quad \wedge ((g(1) \wedge x) \vee (g(0) \wedge \bar{x})) \\
&= (f(1) \wedge x \wedge g(1) \wedge x) \vee (f(1) \wedge x \wedge g(0) \wedge \bar{x}) \\
&\quad \vee (f(0) \wedge \bar{x} \wedge g(1) \wedge x) \\
&\quad \vee (f(0) \wedge \bar{x} \wedge g(0) \wedge \bar{x}) \\
&= (f(1) \wedge g(1) \wedge x) \vee 0 \vee 0 \vee (f(0) \wedge g(0) \wedge \bar{x}) \\
&= (((f \wedge g)(1)) \wedge x) \vee (((f \wedge g)(0)) \wedge \bar{x}).
\end{aligned}
$$

It only remains to show that $\overline{f(x)} = (\bar{f}(1) \wedge x) \vee (\bar{f}(0) \wedge \bar{x})$. By De Morgan's law (8) and the law of involution (7), it is sufficient and not difficult to show $h(x) = \bar{x} = (h(1) \wedge x) \vee (h(0) \wedge \bar{x}) = (0 \wedge x) \vee (1 \wedge \bar{x})$. Thus the lemma is proven.

Lemma 4.2 The Boolean polynomial $f(x_1, x_2, \ldots, x_n)$ equals $(f(1, x_2, \ldots, x_n) \wedge x_1) \vee (f(0, x_2, \ldots, x_n) \wedge \bar{x}_1)$.

Proof The set of Boolean polynomials in the variables $x_2, x_3, \ldots, x_n$ is a Boolean algebra B. Thus a Boolean polynomial in the variables $x_1, x_2, \ldots, x_n$ can be considered a Boolean polynomial in the single variable x_1 with coefficients from the Boolean algebra B. Let $h(x_1)$ be a Boolean polynomial $f(x_1, x_2, \ldots, x_n)$ so considered. Hence, by Lemma 4.1, $h(x_1) = (h(1) \wedge x_1) \vee (h(0) \wedge \bar{x}_1) = (f(1, x_2, \ldots, x_n) \wedge x_1) \vee (f(0, x_2, \ldots, x_n) \wedge \bar{x}_1)$, and the lemma is proven.

Lemmas 4.1 and 4.2 show how to express a Boolean polynomial in n variables in terms of a very simple expression depending on Boolean polynomials in $n - 1$ variables. This reduction process is used in the next theorem to determine a canonical form for Boolean polynomials, called the disjunctive normal form. In order to describe this form, let $e_i \in \{0, 1\}$, $i = 1, \ldots, n$ and define $x_i^{e_i}$ to be x_i if $e_i = 1$ and $\overline{x}_i$ if $e_i = 0$. Define

$$\bigvee (f(e_1, e_2, \ldots, e_n) \wedge x_1^{e_1} \wedge x_2^{e_2} \wedge \cdots \wedge x_n^{e_n}) = m_0 \vee m_1 \vee \cdots \vee m_{2^n - 1},$$

where

$$m_i = f(d_1, d_2, \ldots, d_n) \wedge x_1^{d_1} \wedge \cdots \wedge x_n^{d_n}$$

and $d_1, d_2, \ldots, d_n$ is the binary representation of the integer i.

For example, suppose $f(x_1, x_2) = \overline{(x_1 \vee x_2)} \wedge ((x_1 \wedge x_2) \vee \overline{x}_2)$. Thus $f(0, 0) = \overline{(0 \vee 0)} \wedge ((0 \wedge 0) \vee \overline{0}) = 1$, $f(0, 1) = 0$, $f(1, 0) = 0$, and $f(1, 1) = 0$, and the expression

$$(1 \wedge x_1^0 \wedge x_2^0) \vee (0 \wedge x_1^0 \wedge x_2^1) \vee (0 \wedge x_1^1 \wedge x_2^0) \vee (0 \wedge x_1^1 \wedge x_2^1) = \overline{x}_1 \wedge \overline{x}_2$$

is obtained.

Theorem 4.1   If $f(x_1, x_2, \ldots, x_n)$ is a Boolean polynomial then

$$f(x_1, \ldots, x_n) = \bigvee (f(e_1, e_2, \ldots, e_n) \wedge x_1^{e_1} \wedge x_2^{e_2} \wedge \cdots \wedge x_n^{e_n}).$$

Proof   The proof is by induction on the number of variables. If there is one variable, then the theorem is proven by Lemma 4.1. If the theorem is true for all Boolean polynomials in $n - 1$ variables and $f(x_1, \ldots, x_n)$ is a Boolean polynomial in n variables, then by Lemma 4.2,

$$f(x_1, x_2, \ldots, x_n) = (f(1, x_2, \ldots, x_n) \wedge x_1) \vee (f(0, x_2, \ldots, x_n) \wedge \overline{x}_1),$$

and by induction this expression is equal to

$$\left(\left(\bigvee (f(1, e_2, \ldots, e_n) \wedge x_2^{e_2} \wedge \cdots \wedge x_n^{e_n}) \right) \wedge x_1 \right)$$

$$\vee \left(\left(\bigvee (f(0, e_2, \ldots, e_n) \wedge x_2^{e_2} \wedge \cdots \wedge x_n^{e_n}) \right) \wedge \overline{x}_1 \right)$$

$$= \bigvee (f(1, e_2, \ldots, e_n) \wedge x_1^1 \wedge x_2^{e_2} \wedge \cdots \wedge x_n^{e_n})$$

$$\vee \bigvee (f(0, e_2, \ldots, e_n) \wedge x_1^0 \wedge x_2^{e_2} \wedge \cdots \wedge x_n^{e_n})$$

$$= \bigvee (f(e_1, e_2, \ldots, e_n) \wedge x_1^{e_1} \wedge x_2^{e_2} \wedge \cdots \wedge x_n^{e_n}).$$

Thus the theorem is proved.

An expression of the form $x_{i_1}^{e_1} \wedge x_{i_2}^{e_2} \wedge \cdots \wedge x_{i_k}^{e_k}$ is called a *product term*. The union of the set of such product terms is called a *sum of products*. A *disjunctive normal form* for the Boolean polynomial $f(x_1, x_2, \ldots, x_n)$ is a sum of products, which represents f and has $\{i_1, i_2, \ldots, i_k\} = \{1, 2, \ldots, n\}$ for each product term. If the coefficients from the Boolean polynomial are taken from the Boolean algebra $\{0, 1\}$, then the truth table of functional values of the

x_1	x_2	x_3	$(x_1 \wedge (\overline{x_2 \vee x_3})) \vee (((x_1 \wedge x_2) \vee \overline{x_3}) \wedge x_1)$
0	0	0	0
0	0	1	0
0	1	0	0
0	1	1	0
1	0	0	1
1	0	1	0
1	1	0	1
1	1	1	1

Figure 4.9

polynomial determines the disjunctive normal form simply by including each product term that occurs when the function takes the value 1. Figure 4.9 gives an example. Thus the disjunctive normal form of $(x_1 \wedge (x_2 \vee x_3)) \vee (((x_1 \wedge x_2) \vee \overline{x_3}) \wedge x_1)$ is

$$(x_1^1 \wedge x_2^0 \wedge x_3^0) \vee (x_1^1 \wedge x_2^1 \wedge x_3^0) \vee (x_1^1 \wedge x_2^1 \wedge x_3^1)$$
$$= (x_1 \wedge \bar{x}_2 \wedge \bar{x}_3) \vee (x_1 \wedge x_2 \wedge \bar{x}_3) \vee (x_1 \wedge x_2 \wedge x_3).$$

It can be tedious to calculate the functional values for every possible substitution of 0 and 1 into the x_i. The disjunctive normal form of a polynomial can be determined algebraically by using the distributive law and De Morgan's law. First determine a sum-of-products form for the polynomial and then for each variable x_i such that both x_i and $\bar{x}_i$ are missing from the product term adjoin the expression $x_i \vee \bar{x}_i$ to that product term. Then use distributivity to form two new product terms, one containing x_i and the other containing $\bar{x}_i$. For example,

$$(x_1 \wedge (\overline{x_2 \vee x_3})) \vee (((x_1 \wedge x_2) \vee \bar{x}_3) \wedge x_1)$$
$$= (x_1 \wedge (\bar{x}_2 \wedge \bar{x}_3)) \vee (((x_1 \wedge x_2) \vee \bar{x}_3) \wedge x_1)$$
$$= (x_1 \wedge \bar{x}_2 \wedge \bar{x}_3) \vee (x_1 \wedge x_2) \vee (x_1 \wedge \bar{x}_3)$$
$$= (x_1 \wedge \bar{x}_2 \wedge \bar{x}_3) \vee ((x_1 \wedge x_2 \wedge x_3) \vee (x_1 \wedge x_2 \wedge \bar{x}_3))$$
$$\vee ((x_1 \wedge x_2 \wedge \bar{x}_3) \vee (x_1 \wedge \bar{x}_2 \wedge \bar{x}_3))$$
$$= (x_1 \wedge \bar{x}_2 \wedge \bar{x}_3) \vee (x_1 \wedge x_2 \wedge x_3) \vee (x_1 \wedge x_2 \wedge \bar{x}_3).$$

In practice it is not necessary to go through all these steps explicitly. Once a sum of products is obtained, simply construct new product terms containing all combinations of the missing variables x_i and $\bar{x}_i$. Thus

$$(x_1 \wedge \bar{x}_2 \wedge \bar{x}_3) \vee (x_1 \wedge x_2) \vee (x_1 \wedge \bar{x}_3) = (x_1 \wedge \bar{x}_2 \wedge \bar{x}_3) \vee (x_1 \wedge x_2 \wedge x_3)$$
$$\vee (x_1 \wedge x_2 \wedge \bar{x}_3).$$

The notation used is often cumbersome, and it is sometimes convenient to omit the symbol $\wedge$ and simply juxtapose the expressions. Also, using the convention that intersection takes precedence over union, the parentheses enclosing an intersection can be dropped. Thus $\bar{x}_1 \wedge (x_3 \vee (x_2 \wedge x_3))$ can be written $\bar{x}_1(x_3 \vee x_2 x_3)$.

Theorem 4.1 enables us to determine a Boolean expression equal to a given Boolean polynomial simply by knowing the functional values of the Boolean polynomial. Thus the functional values of the Boolean polynomial determine the Boolean polynomial. Conversely, if $f(x_1, \ldots, x_n)$ is a Boolean function, then the Boolean expression

$$\bigvee f(e_1, e_2, \ldots, e_n) x_1^{e_1} x_2^{e_2} \cdots x_n^{e_n} \tag{1}$$

will have the same functional values as f. This is not difficult to see, since $e_i^{e_i} = 1$ for $e_i = 0$ or 1, implies

$$f(e_1, e_2, \ldots, e_n) e_1^{e_1} e_2^{e_2} \cdots e_n^{e_n} = f(e_1, e_2, \ldots, e_n)1$$
$$= f(e_1, e_2, \ldots, e_n)$$

and

$$f(e'_1, e'_2, \ldots, e'_n) e_1^{e_1'} e_2^{e_2'} \cdots e_n^{e_n'} = f(e'_1, e'_2, \ldots, e'_n)0$$
$$= 0,$$

if some e'_i does not equal e_i. Thus the substitution of e_i for x_i, $i = 1, \ldots, n$, in Eq. (1) gives the value $f(e_1, e_2, \ldots, e_n)$. Hence the disjunctive normal form for Boolean polynomials not only is a convenient way to express the polynomial, but also different disjunctive normal forms give different functions, hence different polynomials.

Theorem 4.1 has a counterpart with $\wedge$ and $\vee$ interchanged. This form is called the *conjunctive normal form*, and the corresponding theorem gives the result

$$f(x_1, x_2, \ldots, x_n) = \wedge (f(e_1, e_2, \ldots, e_n) \vee \bar{x}_1^{e_1} \vee \cdots \vee \bar{x}_n^{e_n}).$$

To prove this formula simply note that the complement of a Boolean function is determined from the table of functional values by taking the sum of all product terms that yield the functional value 0. Thus

$$\overline{f(x_1, \ldots, x_n)} = \vee \overline{f(e_1, \ldots, e_n)} x_1^{e_1} x_2^{e_2} \cdots x_n^{e_n},$$

so that

$$\overline{\overline{f(x_1, \ldots, x_n)}} = f(x_1, \ldots, x_n)$$
$$= \vee \overline{f(e_1, \ldots, e_n)} x_1^{e_1} x_2^{e_2} \cdots x_n^{e_n}$$
$$= \wedge (f(e_1, \ldots, e_n) \vee \bar{x}_1^{e_1} \vee \bar{x}_2^{e_2} \cdots \vee \bar{x}_n^{e_n}).$$

Thus in Figure 4.9 the complement of $x_1 \overline{(x_2 \vee x_3)} \vee (x_1 x_2 \vee x_3)x_1$ is given by the sum of products

$$\bar{x}_1 \bar{x}_2 \bar{x}_3 \vee \bar{x}_1 \bar{x}_2 x_3 \vee \bar{x}_1 x_2 \bar{x}_3 \vee \bar{x}_1 x_2 x_3 \vee x_1 \bar{x}_2 x_3$$
$$= \vee (f(e_1, e_2, \ldots, e_n) x_1^{e_1} x_2^{e_2} \cdots x_n^{e_n}).$$

Hence

$$x_1 \overline{(x_2 \vee x_3)} \vee (x_1 x_2 \vee \bar{x}_3)x_1 = \overline{\overline{x_1 \overline{(x_2 \vee x_3)} \vee (x_1 x_2 \vee \bar{x}_3)x_1}}$$

$$= \overline{\bar{x}_1 \bar{x}_2 \bar{x}_3 \vee \bar{x}_1 \bar{x}_2 x_3 \vee \bar{x}_1 x_2 \bar{x}_3 \vee \bar{x}_1 x_2 x_3 \vee x_1 \bar{x}_2 x_3}$$

$$= (x_1 \vee x_2 \vee x_3)(x_1 \vee x_2 \vee \bar{x}_3)(x_1 \vee \bar{x}_2 \vee x_3)$$

$$\wedge (x_1 \vee \bar{x}_2 \vee \bar{x}_3)(\bar{x}_1 \vee x_2 \vee \bar{x}_3).$$

Thus a Boolean expression can be put into conjunctive normal form by determining the disjunctive normal form of the complement and then taking the complement of this. Another method would be to convert the Boolean expression into a product of sums, and then if variables x_i and $\bar{x}_i$ are both missing from a sum term, simply adjoin the expression $x_i \wedge \bar{x}_i$ and use distributivity to obtain a new product of sums. In short for each sum term in the product of sums which contains neither the variable x_i nor $\bar{x}_i$ make two new sum terms simply by adding the variable x_i to the previous sum term and also adding the variable $\bar{x}_i$ to the sum term. Continue this process until each variable or its complement appears in each sum term.

We thus have two ways for determining the disjunctive normal form for Boolean expressions. The first way will be called the Black Box Method, since if the expression is viewed as a two-terminal switching circuit all we are doing is checking whether current flows or does not flow through the circuit with each possible combination of on and off for each switch. Thus no matter what the internal circuitry of the switching circuit is, an equivalent switching circuit can be built up by this procedure.

Often a switching circuit is represented by a graph in which the edges of the graph represent the switches and the vertices of the graph represent the connections between the switches (Figure 4.10). Thus an edge joins vertex i and vertex j if there is a switch that directly allows current to flow between connector i and connector j. Since current flows between the terminals if and only if there is a chain representing switches all allowing current to flow, a sum of products representing the circuit can be obtained by taking the set of product terms corresponding to the set of all chains between terminal 1 and terminal 2. Figure 4.10 gives an example of the graphical representation of a switching circuit, and in this figure the set of all chains from w_1 to w_6 is $\{x_1, \bar{x}_2, x_3\}, \{x_1, \bar{x}_2, x_2\}, \{x_1, x_4, x_3\}, \{x_1, x_4, x_2\}, \{\bar{x}_4, x_2\}, \{\bar{x}_4, x_4\}, \{\bar{x}_4, x_3\}, \{\bar{x}_2, x_1, x_2\}, \{\bar{x}_2, x_1, x_4\}, \{\bar{x}_2, x_1, x_3\}$ which yields product terms $x_1 \bar{x}_2 x_3$,

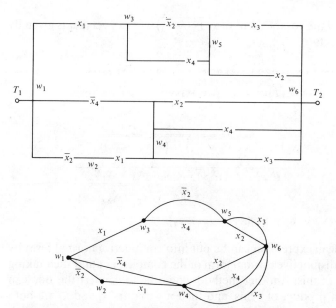

Figure 4.10 Graphical representation of a switching circuit.

$x_1 \bar{x}_2 x_2 = 0$, $x_1 x_3 x_4$, $x_1 x_2 x_4$, $x_2 \bar{x}_4$, $x_4 \bar{x}_4 = 0$, $x_3 \bar{x}_4$, $x_1 x_2 \bar{x}_2 = 0$, $x_1 \bar{x}_2 x_4$, and $x_1 \bar{x}_2 x_3$. This gives the sum-of-products expression for the switching circuit $x_1 \bar{x}_2 x_3 \vee x_1 x_4 x_4 \vee x_1 x_2 x_4 \vee x_2 \bar{x}_4 \vee x_3 \bar{x}_4 \vee x_1 \bar{x}_2 x_4$, which has the disjunctive normal form $\bar{x}_1 \bar{x}_2 x_3 \bar{x}_4 \vee \bar{x}_1 x_2 \bar{x}_3 \bar{x}_4 \vee \bar{x}_1 x_2 x_3 \bar{x}_4 \vee x_1 \bar{x}_2 \bar{x}_3 x_4 \vee x_1 \bar{x}_2 x_3 \bar{x}_4 \vee x_1 \bar{x}_2 x_3 x_4 \vee x_1 x_2 \bar{x}_3 \bar{x}_4 \vee x_1 x_2 \bar{x}_3 x_4 \vee x_1 x_2 x_3 \bar{x}_4 \vee x_1 x_2 x_3 x_4$. By taking the complement of the disjunctive normal form of the complement, the conjunctive normal form of the switching circuit $(\bar{x}_1 \vee x_2 \vee x_3 \vee x_4)(x_1 \vee \bar{x}_2 \vee \bar{x}_3 \vee \bar{x}_4)(x_1 \vee \bar{x}_2 \vee x_3 \vee \bar{x}_4)(x_1 \vee x_2 \vee x_3 \vee \bar{x}_4)(x_1 \vee x_2 \vee x_3 \vee x_4)$ is obtained. An alternative method for obtaining a product-of-sums expression for the circuit is simply to take the set of cut sets that separate the nodes representing terminal points and take as sum terms the terms corresponding to these cut sets. Since the function representing the circuit is 0 if and only if there is a cut set in which none of the switches, represented by the edges of the cut set, allows current to flow, the sum terms correspond to the cut sets. Thus the set of cut sets in Figure 4.10 is $\{\{x_1, \bar{x}_4, x_2\}, \{x_1, \bar{x}_4\}, \{x_1, x_2, x_3, x_4\}, \{\bar{x}_2, x_4, \bar{x}_4\}, \{\bar{x}_2, x_4, \bar{x}_4, x_1\}, \{\bar{x}_2, x_4, x_2, x_3\}, \{x_3, x_2, \bar{x}_4, \bar{x}_2\}, \{x_3, x_2, \bar{x}_4, x_1\}, \{x_3, x_2, x_4\}\}$ which yields the product of sums $(x_1 \vee \bar{x}_4)(x_2 \vee x_3 \vee x_4)$. From this product-of-sums representation for the switching circuit, the conjunctive normal form $(\bar{x}_1 \vee x_2 \vee x_3 \vee x_4)(x_1 \vee \bar{x}_2 \vee \bar{x}_3 \vee \bar{x}_4)(x_1 \vee \bar{x}_2 \vee x_3 \vee \bar{x}_4)(x_1 \vee x_2 \vee \bar{x}_3 \vee \bar{x}_4)(x_1 \vee x_2 \vee x_3 \vee \bar{x}_4)(\bar{x}_1 \vee x_2 \vee x_3 \vee x_4)$ is easily obtained.

The notation used in the previous paragraphs can be further abbreviated by expressing a product term in the n variables $x_1, \dots, x_n$ as an

n-digit binary integer, where a 0 in the ith digit stands for $\bar{x}_i$ and a 1 in the ith digit stands for x_i. Thus the complement of a polynomial in disjunctive normal form is the sum of products, where the product terms are represented by binary integers between 0 and $2^n - 1$ not contained in the disjunctive normal form of the polynomial.

Exercises

4-22 Let p_1 and p_2 be Boolean expressions. Define $p_1 \simeq p_2$ if there is a sequence $p_1 = q_1, q_2, \ldots, q_k = p_2$ of Boolean expressions such that the Boolean expression q_{i+1} is obtained from the Boolean expression q_i by using one of the laws (1) through (8) of Boolean algebra to change a subexpression of q_i. Prove that $\simeq$ is an equivalence relation on the set of all Boolean expressions in variables $x_1, \ldots, x_n$ and with coefficients from the Boolean algebra B.

4-23 Determine the table of functional values for the circuit in Figure 4.11. Write the disjunctive normal form that represents this circuit.

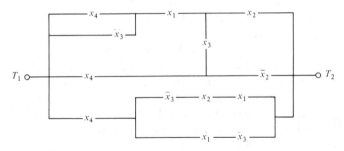

Figure 4.11

4-24 Determine the set of all paths in Figure 4.11 from T_1 to T_2, and from this set determine the disjunctive normal form for the switching circuit.

4-25 Determine the conjunctive normal form for the Boolean polynomial
$\bar{x}_1\bar{x}_2 x_3\bar{x}_4 \;\lor\; \bar{x}_1\bar{x}_2 x_3 x_4 \;\lor\; \bar{x}_1 x_2 \bar{x}_3 x_4 \;\lor\; \bar{x}_1 x_2 x_3 \bar{x}_4 \;\lor\; x_1\bar{x}_2 \bar{x}_3 \bar{x}_4 \;\lor\;$
$x_1\bar{x}_2 \bar{x}_3 x_4 \;\lor\; x_1 x_2 \bar{x}_3 \bar{x}_4 \;\lor\; x_1 x_2 x_3 \bar{x}_4 \;\lor\; x_1 x_2 x_3 x_4$. (Alternatively written
$0010 \lor 0011 \lor 0101 \lor 0110 \lor 1000 \lor 1001 \lor 1100 \lor 1110 \lor 1111$.)

4-26 Determine the set of cut sets in Figure 4.11, hence write a product-of-sums representation of the switching circuit. From this product-of-sums representation determine the conjunctive normal form for the Boolean polynomial.

4-27 Describe a simple method for obtaining the disjunctive normal form of a Boolean polynomial from the conjunctive normal form of that polynomial.

4-28 Determine the disjunctive normal form for $(x_1 x_2 \lor x_3 x_4)\bar{x}_3 \lor x_3 x_4$.

4-29 The following graph represents a switching circuit. Determine the cut sets, hence write the conjunctive normal form for the corresponding Boolean polynomial.

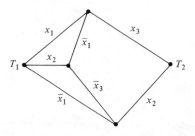

4.5   MINIMIZATION OF BOOLEAN POLYNOMIALS

Often in the design of switching circuits, the only requirement is that the circuitry have certain functional values. Within this limitation, the designer has considerable flexibility. In industrial applications, it is extremely important that the circuitry be designed in as efficient a manner as possible. This efficiency often is measured in terms of cost. Each switch or each electronic gate has a certain cost associated with it, and the switching circuit must be designed to minimize the total cost of the components in that circuit. This section gives certain minimization procedures.

A variable x_i or its complement $\bar{x}_i$ is called a *literal*. If an expression represents a Boolean polynomial and the number of literals occurring in that expression is minimal among all expressions that represent that Boolean polynomial, then the expression is said to be minimal with respect to the fewest occurrences of literals. Although much effort has been expended to determine an efficient method for finding an expression containing the fewest number of literals, no efficient general method is yet known. Another criterion for minimality is to restrict the expressions representing the polynomial to sum-of-products expressions and then pick, from this set of sum-of-products expressions, one with the fewest occurrences of literals. Even this problem we do not solve. However, if we restrict ourselves to sum-of-products expressions representing the polynomial and insist only that the expression contain the minimal number of product terms, with the additional restriction that from among these candidates we must pick the one with the fewest occurrences of literals, then there is a procedure for determining a minimal expression. This procedure was discovered by Quine and improved by McCluskey in the early 1950s and is called the Quine-McCluskey algorithm.

The only axioms for Boolean algebra that reduce the number of literals occurring in an expression are the axioms of absorption, distributivity, universal bound, and complementation. These are the basic tools in our minimization procedure. This procedure is illustrated by the following simplification of a sum-of-products expression.

$$x_1 x_2 x_3 \vee x_1 \bar{x}_2 x_3 \vee \bar{x}_1 \bar{x}_2 \bar{x}_3$$

$$= x_1 x_3 (x_2 \vee \bar{x}_2) \vee \bar{x}_1 \bar{x}_2 \bar{x}_3 \qquad \text{(by distributivity)}$$

$$= x_1 x_3 1 \vee \bar{x}_1 \bar{x}_2 \bar{x}_3 \qquad \text{(by complementation)}$$

$$= x_1 x_3 \vee \bar{x}_1 \bar{x}_2 \bar{x}_3 \qquad \text{(by universal bound).} \qquad (2)$$

This procedure reduced the number of product terms by 1 and, furthermore, reduced the number of occurrences of literals by 4. In formula (2), the product term $x_1 x_3$ appears in the final expression, and its literals form a subset of the literals of $x_1 x_2 x_3$ and $x_1 \bar{x}_2 x_3$. A product term whose literals are a subset of the literals of a second product term is called a *subproduct* of the second. A product term in a sum-of-products representation of a polynomial may take the value 1 only when the polynomial takes the value 1. Any product term that takes the value 1 only if the polynomial does is called an *implicant* of the polynomial, and the product term is said to imply the polynomial. A *prime implicant* of a polynomial is a product term that implies the polynomial but has no other subproduct term that implies the polynomial. Thus in formula (2) the product term $x_1 x_3$ implies the polynomial and, since neither x_1 nor x_3 implies the polynomial, there is no proper subproduct of $x_1 x_3$ that implies the polynomial. Hence $x_1 x_3$ is a prime implicant. Since a Boolean polynomial representing a switching circuit takes its coefficients from the Boolean algebra $\{0, 1\}$, we assume for the rest of this section that the Boolean polynomials in the variables $x_1, \ldots, x_n$ take their coefficients from 0, 1. Thus we state the following proposition.

Proposition 4.1   A Boolean polynomial $f(x_1, \ldots, x_n)$ is equal to the sum of all prime implicants of f.

Proof   Since each prime implicant takes the value 1 only if f takes the value 1, the sum of the prime implicants takes the value 1 only if f takes the value 1. If $f(e_1, \ldots, e_n) = 1$ for $e_i = 0, 1$, then some product term of the disjunctive normal form for f must also equal 1 under this substitution. If that product term equals 1, then any subproduct term of the product term also equals 1. In particular, there must be a subproduct term that is a prime implicant of f and takes the value 1. Thus the sum of all prime implicants of f takes the value 1 if and only if f takes the value 1. Thus the two expressions as functions are equal, hence as polynomials must also be equal.

Proposition 4.1 shows that a polynomial can be written as a sum of prime implicants. The proposition does not explicitly outline an algorithm for determining the prime implicants, but this is not difficult to do. If the polynomial $f(x_1, \ldots, x_n)$ is in disjunctive normal form, the product terms are exactly the implicants containing n literals. Since any implicant must be a subproduct of a product term of the disjunctive normal form, the implicants containing $n - 1$ literals are subproducts of the product terms of the normal form. An implicant containing $n - 1$ literals remains an implicant when an arbitrary value is assigned to the missing literal. Thus the disjunctive normal form must contain product terms corresponding to both the subproduct with the missing literal adjoined and the subproduct with the complement of the missing literal adjoined. For example, if

$$\bar{x}_1 \bar{x}_2 \bar{x}_3 \vee \bar{x}_1 x_2 \bar{x}_3 \vee \bar{x}_1 x_2 x_3 \vee x_1 \bar{x}_2 \bar{x}_3 \vee x_1 \bar{x}_2 x_3 \vee x_1 x_2 x_3 = f(x_1, x_2, x_3),$$

then the subproduct $\bar{x}_1 \bar{x}_3$ of $\bar{x}_1 \bar{x}_2 \bar{x}_3$ is an implicant, since both $\bar{x}_1 \bar{x}_2 \bar{x}_3$ and $\bar{x}_1 x_2 \bar{x}_3$ are implicants. Likewise, $\bar{x}_1 x_2$ is a subproduct of both $\bar{x}_1 x_2 x_3$ and $\bar{x}_1 x_2 \bar{x}_3$, so that $\bar{x}_1 x_2$ is an implicant. By checking the remaining subproducts containing two literals, the additional implicants $\bar{x}_2 \bar{x}_3$, $x_1 \bar{x}_2$, $x_2 x_3$, and $x_1 x_3$ are found. These implicants are easily found to be prime implicants, hence

$$f(x_1, x_2, x_3) = \bar{x}_1 \bar{x}_3 \vee \bar{x}_1 x_2 \vee \bar{x}_2 \bar{x}_3 \vee x_1 \bar{x}_2 \vee x_2 x_3 \vee x_1 x_3.$$

Even though f is written as a sum of prime implicants, it may be possible to delete several prime implicants and still obtain the sum of prime implicants, which equals f. In fact,

$$f(x_1, x_2, x_3) = \bar{x}_1 \bar{x}_3 \vee \bar{x}_1 x_2 \vee x_1 \bar{x}_2 \vee x_1 x_3.$$

None of the prime implicants in this expression for f can be deleted. However, there may be other sums of prime implicants that have fewer product terms than this expression. As a matter of fact,

$$f(x_1, x_2, x_3) = \bar{x}_1 \bar{x}_3 \vee x_2 x_3 \vee x_1 \bar{x}_2,$$

or even

$$f(x_1, x_2, x_3) = \bar{x}_1 x_2 \vee \bar{x}_2 \bar{x}_3 \vee x_1 x_3.$$

These two expressions for f have the minimal number of product terms possible. Such a sum of prime implicants that has the smallest number of product terms possible out of all sums of prime implicants representing the polynomial f is called *irredundant*. It is not difficult to see that a minimal sum-of-products expression must be irredundant. Thus to determine the minimal expression it is sufficient to check the set of irredundant expressions to find which irredundant expression contains the fewest literals.

We now give the Quine-McCluskey algorithm for determining such a minimal expression. First the prime implicants of the Boolean polynomial $f(x_1, \ldots, x_n)$ must be determined. To do this, find the disjunctive normal form for the Boolean polynomial. This gives all nonzero product terms containing n literals. Any product term with more than n literals must either equal 0 or a product term with at most n literals. Thus the prime implicants must be subproduct terms of these product terms. List the product terms of the disjunctive normal form in a column, using their binary representation. Order the columns so that the number of ones in the binary representation increases as one goes down the column. For example, $\bar{x}_1 \bar{x}_2 \bar{x}_3 \bar{x}_4 \vee \bar{x}_1 \bar{x}_2 \bar{x}_3 x_4 \vee \bar{x}_1 \bar{x}_2 x_3 \bar{x}_4 \vee \bar{x}_1 \bar{x}_2 x_3 x_4 \vee \bar{x}_1 x_2 x_3 x_4 \vee x_1 \bar{x}_2 \bar{x}_3 \bar{x}_4 \vee x_1 x_2 \bar{x}_3 \bar{x}_4$ yields

$$0000$$

$$0001$$

$$0010$$

$$1000$$

$$0011$$

$$1100$$

$$0111.$$

Since $(p \wedge x) \vee (p \wedge \bar{x})$ equals p, where x is a literal and p is a subproduct term, the implicants with one less occurrence of a literal can be found by examining product terms that differ in at most one component. Thus take the first product term in the column and compare it pairwise with all other product terms that differ from it in at most one entry. For each such pair, put a term in a second column having a dash for the component in which the members of the pair differ, and is otherwise equal to the first product term. Continue this process with the second and succeeding terms of the first column. Check off each product term in the first column that has been used to determine a product term with fewer literals. After this procedure we then have two columns. The unchecked entries in the first column represent prime implicants, since there are no implicants with exactly one less literal that are subproducts of that implicant. Continue this procedure with the second and succeeding columns until no new terms are obtained. Thus, in the example, we have

0000 ✓	000_ ✓	(1 and 2)	00_ _	(1 and 5)
0001 ✓	00_0 ✓	(1 and 3)	00_ _	(2 and 4)
0010 ✓	_000	(1 and 4)		
1000 ✓	00_1 ✓	(2 and 5)		
0011 ✓	001_ ✓	(3 and 5)		
1100 ✓	1_00	(4 and 6)		
0111 ✓	0_11	(5 and 7)		

Since there are no product terms in the third column that differ from each other in exactly one component, the procedure is completed, and the prime implicants are the unchecked product terms in the table.

In order to determine a minimal expression the irredundant sums of prime implicants must be found. If a product term appears in the disjunctive normal form and the values corresponding to the binary representation of the product term are substituted into the polynomial, then the polynomial has the functional value 1. If no prime implicant in a sum of prime implicants is a subproduct of this term, then when this substitution is made into the sum of prime implicants, each product term of that sum must be 0, hence the sum of prime implicants takes the value 0. Therefore, if a sum of prime implicants is going to be equal to the polynomial, then for each product term in the disjunctive normal form there must be a prime implicant in the sum of prime implicants that is a subproduct of that product term. Thus the next step in the procedure is to determine which prime implicants are subproducts of which product term of the disjunctive normal form. This is accomplished by means of a prime implicant table which has rows corresponding to each prime implicant and columns corresponding to each product term of the disjunctive normal form. An × is placed in the ith row and jth column if the prime implicant corresponding to the ith row is a subproduct of the product term corresponding to the jth column, as in Figure 4.12. A product term p is said to cover a product term q if p is a subproduct of q. Thus to determine a sum of prime implicants equal to a Boolean polynomial pick a subset of the set of prime implicants such that each product term of the disjunctive normal form is covered by at least one prime implicant in the subset. A minimal expression is such a sum of prime implicants that has the smallest number of terms and the smallest number of literals.

In Figure 4.12 the only prime implicant that covers 0001 is the prime implicant 00_ _ . The only prime implicant that covers 1100 is 1_00, and the only prime implicant that covers 0111 is 0_11. Thus these three prime implicants must be contained in any sum of prime implicants equal to the Boolean polynomial. A prime implicant that covers a product term of the disjunctive normal form, where that product term is covered by no other prime implicant, is called *essential*. The sum of the essential implicants is called the *core*. Since these three prime implicants cover every product term in the disjunctive normal form for the polynomial, a minimal sum of prime implicants is

$$x_1 \bar{x}_3 \bar{x}_4 \vee \bar{x}_1 x_3 x_4 \vee \bar{x}_1 \bar{x}_2 .$$

The procedure for finding a minimal sum of prime implicants from the prime implicant table can be formalized. First determine the core. Rename the product terms not convered by prime implicants in the core $q_1, q_2, \ldots, q_k$ and

	0000	0001	0010	1000	0011	1100	0111
_000	×			×			
1_00				×		×	
0_11					×		×
00_ _	×	×	×		×		

Figure 4.12 Prime implicant table.

	q_1	q_2	q_3	q_4	q_5
p_1	×		×		×
p_2		×		×	×
p_3	×	×		×	
p_4		×	×		×

Figure 4.13

label the prime implicants not in the core $p_1, \ldots, p_m$. Construct a table in which the columns correspond to the q_j's and the rows correspond to the p_i's. Put an × in the ith row and jth column if the prime implicant p_i covers q_j. Figure 4.13 shows a hypothetical example. Construct a product of sums in the variables p_i such that the sum terms are determined by the prime implicants in the table that cover each column. Determine a sum-of-products expression for this product of sums by expanding and using the absorption law. The product terms of this expression yield the possible set of prime implicants necessary to add to the core to obtain an irredundant expression. Thus, in Figure 4.13, we have

$$(p_1 \vee p_3)(p_2 \vee p_3 \vee p_4)(p_1 \vee p_4)(p_2 \vee p_3)(p_1 \vee p_2 \vee p_4) = p_1 p_2 \vee p_1 p_3 \vee p_3 p_4,$$

and the irredundant sums of prime implicants are

$$\text{core} \vee p_1 \vee p_2, \qquad \text{core} \vee p_1 \vee p_3, \qquad \text{and} \qquad \text{core} \vee p_3 \vee p_4.$$

Exercises

4-30 Determine the set of prime implicants for each of the following Boolean polynomials.
 a $\bar{x}_1 \bar{x}_2 \bar{x}_3 \vee \bar{x}_1 x_2 x_3 \vee x_1 \bar{x}_2 \bar{x}_3 \vee x_1 x_2$
 b $0000 \vee 0010 \vee 0100 \vee 1010 \vee 1101 \vee 1110$
 c $0001 \vee 0011 \vee 1001 \vee 1011 \vee 1100 \vee 1101$
 d $1000 \vee 0011 \vee 0111 \vee 1011 \vee 1110 \vee 1111$
 e $0010 \vee 0100 \vee 0111 \vee 1010 \vee 1100 \vee 1110 \vee 1111.$

4-31 Construct prime implicant tables for the Boolean polynomials in Exercise 4-30 and determine the core for each polynomial. Determine a minimal sum-of-products expression for each polynomial.

4-32 Draw the gating network for each of the polynomials in Exercise 4-30 and the gating network corresponding to the minimal sum-of-products expression for each polynomial.

4-33 Minimize the following gating network and diagram the result.

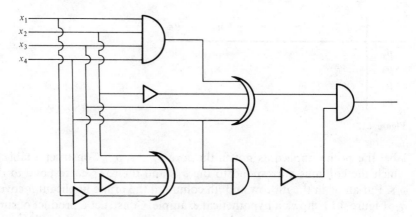

4-34 Construct a minimization procedure that yields a minimal product-of-sums expression.

---

*4.6 DECOMPOSITION OF FUNCTIONS

In Section 4.5 the variables in a Boolean expression are considered inputs to a gating network consisting of various series and parallel arrangements of and gates, or gates, and inverters. Often, components that are not simple gates or inverters are used to construct more complicated electronic devices. The outputs from these components are used as inputs to the devices. Hence, although the total device can be considered a Boolean function of the inputs, it may also be a function of the outputs of certain components, and some of the original inputs. A Boolean function $f(x_1, x_2, \ldots, x_n)$ is said to be *decomposable* if f can be expressed as a composition of several functions, each of which is a function of less than n variables. In particular, a Boolean function $f(x_1, x_2, \ldots, x_n)$ is *simple disjunctive decomposable* if $f = F(g(y_1, \ldots, y_s), z_1, \ldots, z_r)$, where $\{y_1, y_2, \ldots, y_s\}$ and $\{z_1, z_2, \ldots, z_r\}$ partition $\{x_1, x_2, \ldots, x_n\}$.

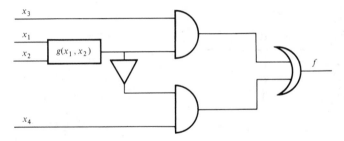

Figure 4.14

For example,

$$f(x_1, x_2, x_3, x_4) = x_1 x_2 x_3 \vee x_1 \bar{x}_2 x_3 \vee \bar{x}_1 \bar{x}_2 x_4 \vee \bar{x}_1 x_2 x_4$$
$$= (x_1 x_2 \vee x_1 \bar{x}_2) x_3 \vee (\bar{x}_1 \bar{x}_2 \vee \bar{x}_1 x_2) x_4$$
$$= (x_1 x_2 \vee x_1 \bar{x}_2) x_3 \vee \overline{(x_1 x_2 \vee x_1 \bar{x}_2)} x_4$$
$$= g(x_1, x_2) x_3 \vee \overline{g(x_1, x_2)} x_4,$$

where $g(x_1, x_2) = x_1 x_2 \vee x_1 \bar{x}_2$. If we diagram the above expression in terms of and gates, or gates, inverters, and the device, which corresponds to $g(x_1, x_2)$, then we will have Figure 4.14.

If f has a simple disjunctive decomposition, then f is a function of the variable g and the variables $z_1, \ldots, z_r$. In Theorem 4.1 an inductive procedure shows that any Boolean polynomial can be expressed in disjunctive normal form. Following this inductive procedure,

$$f(y_1, \ldots, y_s, z_1, \ldots, z_r) = \vee f(y_1, \ldots, y_s, e_1, \ldots, e_r) z_1^{e_1} \cdots z_r^{e_r},$$

and the coefficients $f(y_1, \ldots, y_s, e_1, \ldots, e_r)$ are unique. Since f is also a function of $g, z_1, \ldots, z_r$, we have

$$f(g, z_1, \ldots, z_r) = \vee f(c_1, e_1, \ldots, e_r) g^{c_1} z_1^{e_1} \cdots z_r^{e_r},$$

where c_1 is 0 or 1, and thus $f(y_1, \ldots, y_s, e_1, \ldots, e_r)$ must be either $g(y_1, \ldots, y_s)$, $\overline{g(y_1, \ldots, y_s)}$, 0, or 1. Thus to determine a simple disjunctive decomposition it is necessary to show that there are only four possibilities for $f(y_1, \ldots, y_s, e_1, \ldots, e_r)$ for each choice of $e_1, \ldots, e_r$. The function $f(y_1, \ldots, y_s, e_1, \ldots, e_r)$ can be illustrated by means of a matrix, called the *partition matrix*, with rows corresponding to each of the products $z_1^{e_1} \cdots z_r^{e_r}$, columns corresponding to $y_1^{c_1} \ldots y_s^{c_s}$, where c_i takes the values 0 or 1, $f(c_1, \ldots, c_s, e_1, \ldots, e_r)$ being the entry in the $z_1^{e_1} \ldots z_r^{e_r}$ row and $y_1^{c_1} \ldots y_s^{c_s}$ column. The rows of the matrix are the functions $f(y_1, \ldots, y_s, e_1, \ldots, e_r)$. Thus for the function f to be simple disjunctive decomposable, there must be at most four distinct rows in the matrix, and these rows must be all 1's, all

$x_3 x_4$ \ $x_1 x_2$	00	01	10	11
00	0	0	0	0
01	1	1	0	0
10	0	0	1	1
11	1	1	1	1

Figure 4.15

0's, the row corresponding to the function g, or a row corresponding to $\bar{g}$. Thus the partition matrix corresponding to

$$f(x_1 x_2 \vee x_1 \bar{x}_2, x_3, x_4) = (x_1 x_2 \vee x_1 \bar{x}_2)x_3 \vee \overline{(x_1 x_2 \vee x_1 \bar{x}_2)}x_4$$

is shown in Figure 4.15.

Since there are exactly four possibilities for the rows and two of these possibilities, namely, the 0 and the 1 row, have exactly the same entries in every column, while the other two rows are complements, there are at most two distinct columns in the partition matrix. We now can state the main theorem of this section.

Theorem 4.2 The Boolean function $f(x_1, \ldots, x_n)$ has a simple disjunctive decomposition into $f(g(y_1, \ldots, y_s), z_1, \ldots, z_r)$ if and only if the partition matrix corresponding to the partition of $\{x_1, \ldots, x_n\}$ into $\{y_1, \ldots, y_s\}$ and $\{z_1, \ldots, z_r\}$ has at most two distinct columns.

Proof We have already shown that, if f has such a simple disjunctive decomposition, then the partition matrix has at most the rows 0, 1, g, or $\bar{g}$. Thus there are at most two distinct columns. Suppose now that there exists a partition of $\{x_1, \ldots, x_n\}$ into $\{y_1, \ldots, y_s\}$ and $\{z_1, \ldots, z_r\}$ such that the partition matrix has at most two distinct columns. If there is exactly one column, then the rows will be either all 0's or all 1's, and f will depend only on $z_1, \ldots, z_r$. If there are exactly two distinct columns and if two corresponding entries in these columns are equal, then the whole row will be equal, hence it will consist of all 0's or all 1's. The two columns could have different corresponding entries either by having a 0 in the first column and a 1 in the other column, or having a 1 in the first column and a 0 in the other. The first case yields a row that is the complement of the row determined by the second case. Thus any row that is not a row of 0's or a row of 1's must be a fixed third row or its complement. This fixed row gives a sum-of-products expression in the variables $y_1, \ldots, y_s$ for the function $g(y_1, \ldots, y_s)$. Thus the function f is equal to a sum-of-products expression with the product terms of the form $g^{c_1} z_1^{e_1} \cdots z_r^{e_r}$, where g^{c_1} corresponds to the $z_1^{e_1} \cdots z_r^{e_r}$ row, and product terms of the form $z_1^{e_1} \cdots z_r^{e_r}$ if that row is all 1's.

	00	01	10	11
000	1	1	1	1
001	0	0	1	0
010	0	0	0	0
011	1	1	0	1
100	1	1	0	1
101	1	1	1	1
110	0	0	1	0
111	1	1	0	1

Figure 4.16

Theorem 4.2 shows that the partition matrix of Figure 4.16, which represents the function

$$f(x_1, x_2, x_3, x_4, x_5)$$

$$= 00000 \vee 00001 \vee 00010 \vee 00011$$

$$\vee\, 00110 \vee 01100 \vee 01101 \vee 01111 \vee 10000 \vee 10001 \vee 10011$$

$$\vee\, 10100 \vee 10101 \vee 10110 \vee 10111 \vee 11010 \vee 11100 \vee 11101 \vee 11111,$$

yields a simple disjunctive decomposition of f into

$$f = \bar{x}_1 \bar{x}_2 \bar{x}_3 \vee g\bar{x}_1 \bar{x}_2 x_3 \vee \bar{g}\bar{x}_1 x_2 x_3 \vee \bar{g}x_1 \bar{x}_2 \bar{x}_3 \vee x_1 \bar{x}_2 x_3 \vee gx_1 x_2 \bar{x}_3$$

$$\vee\, \bar{g}x_1 x_2 x_3,$$

where

$$g(x_4, x_5) = x_4 \bar{x}_5, \qquad \overline{g(x_4, x_5)} = \bar{x}_4 \bar{x}_5 \vee \bar{x}_4 x_5 \vee x_4 x_5.$$

Using the Quine-McCluskey algorithm, f can be further simplified to

$$f(g, x_1, x_2, x_3) = \bar{x}_1 \bar{x}_2 \bar{x}_3 \vee \bar{g}x_1 \bar{x}_2 \vee g\bar{x}_2 x_3 \vee \bar{g}x_2 x_3 \vee gx_1 x_2 \bar{x}_3.$$

The switching circuit corresponding to the expression for f in terms of g, x_1, x_2, and x_3 is given in Figure 4.17. If the Quine-McCluskey minimization procedure is applied to $f(x_1, x_2, x_3, x_4, x_5)$, then a minimal sum-of-products expression is obtained which is significantly longer than a minimal expression obtained for f as a simple disjunctive decomposition.

Theorem 4.2 enables us to determine simple disjunctive decompositions of a function f. To do this, the partition matrices must be determined and then examined to see if any have at most two distinct columns. This would require examining 2^n partition matrices. However, we need compute only those partitions in which the first subset of the partition has at most as many elements as the second subset of the partition. The partition matrices in which the first subset of the partition has more elements than the second

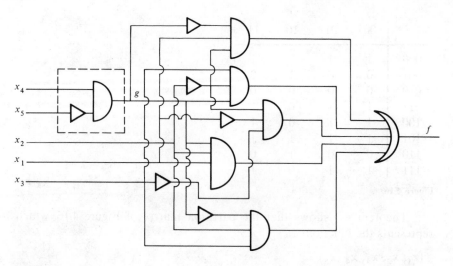

Figure 4.17

subset of the partition can be found by taking the transpose of a matrix previously found. In other words, it is sufficient to determine whether the partition matrices of size $k \times l$, where $k \leq l$, have at most two distinct columns or at most two distinct rows.

Exercises

4-35 Use the Quine-McCluskey minimization procedure to determine a minimal sum-of-products expression for the function

$$f(x_1, x_2, x_3, x_4, x_5) = 00000 \vee 00001 \vee 00010 \vee 00110 \vee 01101 \vee 01111$$

$$\vee\, 10000 \vee 10001 \vee 10011 \vee 10100 \vee 10101 \vee 10110$$

$$\vee\, 10111 \vee 10010 \vee 11011 \vee 11111.$$

4-36 Determine a simple disjunctive decomposition for the function

$$h(x_1, x_2, x_3, x_4, x_5) = 00000 \vee 00011 \vee 00100 \vee 00101 \vee 01000 \vee 01010$$

$$\vee\, 01011 \vee 01110 \vee 10000 \vee 10011 \vee 10100 \vee 10111$$

$$\vee\, 10111 \vee 11010 \vee 11011 \vee 11111.$$

4-37 Minimize the function h in Exercise 4-36 in terms of the variables of the simple disjunctive decomposition.

Chapter 5

Finite Machines

5.1 INTRODUCTION

Machines affect almost every facet of our lives. They may be very simple, such as hammers, screwdrivers, or switches, or exceedingly complex, such as automobiles, jet airplanes, or digital computers. Each machine is physically different, but certain aspects are common to all. One such aspect is the fact that a machine can assume only certain physical configurations. At a particular instant in time, an automobile may be traveling down the street with gas flowing to the engine at a particular rate, a specified pressure on the brake pedal, and the steering wheel turned at a specific angle. Thus the state of the automobile depends on the actions of the operator, and these actions represent some of the inputs to the machine. The result of these inputs to the machine and the state of the machine at a particular instance yield the outputs of the machine, which may be the velocity in a specified direction and with a certain acceleration. Thus with any machine we associate a set of states of the machine, the set of possible inputs to the machine, and a set of possible outputs of the machine.

As a machine, the automobile exhibits continuous dependencies on its inputs through time and has infinitely many distinct states with an output which also changes continuously with time. Furthermore, the continuity and the infinity of states are both important in the description of the automobile. There are, however, many machines whose operations can be described effectively in terms of a finite number of states, a finite number of inputs, and a finite number of outputs. For example, an automatic elevator can be considered to have only a finite number of inputs, corresponding to the signal buttons both in the elevator and on each floor. The state of the elevator corresponds to going up, going down, or resting, along with the inventory of stops it must make as it ascends or descends. The output of the machine is movement between floors or no movement. It is clear that the operation of any particular automatic elevator can be described in terms of a finite number of states, a finite number of inputs, and a finite number of outputs. Such a description ignores the continuous aspects of movement, hence it is only an approximation. However, most machines can be described in terms of such a finite approximation. Even the continuous output of a meter can be digitalized to the desired degree of accuracy, resulting in only a finite number of outputs.

Although many machines can be represented in this manner, the most important examples are digital devices. The basic components of a digital system consist of various two-state devices. These are combined in a finite number of ways, so that the digital system has a finite number of possible internal states. Also, only a finite number of possible inputs is accepted by the machine, and a finite number of outputs results.

This chapter is concerned only with machines that exhibit a finite number of states, have a finite number of possible inputs, and yield a finite number of possible outputs. These machines form two classes according to whether the output exists or does not exist. The first class of machines is called the class of input-output (i/o) machines.

Definition   An i/o machine M is equal to $(\mathcal{S}, \mathcal{I}, \mathcal{O}, \delta, \theta)$, where $\mathcal{S}$ is a finite set called the states of the machine, $\mathcal{I}$ is a finite set called the input alphabet, $\mathcal{O}$ is a finite set called the output alphabet, δ is a function from $\mathcal{S} \times \mathcal{I}$ to $\mathcal{S}$, called the next state function, and θ is a function from $\mathcal{S} \times \mathcal{I}$ to $\mathcal{O}$, called the output function.

The non-negative integers N denote successive instances of time, and a_t, $t \in N$, is the input to the i/o machine M at time t. The machine M operates in time as follows. If $s(t)$ is the state of the machine at time t, then $s(t + 1) = \delta(s(t), a_t)$ and, if $w(t)$ is the output at time t, then $w(t) = \theta(s(t), a_t)$. Thus δ gives the next state, and θ gives the current output.

If we are not concerned about output, then we omit $\mathcal{O}$ and θ and call the machine a state machine.

Definition   A state machine M is equal to $(\mathcal{S}, \mathcal{I}, \delta)$, where $\mathcal{S}$ is a finite set, $\mathcal{I}$ is a finite set, and δ is a function from $\mathcal{S} \times \mathcal{I}$ to $\mathcal{S}$. $\mathcal{S}$, $\mathcal{I}$, and δ are called states, inputs, and next-state function, respectively.

We use the term *machine* to refer to either an i/o machine or a state machine.

This chapter examines some of the properties of machines and various concepts which reduce to machines. Equivalent machines are defined, and a minimization procedure exhibited which in a precise sense yields the smallest possible machine in an equivalence class of machines. Furthermore, we shall see that any machine can be realized as an electronic gating network with various delay elements.

5.2   STATE TABLES AND STATE DIAGRAMS

Machines have been defined in terms of certain finite sets and certain functions between these sets. Since there can be only a finite number of such functions, each finite state machine can be described by listing the possible states, the possible inputs, and the possible outputs, along with the values the function δ and, if applicable, θ take for each element of the set $\mathcal{S} \times \mathcal{I}$. This description can be conveniently arranged in tabular (or matrix) form. The rows of the table are labeled with the possible states of the machine. The first set of columns of the table is labeled with the possible inputs of the machine, and the entry corresponding to the s-row and the a-column is $\delta(s, a)$. If needed, a second set of columns of the table is again labeled with the possible inputs of the machine, and the entry in the s-row and a-column is $\theta(s, a)$. Such a table is called the state table for the machine.

A very simple i/o machine is the parity-check machine. This machine is designed to show whether the total number of 1's in a finite sequence of 0's and 1's is even or odd. This machine has an input 0 or 1, states corresponding to even or odd, and outputs corresponding to even or odd. If the machine is in the state corresponding to even, and a sequence of 0's and 1's is fed into it, it outputs a symbol corresponding to even if an even number of 1's has been received, and outputs a symbol corresponding to odd if an odd number of 1's has been received. The functions δ and θ are easily described for this machine. If the machine is in state even and a 1 is received, then it moves to state odd and outputs the symbol corresponding to odd. If the input 0 is received while the machine is in state even, then it remains in state even and outputs the symbol corresponding to state even. If the machine is in state odd and receives an input of 1, then it changes to state even and

	$\delta(s, a)$		$\theta(s, a)$	
	0	1	0	1
Even	Even	Odd	E	O
Odd	Odd	Even	O	E

Figure 5.1 Parity-check machine.

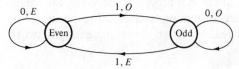

Figure 5.2 Parity-check machine.

outputs an even. If an input of 0 is received when the machine is in state odd, then it does not change state and outputs the symbol corresponding to odd. This behavior is described by the state table in Figure 5.1.

In addition to the tabular form, a machine can also be described in terms of a directed graph with labels. The nodes of the graph correspond exactly to the state of the machine. For each possible input a and each possible state s, define an arc that originates at the node s and terminates at the node $\delta(s, a)$. Label this arc with the input a followed by the output $\theta(s, a)$. Thus the directed graph of the parity-check machine is given in Figure 5.2.

The directed graph representation of a machine is called the state diagram of that machine. If the state diagram is known, then it is a simple matter to write out the state table for the machine, and vice versa.

Exercises

5-1 Draw the state diagram of the machine given in Figure 5.3.

	δ		θ	
	0	1	0	1
s_1	s_1	s_2	x	y
s_2	s_2	s_4	z	x
s_3	s_3	s_3	x	y
s_4	s_1	s_2	y	z

Figure 5.3

5-2   Write the state table for the machine in Figure 5.4.

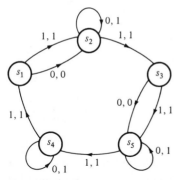

Figure 5.4

5-3   Determine the state table and the state diagram for a machine that has input 0 or 1 and outputs the previous input (i.e., remembers the input for 1 unit of time).

5-4   Determine the state table and the state diagram for a machine that has inputs 0 or 1 and outputs the remainder when the number of received 1's is divided by 5.

5-5   Determine a state diagram for a machine that has input 0 or 1 and outputs a 1 if the number of 1's in the preceding four inputs is greater than the number of 0's, and outputs a 0 otherwise.

5-6   Draw the state diagram for a machine with an input alphabet consisting of the letters of the English alphabet, which outputs a 1 if the sequence ALERT is received and outputs a 0 otherwise (do not draw 26 arcs from each vertex—just label the arcs in an abbreviated manner).

5-7   Draw the state diagram for a finite state machine with input and output alphabet {0, 1}, which outputs a 0 if it receives 010 or 101 and outputs a 1 otherwise.

5-8   Determine a state table for an automatic elevator that services three floors.

5.3   SIMPLE PROPERTIES

Since digital devices can be modeled by machines, the capability of machines is enormous. However, there are many arithmetical tasks a machine cannot do. Let us examine the arithmetical processes of addition and multiplication of two binary integers. In the usual hand computations for the addition of two binary integers, corresponding digits of the two integers are operated on starting with the rightmost pair of digits. Thus we assume

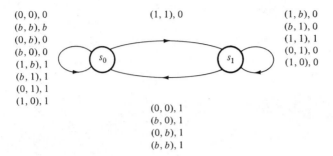

(0, 0), 0
(b, b), b
(0, b), 0
(b, 0), 0
(1, b), 1
(b, 1), 1
(0, 1), 1
(1, 0), 1

(1, 1), 0

(1, b), 0
(b, 1), 0
(1, 1), 1
(0, 1), 0
(1, 0), 0

(0, 0), 1
(b, 0), 1
(0, b), 1
(b, b), 1

Figure 5.5

that the corresponding digits of the binary integers are fed into the machine
simultaneously. In order to add integers that may not have the same number
of significant digits, we assume that the symbol b (for blank) is fed in when
an integer has no more significant digits. Thus the input to the machine is
any element of the form (x, y), where x and y are contained in $\{0, 1, b\}$. A
machine that can carry out this addition is very simple, since the only thing
to remember in adding two integers in the usual hand computation is how to
add single-digit binary integers and when to carry a 1 or a 0. Thus our
machine has two states: a state s_0, which signifies that 0 is being carried, and
a state s_1, which signifies that 1 is being carried. The state diagram for such
an addition machine is given in Figure 5.5. In this diagram, we have eliminated numerous arrows by simply labeling a single arrow with various
possible inputs and outputs.

Designing a machine that will multiply two binary integers is a much
more difficult problem. In fact, we show that it is impossible for a single
machine to multiply every pair of arbitrary binary integers. A machine can
of course be designed that will multiply two single-digit binary integers, a
slightly larger machine that will multiply two two-digit binary integers, and
a still larger machine that will multiply two three-digit binary integers. In
general, machines of increasing size can be designed to multiply two n-digit
(or smaller) binary integers for each n. However, a very simple machine can
add two arbitrary binary integers.

To see why no single machine can multiply two arbitrary integers, the
operation of a machine through time must be examined. If the machine
receives a constant input (the same symbol after each interval of time), then
the machine must exhibit periodic behavior. Since there is only a finite
number of states, a sequence of inputs must result in a corresponding sequence of states and a state must eventually be repeated. At the second
occurrence of the repeated state, the sequence of states becomes periodic,
since the next state is dependent only on the previous repeated state and the
input (which is constant). Similarly, the output is dependent only on
the previous state and the input (which is constant), hence the output is

periodic. Furthermore, if there are n states, then the period must begin on or before the nth input. These simple observations imply that no machine can be built that can multiply two arbitrary binary integers. For suppose such a machine exists, and has n states. Using this machine, multiply the binary representation of 2^{n+1} (1 followed by $n + 1$ 0's) by the binary representation of 2^{n+1}. These integers are fed simultaneously into the machine digit by digit, starting with the unit digit. Since an output occurs only when an input is received, and the answer is a 1 followed by $2n + 2$ 0's, the machine must still receive an input $n + 1$ more times after the integers have been fed in. The additional input consists of the letters b, hence there is a constant input for the next $n + 1$ times. Since the number of states is n, there is a constant input [namely, (b, b)] for a longer time period than there are states of the machine. Hence the output must be periodic and, since the output consists entirely of 0's, the machine must continue to output 0's. Thus the answer 1 followed by $2n + 2$ 0's is never achieved.

This example shows that the capability of a machine is essentially limited by the amount of information it can remember (its number of states).

Exercises

5-9 Draw the state diagram of a machine with $\mathscr{I} = \{0, 1, b\} = \mathcal{O}$, which adds two two-digit binary integers when the input is the first two-digit integer, followed by a b (blank), followed by the second two-digit integer. Prove that no single machine can add arbitrary n-digit binary integers when the input is presented in this manner.

5-10 Let M be an i/o machine with n states. Prove that a periodic input sequence of period m received by the machine eventually produces a periodic output sequence. Determine an upper bound on the period of the output sequence in terms of m and n. Give reasons.

5.4 DYNAMICS

The structure of a machine is of great importance in its design and determines its dynamics of operation. This section discusses structure abstractly in terms of the operation of the next-state function, without regard to the output function. Thus we are concerned only with state machines, although what we prove is applicable to i/o machines as long as the output and output function are disregarded.

The next-state function can be extended to a function from the set of input sequences to the set of states. We can think of this as taking an input

	δ	
	0	1
1	3	1
2	2	3
3	2	1

Figure 5.6

sequence, starting in a given state s, and generating a sequence of states by applying the inputs of the sequence successively until the final state is obtained.

To be precise, if X is any set, define X^* to be the set of all finite sequences of elements from X. These finite sequences are often called *strings*. The binary operation of *concatenation* in X^* is defined by $x_1 x_2 \cdots x_n \circ y_1 y_2 \cdots y_k = x_1 x_2 \cdots x_n y_1 y_2 \cdots y_k$. The length $l(w)$ of the sequence $w = x_1 x_2 \cdots x_n$ is defined to be n, and thus $l(w_1 \circ w_2) = l(w_1) + l(w_2)$. The operation of concatenation is associative, and the empty sequence (denoted by e) is explicitly assumed to be in X^*, with $w \circ e = e \circ w = w$, so that X^* has an identity element.

The next-state function of the state machine $M = (\mathscr{S}, \mathscr{I}, \delta)$ can be extended to a function δ^* from $\mathscr{S} \times \mathscr{I}^*$ to $\mathscr{S}$. By extended we mean that δ^* is a function from $\mathscr{S} \times \mathscr{I}^*$ to $\mathscr{S}$ with $\delta^*(s, a) = \delta(s, a)$ for all $s \in \mathscr{S}$ and $a \in \mathscr{I}$. Thus we require that $\delta^*(s, a_1) = \delta(s, a_1)$ for $a_1 \in \mathscr{I}$ and $s \in \mathscr{S}$. If $\delta^*(s, a_1 a_2 \cdots a_{k-1})$ has been defined, then $\delta^*(s, a_1 a_2 \cdots a_{k-1} a_k)$ is defined as $\delta(\delta^*(s, a_1 a_2 \cdots a_{k-1}), a_k)$. By convention, $\delta^*(s, e) = s$, where e is the empty sequence in $\mathscr{I}^*$ and $s \in \mathscr{S}$.

Although it may appear difficult actually to compute δ^*, since $\mathscr{I}^*$ is infinite, we are helped by the fact that $\mathscr{S}$ is finite. Thus the number of functions from $\mathscr{S}$ to $\mathscr{S}$ is finite, and each $w \in \mathscr{I}^*$ determines one such function $\delta^*(\ , w)$ from $\mathscr{S}$ to $\mathscr{S}$. Furthermore, if w_1 and w_2 are elements of $\mathscr{I}^*$ such that $\delta^*(s, w_1) = \delta^*(s, w_2)$ for all $s \in \mathscr{S}$, then, for a in $\mathscr{I}$,

$$\delta^*(s, w_2 a) = \delta(\delta^*(s, w_2), a) = \delta(\delta^*(s, w_1), a) = \delta^*(s, w_1 a).$$

Thus $\delta^*(s, w_2 a)$ can be computed if $\delta^*(s, w_1 a)$ is known. This observation is particularly useful when applied to the case $l(w_2) > l(w_1)$. For example, δ^* for the machine in Figure 5.6 is computed as follows:

$$\delta^*(1, 00) = \delta(\delta^*(1, 0), 0) = \delta(3, 0) = 2$$
$$\delta^*(2, 00) = \delta(\delta^*(2, 0), 0) = \delta(2, 0) = 2$$
$$\delta^*(3, 00) = \delta(\delta^*(3, 0), 0) = \delta(2, 0) = 2.$$

If we use the shorthand notation $(s)w$ to mean $\delta^*(s, w)$ for any state s and input string w, then

$$(1)01 = ((1)0)1 = (3)1 = 1$$
$$(2)01 = ((2)0)1 = (2)1 = 3$$
$$(3)01 = ((3)0)1 = (2)1 = 3$$

$$(1)10 = ((1)1)0 = (1)0 = 3$$
$$(2)10 = ((2)1)0 = (3)0 = 2$$
$$(3)10 = ((3)1)0 = (1)0 = 3$$

$$(1)11 = ((1)1)1 = (1)1 = 1$$
$$(2)11 = ((2)1)1 = (3)1 = 1$$
$$(3)11 = ((3)1)1 = (1)1 = 1.$$

Figure 5.7 shows δ^* for the strings 0, 1, 00, 01, 10, and 11. If δ^* is computed for the strings 000, 001, 010, 011, 100, 101, 110, and 111, then we observe that, for all states s,

$$(s)000 = (s)00$$
$$(1)001 = 3$$
$$(2)001 = 3$$
$$(3)001 = 3$$
$$(s)010 = (s)0$$
$$(s)011 = (s)11$$
$$(s)100 = (s)00$$
$$(s)101 = (s)1$$
$$(s)110 = (s)001$$
$$(s)111 = (s)11.$$

Thus for each input string $w \notin \{001, 110\}$ of length 3, there exists an input string v_w of length less than 3 with $\delta^*(s, w) = \delta^*(s, v_w)$.

The final state reached by applying the input string $w_1 w_2$ to the machine in state s is the same as the state reached by applying the input string w_2 to the machine in state $(s)w_1$ for all inputs w_1 and w_2. Formally, we have $(s)w_1 w_2 = ((s)w_1)w_2$. This fact follows easily by induction and is left as an exercise. If $(s)w_1$ equals $(s)w$ for all states s and some input string w, then

	δ^*					
	0	1	00	01	10	11
1	3	1	2	1	3	1
2	2	3	2	3	2	1
3	2	1	2	3	3	1

Figure 5.7

$(s)w_1w_2 = ((s)w_1)w_2 = ((s)w)w_2 = (s)ww_2$ for all input strings w_2. For example,

$$(s)00110 = ((s)0)0110 = (t)0110 = ((t)011)0 = ((t)11)0 = (((s)0)11)0$$
$$= ((s)011)0 = ((s)11)0 = (s)110$$

for all states s, where $t = ((s)0)$. Every string w_1 of length 3, except 001 and 110, satisfies $(s)w_1 = (s)w$ for w of length less than 3. Also, $(s)0010 = ((s)0)010 = ((s)0)0 = (s)00$ and

$$(s)0011 = ((s)0)011 = ((s)0)11 = (s)011 = (s)11,$$

so that any string w_1 of length 4 satisfies $(s)w_1 = (s)w$ for w of length less than 3. Thus just using the facts that

$$(s)000 = (s)100 = (s)0010 = (s)00$$
$$(s)010 = (s)0$$
$$(s)011 = (s)111 = (s)0011 = (s)11$$
$$(s)101 = (s)1$$
$$(s)110 = (s)001$$

and

$$(s)w_1w_2 = ((s)w_1)w_2,$$

we can compute $(s)w$ for any string w.

Machines may act the same way internally, although their physical components may differ (transistors instead of triodes, for example) and the spatial organization may be different. Machines that act the same way internally are called state isomorphic. This idea is formalized in the following definition.

Definition The state machine $M_1 = (\mathscr{S}_1, \mathscr{I}, \delta_1)$ is *state isomorphic* to the machine $M_2 = (\mathscr{S}_2, \mathscr{I}, \delta_2)$ if there exists a one-to-one function f from $\mathscr{S}_1$ onto $\mathscr{S}_2$ such that $f(\delta_1(s, a)) = \delta_2(f(s), a)$ for all s in $\mathscr{S}_1$ and a in $\mathscr{I}$.

The map f in the above definition is called a *state isomorphism* and essentially is just an identification of the states of M_1 with states of M_2 that act the same way under the same input.

Even more important than the concept of state isomorphism is the generalization, state homomorphism. There is a state homomorphism from one machine to another if the second machine only crudely approximates the first in the sense that each state of the second represents a number of states in the first and that the dynamic action of the machines is roughly the same.

Definition   Let $M_1 = (\mathscr{S}_1, \mathscr{I}, \delta_1)$ and $M_2 = (\mathscr{S}_2, \mathscr{I}, \delta_2)$ be state machines. The function f from $\mathscr{S}_1$ into $\mathscr{S}_2$ is called a state homomorphism of M_1 into M_2 if

$$f(\delta_1(s, a)) = \delta_2(f(s), a)$$

for all $s \in \mathscr{S}_1$ and $a \in \mathscr{I}$.

If f maps $\mathscr{S}_1$ onto $\mathscr{S}_2$, then f is said to be a state homomorphism from M_1 onto M_2. The homomorphism f not only preserves the next-state function δ but also preserves δ^*. In other words, $f(\delta_1^*(s, w)) = \delta_2^*(f(s), w)$ for all w in $\mathscr{I}^*$. This fact follows by induction and is left as an exercise.

As an example, the machine in Figure 5.8 keeps track of whether the number of 1's in an input string is 0, 1, 2, 3, 4, or 5 plus some multiple of 6. The output function is not essential, since this information is actually contained in the states. The states u, v, w, x, y, and z indicate 0, 1, 2, 3, 4, and 5, plus some multiple of 6, ones, respectively, in the input string. The parity-check machine with two states, even and odd, gives much cruder information about the input strings and, if we interpret u, w, and y as being even states and v, x, and z as being odd, then there is a state homomorphism from the machine in Figure 5.8 to the parity-check machine given by

$$f(u) = \text{Even}$$
$$f(v) = \text{Odd}$$
$$f(w) = \text{Even}$$
$$f(x) = \text{Odd}$$
$$f(y) = \text{Even}$$
$$f(z) = \text{Odd}.$$

This fact is easily checked, since applying f to each state in the state table (disregarding the outputs) yields Figure 5.9, and each row in the table is consistent with the state table for the parity-check machine.

	δ		θ	
State	0	1	0	1
u	u	v	0	1
v	v	w	1	2
w	w	x	2	3
x	x	y	3	4
y	y	z	4	5
z	z	u	5	0

Figure 5.8

	δ	
f(state)	0	1
Even	Even	Odd
Odd	Odd	Even
Even	Even	Odd
Odd	Odd	Even
Even	Even	Odd
Odd	Odd	Even

Figure 5.9

	δ	
	0	1
$\{u, w, y\}$	$\{u, w, y\}$	$\{v, x, z\}$
$\{v, x, z\}$	$\{v, x, z\}$	$\{u, w, y\}$

Figure 5.10

The state homomorphisms from a given machine M onto a machine are determined up to isomorphism by M. In fact, for the previous example, the set of states is partitioned into $\{u, w, y\}$ and $\{v, x, z\}$. Each input a maps $\{u, w, y\}$ and $\{v, x, z\}$ into $\{\delta(u, a), \delta(w, a), \delta(y, a)\}$ and $\{\delta(v, a), \delta(x, a), \delta(z, a)\}$, respectively, and each of these sets is a subset of either $\{u, w, y\}$ or $\{v, x, z\}$. This yields the next-state function for a machine with states $\{u, w, y\}$ and $\{v, x, z\}$, as in Figure 5.10. In fact, there is a state isomorphism between this machine and the parity-check machine.

This phenomenon always occurs for state homomorphisms, as we now show. Let $M = (\mathscr{S}, \mathscr{I}, \delta)$ be a state machine. For any subset P of $\mathscr{S}$ and input a in $\mathscr{I}$ define $\delta(P, a) = \{\delta(p, a) : p \in P\}$. If $\mathscr{P}$ is a partition of $\mathscr{S}$, denote the subset of the partition containing the state s by $[s]$. The partition $\mathscr{P}$ is defined to be a *state machine congruence* if, for each subset P in $\mathscr{P}$ and each input a of $\mathscr{I}$, $\delta(P, a)$ is contained in a unique class of the partition. This class is denoted $[\delta(P, a)]$. A state machine congruence $\mathscr{P}$ on $M = (\mathscr{S}, \mathscr{I}, \delta)$ gives rise to the machine $\overline{M} = (\mathscr{P}, \mathscr{I}, \overline{\delta})$, where $\overline{\delta}(P, a) = [\delta(P, a)]$.

Theorem 5.1 Let $\mathscr{P}$ be a state machine congruence on $M = (\mathscr{S}, \mathscr{I}, \delta)$. Then there is a state homomorphism f from M onto $\overline{M} = (\mathscr{P}, \mathscr{I}, \overline{\delta})$ given by $f(s) = [s]$.

Proof We need only show that $f(\delta(s, a)) = \overline{\delta}(f(s), a)$. In other words, $[\delta(s, a)] = \overline{\delta}([s], a)$. However, $\mathscr{P}$ being a machine congruence ensures that $\overline{\delta}([s], a) = [\delta([s], a)]$. However, $\delta(s, a) \in \delta([s], a)$, and so $[\delta([s], a)] = [\delta(s, a)]$, proving the theorem.

Theorem 5.1 shows that some state homomorphisms originate from a state machine congruence. Theorem 5.2 shows that all state homomorphisms originate essentially in this manner.

Theorem 5.2 Let f be a state homomorphism from the state machine $M = (\mathscr{S}, \mathscr{I}, \delta)$ onto the state machine $M_1 = (\mathscr{S}_1, \mathscr{I}, \delta_1)$. Then there is a state machine congruence on M such that $\overline{M}$ is isomorphic to M_1.

Proof The relation $x \sim y$, whenever $f(x) = f(y)$, is an equivalence relation on $\mathscr{S}$, hence the set $\mathscr{P}$ of equivalence classes is a partition of $\mathscr{S}$ (Theorem 1.1). In other words, the partition consists of the sets of all elements of $\mathscr{S}$ that map to the same element in $\mathscr{S}_1$. Let P be the subset in $\mathscr{P}$ of all elements s in $\mathscr{S}$ that satisfy $f(s) = s_1$ for a given state s_1 in $\mathscr{S}_1$. Thus $\delta(P, a) = \{\delta(s, a) : f(s) = s_1\}$. Since f is a homomorphism, $f(\delta(s, a)) = \delta(f(s), a) = \delta(s_1, a)$ for all s in P and a in $\mathscr{I}$. Thus $\delta(P, a) \subset \{t : f(t) = \delta(s_1, a)\}$, which is one of the subsets of the partition. Thus $\mathscr{P}$ is a state machine congruence, and it remains to show that $\overline{M}$ is isomorphic to M_1. Define $g([s])$ to be $f(s)$ for each class $[s]$ in the partition. The correspondence g is a function, since $[u] = [s]$ implies $u \in [s]$, so that $f(u) = f(s)$. Since f maps $\mathscr{S}$ onto $\mathscr{S}_1$, g maps $\mathscr{P}$ onto $\mathscr{S}_1$ and, furthermore, if $g([s]) = g([u])$, we have $f(s) = f(u)$, so that s and u are elements in the same equivalence class, that is, $[s] = [u]$. Thus g is a one-to-one function from $\mathscr{P}$ onto $\mathscr{S}_1$. To complete the proof that g is an isomorphism, we must show that

$$g(\overline{\delta}([s], a)) = \delta_1(g([s]), a)$$

for all equivalence classes $[s]$ in $\mathscr{P}$ and all a in $\mathscr{I}$. However, f being a homomorphism implies

$$\delta_1(f(s), a) = f(\delta(s, a))$$

so that

$$g(\bar{\delta}([s], a)) = g([\delta(s, a)]) = f(\delta(s, a)) = \delta_1(f(s), a) = \delta_1(g([s]), a)$$

for all $[s]$ in $\mathscr{P}$ and a in $\mathscr{I}$.

This homomorphism theorem is the beginning step in the study of the structure of machines and shows how homomorphisms are determined by certain partitions.

Exercises

5-11 Determine $(s)110101$ for all states s of the machine in Figure 5.6.

5-12 Determine all onto state homomorphisms (not counting homomorphisms that yield isomorphic images as distinct) of the state machine given by the following diagram.

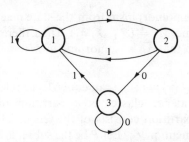

5-13 Determine all state machine congruences of the machine in Figure 5.8.

5-14 Prove that, if $M = (\mathscr{S}, \mathscr{I}, \delta)$ is a state machine, then $(s)(w_1 w_2) = ((s)w_1)w_2$, where w_1, w_2 are in $\mathscr{I}^*$ and s is in $\mathscr{S}$.

5-15 Let f be a state homomorphism from $M = (\mathscr{S}, \mathscr{I}, \delta)$ to $M_1 = (\mathscr{S}_1, \mathscr{I}, \delta_1)$. Prove that $f(\delta^*(s, w)) = \delta_1^*(f(s), w)$ for all w in $\mathscr{I}^*$.

5.5 BEHAVIOR AND MINIMIZATION

In addition to the aspects of internal structure described in Section 5.4, the external behavior of an i/o machine is of great importance. If the internal structure and circuitry are ignored and the machine treated as a black box,

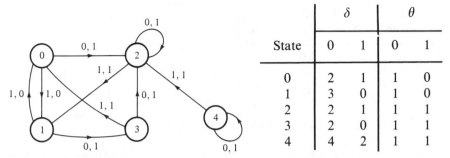

		δ		θ	
State	0	1	0	1
0	2	1	1	0
1	3	0	1	0
2	2	1	1	1
3	2	0	1	1
4	4	2	1	1

Figure 5.11 i/o Machine M.

Input string, leftmost first	Starting state	First state	Second state	Third state	First output	Second output	Third output
000	3	2	2	2	1	1	1
001	3	2	2	1	1	1	1
010	3	2	1	3	1	1	1
011	3	2	1	0	1	1	0
100	3	0	2	2	1	1	1
101	3	0	2	1	1	1	1
110	3	0	1	3	1	0	1
111	3	0	1	0	1	0	0

Figure 5.12 Sequence of states and outputs for the machine M in starting state 3 under inputs of length 3.

then we can only observe the sequence of outputs that result from a sequence of inputs. This section defines behavior, introduces the concept of state output machine, relates i/o machines to state output machines in terms of behavior, and defines a reduced machine which turns out to be the i/o machine with fewest states that exhibits the same behavior as a given i/o machine. The concept of homomorphism plays a fundamental role in understanding the reduced machine.

Definition A behavior from $\mathscr{I}$ to $\mathcal{O}$ is any function β from $\mathscr{I}*\backslash\{e\}$ to $\mathcal{O}$, where $\mathscr{I}$ and $\mathcal{O}$ are sets and e is the empty string in $\mathscr{I}*$.

If $M = (\mathscr{S}, \mathscr{I}, \mathcal{O}, \delta, \theta)$ is an i/o machine and s_0 is a specified state, called the starting state, then M and s_0 determine a behavior β_{s_0} on $\mathscr{I}$, defined inductively by $\beta_{s_0}(a) = \theta(s_0, a)$ for all $a \in \mathscr{I}$ and for $wa \in \mathscr{I}*\backslash\{e\}$, $\beta_{s_0}(wa) = \theta(\delta*(s_0, w), a)$. Thus for an i/o machine M and starting state s_0, $\beta_{s_0}(wa)$ is obtained by determining the last output when the input sequence wa is fed into the machine in starting state s_0.

For the machine in Figure 5.11, we obtain the data in Figure 5.12, which indicates the behavior given in Figure 5.13. In Figure 5.12, the start-

Input string	β_3	Input string	β_3	Input string	β_3	Input string	β_3
0	1	00	1	000	1	100	1
1	1	01	1	001	1	101	1
		10	1	010	1	110	1
		11	0	011	0	111	0

Figure 5.13 Input strings w and $\beta_3(w)$ for all w with $l(w) \leq 3$.

ing state is taken to be state 3, the first state is the result of applying the first input (the leftmost in the string) to the machine in the starting state, the second state is the result of applying the second input (the middle digit in the string) to the machine in the first state, and the third state is the result of applying the third input (the rightmost in the string) to the machine in the second state. The first, second, and third outputs are found analogously.

Figure 5.13 is obtained from Figure 5.12 with $\beta_3(w)$ for strings of length 3 simply being the third output, for strings of length 2 being the second output of any string beginning with w, and for strings of length 1 being the first output of any string beginning with w. We now introduce state output machines and show their relationship to i/o machines in terms of behavior. State output machines are i/o machines in which the output function θ is independent of the input. In other words, the output of a state output machine depends only on the state. We in fact show that every i/o machine can be considered a state output machine. The basic idea is simple. To each state we attach a register which keeps track of the output. Thus, to test the output, we read the register. This procedure gives the output one time unit later, since the output is first stored in the register and then read. The concept of state output machine is formalized by the following definition.

Definition A *state output machine* is an i/o machine $(\mathcal{S}, \mathcal{I}, \mathcal{O}, \delta, \theta)$ such that $\theta(s, a) = \rho(\delta(s, a))$ for a function ρ from $\mathcal{S}$ to $\mathcal{O}$.

The state output machine just defined is denoted by $(\mathcal{S}, \mathcal{I}, \mathcal{O}, \delta, \rho)$. The machine given by the diagram in Figure 5.14 is not a state output machine since, for example, inputs of 0 and 1, respectively, take states x and y, respectively, to state x, but with outputs of 4 and 1, respectively. However, if the previous output is stored along with the state, then the new set of states will be denoted by $x|2$, $x|3$, $x|4$, and $y|5$. This new set of states indicates that there are three arcs terminating at x with output labels 2, 3, and 4, respectively, and that there is one arc terminating at y with output label 5. The new state output machine is diagramed in Figure 5.15. The arcs are labeled with input only, since the output is indicated by the number in the state name.

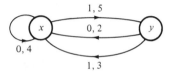

Figure 5.14

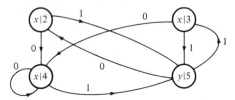

Figure 5.15

Since every state output machine is an i/o machine, each state of a state output machine also determines a behavior from $\mathcal{I}^*$ to $\mathcal{O}$ by $\beta_s(wa) = \theta(\delta^*(s, w), a) = \rho(\delta(\delta^*(s, w), a)) = \rho(\delta^*(s, wa))$. The relationship between an i/o machine and a corresponding state output machine is given in terms of behavior in the following theorem.

Theorem 5.3 Let $M = (\mathcal{S}, \mathcal{I}, \mathcal{O}, \delta, \theta)$ be an i/o machine. Then there exists a state output machine $M_1 = (\mathcal{S}_1, \mathcal{I}, \mathcal{O}, \delta_1, \rho)$ and a one-to-one function f from $\mathcal{S}$ into $\mathcal{S}_1$ such that $\beta_s = \beta_{f(s)}$ for all s in $\mathcal{S}$.

Proof First define $\mathcal{S}_1 = \{s \mid z : s \in \mathcal{S}$ and there exists some state t and input a with $\delta(t, a) = s$ and $\theta(t, a) = z\} \cup \{s \mid \varnothing : s \in \mathcal{S}$ and there is no state t and input a with $\delta(t, a) = s\}$. The symbol $s \mid z$ is used to denote the ordered pair (s, z). Define

$$\delta_1(s \mid z, a) = \delta(s, a) \mid \theta(s, a).$$

If $z \in \mathcal{O}$, define $\rho(s \mid z) = z$. For any remaining states of the form $s \mid \varnothing$ pick some z_0 in $\mathcal{O}$ and define $\rho(s \mid \varnothing) = z_0$. Thus $M_1 = (\mathcal{S}_1, \mathcal{I}, \mathcal{O}, \delta_1, \rho)$ is a state output machine. We now wish to define the map f from $\mathcal{S}$ to $\mathcal{S}_1$ such that $\beta_s = \beta_{f(s)}$ for all s in $\mathcal{S}$. We simply pick for each s in $\mathcal{S}$ some state $s \mid z$ in $\mathcal{S}_1$. Thus, for each state s, choose some output z such that there exists t in $\mathcal{S}$ and a in $\mathcal{I}$, with $\delta(t, a) = s$ and $\theta(t, a) = z$, and define $f(s) = s \mid z$. If no such output z exists, then define $f(s) = s \mid \varnothing$. We wish now to show that $\beta_s = \beta_{f(s)}$. If we can prove

$$\delta_1^*(f(s), wa) = \delta^*(s, wa) \mid \theta(\delta^*(s, w), a) \tag{1}$$

for $w \in \mathscr{I}^*$ and $a \in \mathscr{I}$, then the theorem follows, since

$$\beta_{f(s)}(wa) = \rho(\delta_1^*(f(s), wa))$$
$$= \rho(\delta^*(s, wa) | \theta(\delta^*(s, w), a))$$
$$= \theta(\delta^*(s, w), a) = \beta_s(wa).$$

We prove Eq. (1) by induction on the length k of wa. If $k = 1$, then w is the empty string, so that $wa = a$, $\delta(s, w) = s$. Thus

$$\delta_1^*(f(s), wa) = \delta_1^*(f(s), a) = \delta_1(f(s), a) = \delta(s, a) | \theta(s, a)$$
$$= \delta^*(s, wa) | \theta(\delta^*(s, w), a),$$

showing that Eq. (1) holds if $k = 1$. Suppose now that Eq. (1) holds for any string $w_1 a_1$ of length k, $w_1 \in \mathscr{I}^*$, $a_1 \in \mathscr{I}$, and suppose wa has length $k + 1$, $w \in \mathscr{I}^*$, $a \in \mathscr{I}$. Since $k \geq 1$, $l(w) \geq 1$, and $w = w_1 a_1$ for some $w_1 \in \mathscr{I}^*$, $a_1 \in \mathscr{I}$ with $l(w_1 a_1) = k$. We have $\delta_1^*(f(s), wa) = \delta_1(\delta_1^*(f(s), w_1 a_1), a)$ which by induction equals

$$\delta_1(\delta^*(s, w_1 a_1) | \theta(\delta^*(s, w_1), a_1), a).$$

However,

$$\delta_1(\delta^*(s, w_1 a_1) | \theta(\delta^*(s, w_1), a_1), a)$$
$$= \delta(\delta^*(s, w_1 a_1), a) | \theta(\delta^*(s, w_1 a_1), a)$$
$$= \delta^*(s, w_1 a_1 a) | \theta(\delta^*(s, w_1 a_1), a)$$
$$= \delta^*(s, wa) | \theta(\delta^*(s, w), a),$$

so that Eq. (1) has been proved by induction. As shown previously, the theorem now follows.

Theorem 5.3 shows that an i/o machine can be simulated by a state output machine if behavior is the only consideration. In the proof of the theorem, we actually showed that, for any state $s | y$ of the constructed state output machine, $\beta_s = \beta_{f(s)}$. Thus in terms of behavior all states $s | y$ are the same as s. In fact there is a state homomorphism from the state output machine to the i/o machine in Theorem 5.3. The proof of this fact is left to the exercises.

The concept of state homomorphism is a gauge for judging similarities in internal machine dynamics, but state homomorphism does not in general preserve behavior. There can be a state homomorphism from one machine to another machine and yet the behavior of the two machines may be quite unrelated. If the behavior is to be somehow related, the outputs, for a given input into corresponding states, must be related. This is done in the concept of input-output homomorphism.

	δ'		θ'	
State	0	1	0	1
a	b	a	1	0
b	b	a	1	1
c	c	b	1	1

Figure 5.16 Machine M'.

	δ		θ	
f(state)	0	1	0	1
a	b	a	1	0
a	b	a	1	0
b	b	a	1	1
b	b	a	1	1
c	c	b	1	1

Figure 5.17

Definition   Let $M = (\mathscr{S}, \mathscr{I}, \mathscr{O}, \delta, \theta)$ and $M' = (\mathscr{S}', \mathscr{I}, \mathscr{O}, \delta', \theta')$ be i/o machines. A function f from $\mathscr{S}$ to $\mathscr{S}'$ is an i/o homomorphism if

$$f(\delta(s, a)) = \delta'(f(s), a)$$

and

$$\theta(s, a) = \theta'(f(s), a).$$

If the function f is onto, the i/o homomorphism is said to be from M onto M'. If f is one-to-one and onto, then M and M' are said to be i/o isomorphic and f is an i/o isomorphism.

There is an i/o homomorphism from the i/o machine M given in Figure 5.11 onto the i/o machine M' in Figure 5.16, given by

$$f(0) = f(1) = a$$
$$f(2) = f(3) = b$$

and

$$f(4) = c.$$

That this is indeed an i/o homomorphism can be checked by replacing each state s in the state table for M by $f(s)$, to obtain Figure 5.17. Each row in Figure 5.17 beginning with a, b, or c is identical to the row in Figure 5.16 beginning with a, b, or c, respectively.

In i/o homomorphism, the condition $\theta(s, a) = \theta'(f(s), a)$ says that the output is identical for states s and $f(s)$ under any input. Since the next-state function is also preserved under f, then the behavior β_s is the same as the behavior $\beta_{f(s)}$. Thus even though the internal construction (represented by the states) may change under a homomorphism, the behavior does not. This is now shown formally.

Theorem 5.4   Let $M = (\mathscr{S}, \mathscr{I}, \mathscr{O}, \delta, \theta)$ and $M_1 = (\mathscr{S}_1, \mathscr{I}, \mathscr{O}, \delta_1, \theta_1)$ be i/o machines and let f be an i/o homomorphism from M to M_1. If s is a state of M, then $\beta_s = \beta_{f(s)}$.

Proof   Recall that behavior is defined inductively by $\beta_s(w, a) = \theta(\delta^*(s, w), a)$ and $\beta_{f(s)}(w, a) = \theta_1(\delta_1^*(f(s), w), a)$, where $w \in \mathscr{I}^*$ and $a \in \mathscr{I}$. Since f is a homomorphism,

$$\theta(\delta^*(s, w), a) = \theta_1(f(\delta^*(s, w)), a).$$

However, f is also a state homomorphism so, by Exercise 5-15, we have $f(\delta^*(s, w)) = \delta_1^*(f(s), w)$. Thus

$$\theta_1(f(\delta^*(s, w)), a) = \theta_1(\delta_1^*(f(s), w), a) = \beta_{f(s)}(wa).$$

Hence $\beta_s(wa) = \beta_{f(s)}(wa)$ for all w in $\mathscr{I}^*$ and a in $\mathscr{I}$, proving the theorem.

Since an i/o homomorphism is a restricted type of state homomorphism, Theorems 5.1 and 5.2 apply. Thus an i/o homomorphism from M corresponds to a certain partition of the states of M, namely, a class in the partition is composed of all the states that map to some given state.

In the example just given, the set of states of M is partitioned by

$$\mathscr{P} = \{\{0, 1\}, \{2, 3\}, \{4\}\}$$

and

$$\delta(\{0, 1\}, 0) = \{2, 3\} \subset \{2, 3\}$$
$$\delta(\{0, 1\}, 1) = \{0, 1\} \subset \{0, 1\}$$
$$\delta(\{2, 3\}, 0) = \{2\} \subset \{2, 3\}$$
$$\delta(\{2, 3\}, 1) = \{0, 1\} \subset \{0, 1\}$$
$$\delta(\{4\}, 0) = \{4\} \subset \{4\}$$
$$\delta(\{4\}, 1) = \{2\} \subset \{2, 3\},$$

as expected. Furthermore, the output function θ is identical for states 0 and 1 and 2 and 3 under each possible input. This condition distinguishes partitions that yield state homomorphisms from partitions that yield i/o homomorphisms.

Definition A partition $\mathscr{P}_2$ of $\mathscr{S}_2$, where $M_2 = (\mathscr{S}_2, \mathscr{I}, \mathcal{O}, \delta_2, \theta_2)$, is an i/o machine congruence if $\delta_2(P, a)$ is contained in some subset in $\mathscr{P}_2$ for each $P \in \mathscr{P}_2$ and $a \in \mathscr{I}$, and for $s, t \in P$, $\theta_2(s, a) = \theta_2(t, a)$, for all a in $\mathscr{I}$.

Since an i/o machine congruence is also a state machine congruence, any i/o machine M_2 with an i/o machine congruence $\mathscr{P}_2$ satisfies the hypothesis of Theorem 5.1, so there is a state homomorphism from M_2 onto $\overline{M}_2 = (\mathscr{P}_2, \mathscr{I}, \bar{\delta}_2)$, given by $f(s) = [s]$, the subset in $\mathscr{P}_2$ containing s. However, $\overline{M}_2$ can be made into an i/o machine by defining $\bar{\theta}_2([s], a) = \theta_2(s, a)$. To make sure that $\bar{\theta}_2$ is actually a function, we must check that, if $[t] = [s]$, then $\bar{\theta}_2([s], a) = \bar{\theta}_2([t], a)$. However, $[t] = [s]$ implies $t \in [s]$, and thus by assumption $\theta_2(t, a) = \theta_2(s, a)$ for all $a \in \mathscr{I}$. Hence $\bar{\theta}_2([t], a) = \theta_2(t, a) = \theta_2(s, a) = \bar{\theta}_2([s], a)$, so that $\bar{\theta}_2$ is a function. So we denote $(\mathscr{P}_2, \mathscr{I}, \mathcal{O}, \bar{\delta}_2; \bar{\theta}_2)$ by $\overline{M}_2$. The map f is now actually an i/o homomorphism from M_2 onto $\overline{M}_2$, since

$$\theta_2(s, a) = \bar{\theta}_2([s], a) = \bar{\theta}_2(f(s), a).$$

Thus the theorem for i/o machines analogous to Theorem 5.1 for state machines holds. This is presented as Theorem 5.5.

Theorem 5.5 Let $M = (\mathscr{S}, \mathscr{I}, \mathcal{O}, \delta, \theta)$ be an i/o machine and let $\mathscr{P}$ be an i/o machine congruence. Then $\overline{M} = (\mathscr{P}, \mathscr{I}, \mathcal{O}, \bar{\delta}, \bar{\theta})$ is an i/o machine and the function f from $\mathscr{S}$ onto $\mathscr{P}$ given by $f(s) = [s]$ is an i/o homomorphism from M onto $\overline{M}$.

As with state homomorphisms, i/o homomorphisms essentially all arise from i/o machine congruences. Since i/o homomorphism is a special type of state homomorphism, the partition obtained is a state machine congruence. In addition, $\theta(s, a) = \theta(t, a)$ for all inputs a and all states s and t contained in the same class in the partition. Thus we have Theorem 5.6. The proof of this theorem is similar to the proof of Theorem 5.2, which characterizes state homomorphism, and so is left as an exercise.

Theorem 5.6 If f is an i/o homomorphism from $M = (\mathscr{S}, \mathscr{I}, \mathcal{O}, \delta, \theta)$ onto $M_1 = (\mathscr{S}_1, \mathscr{I}, \mathcal{O}, \delta_1, \theta_1)$, then there exists an i/o machine congruence $\mathscr{P}$ of $\mathscr{S}$ such that the mapping $g([s]) = f(s)$ is an i/o isomorphism from $\overline{M}$ onto M_1.

In terms of the i/o homomorphism from the machine M in Figure 5.11 onto the machine M' in Figure 5.16, we have $\overline{M}$ given in Figure 5.18 along with M'. The state tables illustrate that $\overline{M}$ and M' are the same machine except for a relabeling of the states by the i/o isomorphism.

Theorem 5.4 shows that the behavior of states is unchanged by an i/o

State	$\bar{\delta}$		$\bar{\theta}$		State	δ'		θ'	
	0	1	0	1		0	1	0	1
$\{0, 1\}$	$\{2, 3\}$	$\{0, 1\}$	1	0	a	b	a	1	0
$\{2, 3\}$	$\{2, 3\}$	$\{0, 1\}$	1	1	b	b	a	1	1
$\{4\}$	$\{4\}$	$\{2, 3\}$	1	1	c	c	b	1	1

Machine $\bar{M}$ Machine M'

Figure 5.18

homomorphism. The image of a machine under an i/o homomorphism contains fewer states (unless the homomorphism is one-to-one) than the original machine. Hence the image machine may be easier to construct physically and yet still exhibit the same behavior in terms of input and output. The image of a given machine under an i/o homomorphism cannot contain fewer states than the number of distinct behaviors β_s determined by the original machine. In the continuing example M in Figure 5.11, $\beta_0 = \beta_1$ and $\beta_2 = \beta_3$, since 0 and 1 are mapped under an i/o homomorphism to the same state, namely, a, and 2 and 3 are mapped to state b. However, $\beta_0 \neq \beta_2$ and $\beta_0 \neq \beta_4$, since $\beta_0(1) = 0$, $\beta_2(1) = 1$, and $\beta_4(1) = 1$. Similarly, $\beta_2 \neq \beta_4$, since $\beta_2(11) = 0$, but $\beta_4(11) = 1$. Any image of M under an i/o homomorphism must have at least three distinct states to account for the three distinct behaviors β_0, β_2, and β_4. Thus $\bar{M}$ in Figure 5.18 has the fewest number of states of any machine that has the same behavior as M.

This example may lead us to partition the set of states of an i/o machine $M = (\mathscr{S}, \mathscr{I}, \mathscr{O}, \delta, \theta)$ into subsets of states that have the same behavior. If this partition is an i/o machine congruence, then Theorem 5.5 shows that $\bar{M}$ is an i/o machine and that there is an i/o homomorphism from M onto $\bar{M}$.

For states s and t of $\mathscr{S}$, define $s \sim t$ if $\beta_s = \beta_t$. This relation is clearly an equivalence relation, hence partitions $\mathscr{S}$ into classes, the states in any class having identical behaviors. Let $\mathscr{S}_R$ denote this partition.

For $t \in [s]$, where $[s]$ is a class in $\mathscr{S}_R$, we have $\beta_t = \beta_s$. Thus $\theta(t, a) = \beta_t(a) = \beta_s(a) = \theta(s, a)$, for all a in $\mathscr{I}$, so that $\mathscr{S}_R$ satisfies the second condition for an i/o machine congruence. If we can further show that $\delta(t, a) \in [\delta(s, a)]$, then $\delta([s], a) \subset [\delta(s, a)]$, so that the first condition holds and $\mathscr{S}_R$ is an i/o machine congruence. However, $\delta(t, a) \in [\delta(s, a)]$ if and only if $\beta_{\delta(t, a)} = \beta_{\delta(s, a)}$. To see this last equality, observe that

$$\beta_{\delta(s, a)}(w_1 a_1) = \theta(\delta^*(\delta(s, a), w_1), a_1)$$

and

$$\beta_{\delta(t, a)}(w_1 a_1) = \theta(\delta^*(\delta(t, a), w_1), a_1) \qquad \text{for} \ \ w_1 \in \mathscr{I}^*, a \in \mathscr{I}.$$

However, Exercise 5.14 shows that $\delta^*(\delta^*(p, x), y) = \delta^*(p, xy)$ for any state p and input strings x and y in $\mathscr{I}^*$. Thus

$$\beta_{\delta(s,\,a)}(w_1 a_1) = \theta(\delta^*(s, aw_1), a_1) = \beta_s((aw_1)a_1) = \beta_t((aw_1)a_1)$$
$$= \theta(\delta^*(t, aw_1), a_1) = \theta(\delta^*(\delta(t, a), w_1), a_1) = \beta_{\delta(t,\,a)}(w_1 a_1).$$

Hence $\beta_{\delta(s,\,a)} = \beta_{\delta(t,\,a)}$, and $\mathscr{S}_R$ is an i/o machine congruence. To distinguish this congruence, we write δ_R for $\bar{\delta}$, and θ_R for $\bar{\theta}$. By Theorem 5.5, $M_R = (\mathscr{S}_R,$ $\mathscr{I}, \mathcal{O}, \delta_R, \theta_R)$ is an i/o machine and is called the *reduced machine* of M. By the construction, $\delta_R([s], a) = [\delta(s, a)]$, for all $[s] \in \mathscr{S}_R$ and $a \in \mathscr{I}$, and $\theta_R([s], a) = \theta(s, a)$. Again by Theorem 5.5, there is an i/o homomorphism from M onto M_R, which we call the natural i/o homomorphism.

The fact that states with different behaviors must map under an i/o homomorphism to states with different behaviors shows that, out of all machines that are images of M under an i/o homomorphism, M_R has the least number of states, hence should be the simplest to construct. Furthermore, M_R has the property that, if h is an i/o homomorphism from M onto M_1, then there exists an i/o homomorphism g from M_1 onto M_R such that $f = g \circ h$ is the natural map from M onto M_R. This says that M_R really is the machine with simplest internal construction that exhibits the same behavior as M.

Theorem 5.7   Let $M = (\mathscr{S}, \mathscr{I}, \mathcal{O}, \delta, \theta)$ be an i/o machine and M_R its reduced machine. If h is an i/o homomorphism from M onto M_1, then there exists an i/o homomorphism g from M_1 onto M_R such that $f = g \circ h$, where f is the natural i/o homomorphism from M onto M_R.

Proof   Let $M_1 = (\mathscr{S}_1, \mathscr{I}, \mathcal{O}, \delta_1, \theta_1)$. If $s_1 \in \mathscr{S}_1$, then since h is onto, there exists $s \in \mathscr{S}$ with $h(s) = s_1$. Define $g(s_1) = [s] \in \mathscr{S}_R$. We first must show that g is a function, so suppose $h(t) = s_1$ also. Thus $h(s) = h(t)$ and, since h is an i/o homomorphism, Theorem 5.4 shows that $\beta_s = \beta_{h(s)} = \beta_{h(t)} = \beta_t$, so that $[s] = [t]$ in $\mathscr{S}_R$, showing that g is well defined. From the definition of g, $g(h(s)) = [s] = f(s)$, for all $s \in \mathscr{S}$, so that $f = g \circ h$. It remains to show that g is an i/o homomorphism. However,

$$g(\delta_1(s_1, a)) = g(\delta_1(h(s), a))$$
$$= g(h(\delta(s, a))) = [\delta(s, a)]$$
$$= \delta_R([s], a) = \delta_R(g(h(s)), a)$$
$$= \delta_R(g(s_1), a),$$

	δ		θ	
State	0	1	0	1
0	2	1	1	0
1	3	0	1	0
2	2	1	1	1
3	2	0	1	1
4	4	2	1	1

Figure 5.19   State table for M.

and

$$\theta_1(s_1, a) = \theta_1(h(s), a) = \theta(s, a)$$
$$= \theta_R([s], a) = \theta_R(g(h(s)), a) = \theta_R(g(s_1), a),$$

for all a in $\mathscr{I}$, proving the theorem.

Theorem 5.7 shows the importance of the reduced machine but gives no indication of a method for determining the partition $\mathscr{S}_R$. Once $\mathscr{S}_R$ is determined, the functions δ_R and θ_R are easily found, since

$$\delta_R([s], a) = [\delta(s, a)]$$

and

$$\theta_R([s], a) = \theta(s, a).$$

Superficially it may seem difficult to determine $\mathscr{S}_R$, since each behavior is a function from an infinite set $\mathscr{I}^*$ to $\mathscr{O}$. However, there is an efficient algorithm for determining $\mathscr{S}_R$, which we now describe.

States s and t of an i/o machine are said to be *distinguishable* if $\beta_s \neq \beta_t$. An input sequence $w \in \mathscr{I}^*$ is said to *distinguish* s and t if $\beta_s(w) \neq \beta_t(w)$. For the machine M in Figure 5.19 (the state table is reproduced for convenience), if M is in state 0 and the input 1 is applied, then the output will be 0. If the input 1 is applied to machine M in states 0 and 2, respectively, then the resulting output will be 0 and 1, respectively. Thus the single input sequence 1 differentiates, in terms of the resulting output, the states 0 and 2. No single input differentiates states 2 and 4, since input 0 results in outputs 1 and 1, respectively, and input 1 results in outputs 1 and 1, respectively. However, the input sequence 1 followed by another 1 results in output sequences 1, 0 and 1, 1, respectively, so that states 2 and 4 are distinguished by the sequence 11.

For each non-negative integer k, two states s and t are *k-equivalent* if no sequence of length k distinguishes the states. The relation, k-equivalent, is clearly an equivalence relation. For states s and t, $\beta_s = \beta_t$ if s and t are

State	δ		θ	
	0	1	0	1
a	b	a	1	0
b	b	a	1	1
c	c	b	1	1

Figure 5.20

k-equivalent for all k. The states 0, 1, 2, 3, and 4 of machine M are all 0-equivalent. States 0 and 1 are 1-equivalent, as are states 2, 3, and 4. The equivalence classes under k-equivalence are $\{0, 1\}$, $\{2, 3\}$, and $\{4\}$ for all integers $k \geq 2$. Thus the classes under equivalence are $\{0, 1\}$, $\{2, 3\}$, and $\{4\}$. If only output is considered, M needs only three states, say $a = \{0, 1\}$, $b = \{2, 3\}$, and $c = \{4\}$; the state table is given in Figure 5.20.

Determining the k-equivalent classes for a given k is simplified by the following observation. Suppose the $(k - 1)$-equivalent classes have been determined. Since an input sequence of length k consists of a sequence of length 1 followed by a sequence of length $k - 1$, two states will be k-equivalent when they are 1-equivalent (implying that the respective outputs are identical on the first input) and are mapped to $(k - 1)$-equivalent states by the next-state function (implying that the respective outputs for the re-maining $k - 1$ inputs are identical). This yields an algorithm to determine the equivalence classes of states. First determine the 1-equivalent classes. If two 1-equivalent states always map to 1-equivalent states under the next-state function, the states are 2-equivalent. This procedure is continued and, at the kth step, if two $(k - 1)$-equivalent states map to $(k - 1)$-equivalent states under the next-state function, then the two states are k-equivalent. The procedure terminates as soon as the k-equivalent classes are identical to the $(k - 1)$-equivalent classes for some k. Thus at each step the number of equivalence classes must increase, or else the algorithm is finished. Since there are at most n classes, where n is the number of states, the algorithm takes at most n steps to terminate.

Let us illustrate the algorithm with the machine described by the state table in Figure 5.21.

The input 0 does not distinguish any states, while the input 1 distinguishes states 1, 4, and 7 from states 2, 3, 5, 6, and 8. Thus the 1-equivalent classes are $\{1, 4, 7\}$ and $\{2, 3, 5, 6, 8\}$. States 1 and 4 are mapped by input 0 to states 2 and 8, respectively, and are mapped by input 1 to states 5 and 2, respectively. State 2 is 1-equivalent to 8, and state 5 is 1-equivalent to 2, so that 1 is 2-equivalent to 4. Since states 8 and 2 and states 2 and 3 are 1-equivalent, states 4 and 7 are 2-equivalent. However, states 5 and 1 are not 1-equivalent, so states 2 and 3 are not 2-equivalent. States 2 and 5 are

State	δ 0	1	θ 0	1
1	2	5	1	0
2	5	5	1	1
3	1	8	1	1
4	8	2	1	0
5	6	5	1	1
6	1	5	1	1
7	2	3	1	0
8	3	5	1	1

Figure 5.21

States	δ 0	1	θ 0	1
{1}	{2}	{5, 8}	1	0
{2}	{5, 8}	{5, 8}	1	1
{3, 6}	{1}	{5, 8}	1	1
{4}	{5, 8}	{2}	1	0
{5, 8}	{3, 6}	{5, 8}	1	1
{7}	{2}	{3, 6}	1	0

Figure 5.22   Reduced machine M_R.

mapped to the 1-equivalent states 5 and 6 and the 1-equivalent states 5 and 5, so that state 2 is 2-equivalent to state 5. Likewise, state 5 is 2-equivalent to state 8, and state 3 is 2-equivalent to state 6. Thus the 2-equivalent classes are {1, 4, 7}, {2, 5, 8}, and {3, 6}. The 3-equivalent classes are {1, 4}, {7}, {2}, {5, 8}, and {3, 6}, and the 4-equivalent classes are {1}, {4}, {7}, {2}, {5, 8}, and {3, 6}. The 5-equivalent partition is identical to the 4-equivalent, so the process terminates. Since each class consists of elements that are k-equivalent for all positive integers k, the states in a class have the same behavior. Thus this final partition is $\mathscr{S}_R$. In the definition of $M_R = (\mathscr{S}_R, \mathscr{I}, \mathscr{O}, \delta_R, \theta_R)$, $\theta_R([s], a)$ is simply the resulting output when input a is applied to any state in $[s]$. Likewise, $\delta_R([s], a)$ is simply the equivalence class of states obtained when input a is applied to any state in $[s]$. Thus the reduced machine for Figure 5.21 is given in Figure 5.22.

Exercises

5-16 Determine the diagram for the state output machine corresponding to the i/o machine with the given diagram, and find two distinct functions f satisfying Theorem 5.3.

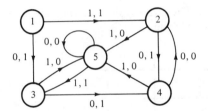

5-17 Let M_1 be the state output machine constructed from the i/o machine M as in Theorem 5.3. Prove that there is an i/o homomorphism from M_1 onto M. Find such an i/o homomorphism for the machine in Exercise 5-16.

5-18 Determine a state homomorphism from machine M_2 onto machine M_3 as given in Figure 5.23. Prove that there is no i/o homomorphism from M_2 onto M_3.

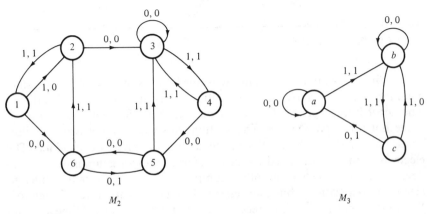

Figure 5.23

5-19 Prove Theorem 5.6.

5-20 Minimize the number of states for the machine given by the following state table.

	δ		θ	
	0	1	0	1
s_0	s_0	s_2	0	0
s_1	s_2	s_5	1	0
s_2	s_2	s_2	1	1
s_3	s_1	s_1	1	1
s_4	s_2	s_3	0	1
s_5	s_4	s_5	1	1
s_6	s_2	s_6	1	1

Give the state table for the reduced machine.

5-21 Minimize the states of the i/o machine given by the following table and draw the state diagram of the reduced machine.

	δ		θ	
	0	1	0	1
s_0	s_0	s_3	0	1
s_1	s_2	s_5	0	1
s_2	s_3	s_4	0	1
s_3	s_0	s_5	1	1
s_4	s_0	s_6	1	1
s_5	s_1	s_4	1	1
s_6	s_1	s_3	1	1

*5.6 CONSTRUCTION

A finite machine is formally described by its state table or its state diagram. This of course gives no indication of its physical realization— whether it is large or small, metal or plastic, or mechanical or electrical, to name but a few possibilities. This section shows how to construct an electronic model that exhibits the i/o behavior of a given i/o machine. The electronic model is designed by means of and gates, or gates, inverters, and delays. The delays, like the other components, may have many different electronic realizations, but their essential function is to store information. We assume that the machine receives input at unit intervals of time and that a delay simply receives input at time t and outputs that input at time $t + 1$.

To give an electronic construction of an i/o machine, the state table must first be described in terms of Boolean functions. To do this, first code the input and output alphabets in binary and then code the set of states in binary. The output and next-state functions can then be described as Boolean functions. This is illustrated by the machine M in Figure 5.24, which has $\mathscr{I} = \{0, 1\}$ and $\mathscr{O} = \{a, b, c, d\}$.

The input alphabet of M is already in binary. The output alphabet $\mathscr{O}$ is $\{a, b, c, d\}$, so label a with 00, b with 01, c with 10, and d with 11. Call the two's digit z_1 and the unit's digit z_2. Likewise, label the states in binary: 0 is 00, 1 is 01, 2 is 10, and 3 is 11. Call the two's digit of this representation x_1 and the unit's digit x_2. Thus the next-state function and the output function are described by Boolean functions on the variables x_1, x_2, and y, where y represents the input and x_1 and x_2 represent the previous state. In fact, if x_1' and x_2' represent the two's digit and the unit's digit, respectively, of the next state, the next-state function and the output function will be given in

	δ		θ	
State	0	1	0	1
0	1	2	c	d
1	2	0	a	b
2	2	3	a	b
3	1	0	c	d

Figure 5.24 *M*.

			δ		θ	
x_1	x_2	y	x_1'	x_2'	z_1	z_2
0	0	0	0	1	1	0
0	0	1	1	0	1	1
0	1	0	1	0	0	0
0	1	1	0	0	0	1
1	0	0	1	0	0	0
1	0	1	1	1	0	1
1	1	0	0	1	1	0
1	1	1	0	0	1	1

Figure 5.25

Figure 5.25. Thus x_1' equals $\bar{x}_1 \bar{x}_2 y \vee \bar{x}_1 x_2 \bar{y} \vee x_1 \bar{x}_2 \bar{y} \vee x_1 \bar{x}_2 y$, x_2' equals $\bar{x}_1 \bar{x}_2 \bar{y} \vee x_1 \bar{x}_2 y \vee x_1 x_2 \bar{y}$, z_1 equals $\bar{x}_1 \bar{x}_2 \bar{y} \vee \bar{x}_1 \bar{x}_2 y \vee x_1 x_2 \bar{y} \vee x_1 x_2 y$, and z_2 equals $\bar{x}_1 \bar{x}_2 y \vee \bar{x}_1 x_2 y \vee x_1 \bar{x}_2 y \vee x_1 x_2 y$. A gating network can represent the functions x_1', x_2', z_1, and z_2. The functions z_1 and z_2 are available as output from the gating network and, since the next state is a function of the previous state, the functions x_1' and x_2' are stored in a delay and are fed along with the input into the machine at the next time period. Thus a diagram of the machine (without being concerned about minimization) is given in Figure 5.26.

The general method for construction is to choose integers k, m, and n such that $|\mathscr{I}| < 2^m$, $|\mathscr{S}| < 2^n$, and $|\mathcal{O}| < 2^k$. Correspond each element of $\mathscr{I}$, $\mathscr{S}$, and $\mathcal{O}$ to a unique m-, n-, and k-digit binary integer, respectively. The next-state function yields n Boolean functions of $m + n$ Boolean variables, which describe the circuitry for obtaining the representation of the next-state function. The output function yields k Boolean functions in $n + m$ variables, which describe the circuitry for obtaining the output function (Figure 5.27).

The Boolean functions for constructing the realization for a finite state machine can be minimized by the techniques in Chapter 4. Furthermore, the reduced machine may be used to determine the functions. These techniques,

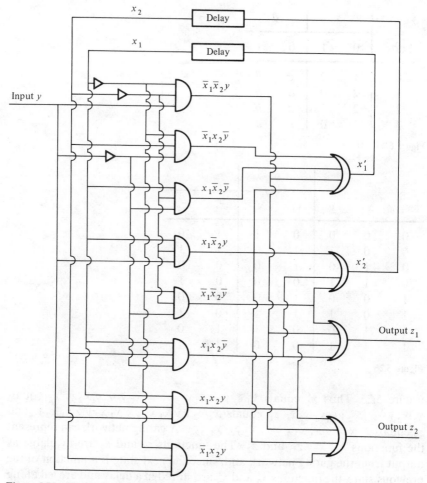

Figure 5.26 Electronic gating network for M.

however, may not yield the simplest realization. In fact, there is no efficient method known for obtaining a simplest realization.

The assignment of binary integers to the elements $\mathscr{I}$, $\mathscr{S}$, and $\mathscr{O}$ is arbitrary, and often yields only a partial Boolean function. For example, if $|\mathscr{S}| = 3$ and $|\mathscr{I}| = 2$, with $\mathscr{S}$ labeled 00, 01, and 10, then z_1 is a function of the six values 000, 001, 010, 011, 100, and 101, while 110 and 111 will never occur as input. Thus the value of $z_1(110)$ and $z_1(111)$ can be arbitrarily chosen. In the Quine-McCluskey minimization the values 110 and 111 can thus be used as implicants in determining the set of prime implicants, yet need not be included in the disjunctive normal form (thus need not be covered in the final step of the Quine-McCluskey method). This yields in general a further simplification of the circuitry.

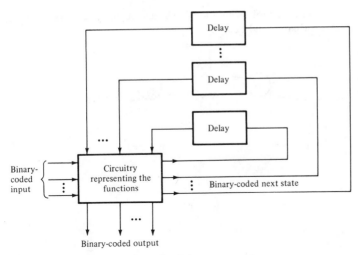

Figure 5.27 Realization scheme for finite state machine.

Exercises

5-22 Determine a minimal machine equivalent to the machine given by the table. Draw the state diagram of the minimal machine.

	δ		θ	
State	0	1	0	1
s_1	s_4	s_2	0	1
s_2	s_5	s_1	0	1
s_3	s_2	s_3	0	1
s_4	s_6	s_1	0	1
s_5	s_6	s_2	0	1
s_6	s_1	s_3	1	1

5-23 Draw a gating network (minimize as much as possible) for the following machine.

	δ		θ	
State	0	1	0	1
s_0	s_2	s_2	1	0
s_1	s_3	s_2	0	0
s_2	s_0	s_0	0	0
s_3	s_1	s_0	0	0

5-24 Give a realization of the following machine as a sequential network of inverters, and gates, or gates, and delays.

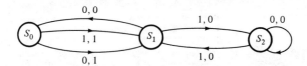

Chapter 6

Languages

---

*6.1   INTRODUCTION

The mathematical structure of languages has been investigated extensively during the past 20 years. The impetus for this study has come from two main sources. The first is the problem of machine translation of one natural language, such as Russian, into another natural language, such as English. The solution to this problem would be of immediate and clear benefit. The second impetus for the study of the mathematical structure of languages involves the design and analysis of computer programming languages. The second aspect has been successfully dealt with, but the problem of machine translation of natural languages has stubbornly resisted all efforts at solution.

A natural language is composed of words, strings of words called sentences, and meanings associated with words and sentences. The rules for forming strings of words into sentences form the grammar of the language. The grammar of the language and the structure of the sentences constitute the syntax of the language. For example, the sentence, "The frost formed lacy patterns" is composed of a noun phrase, namely, "the frost," followed by a verb phrase "formed lacy patterns." A noun phrase followed by a verb phrase is one of the allowed formations in the English language. The noun phrase "the frost" is made up of an article "the" followed by a noun "frost." An article followed by a noun is an allowed formation of a noun phrase in English. The verb phrase consists of the verb "formed" followed by a noun phrase "lacy patterns." Again, in English a verb phrase is allowed to be of the form of a verb followed by a noun phrase. The last remaining noun phrase "lacy patterns." Again, in English a verb phrase is allowed to be of "patterns." Any sentence having this same type of decomposition is grammatically correct but may not be meaningful. For example, the sentence, "The rock slept yellow love" has the same structure as "The frost formed lacy patterns," but the former sentence is meaningless while the latter sentence is easily understood. This chapter is concerned only with the syntactical aspects of languages, even though the meaning associated with sentences, namely, the semantics of the language, is of far greater importance in the problem of machine translation of natural languages.

The above analysis can be described succinctly in the following form. Let s stand for sentence, p stand for noun phrase, q stand for verb phrase, a stand for article, n stand for noun, m stand for adjective, and v stand for verb, with $\rightarrow$ denoting "is replaced by." We then have $s \rightarrow pq$, $pq \rightarrow anq$, $anq \rightarrow anvp$, and $anvp \rightarrow anvmn$. Finally, a is replaced by "the," the first occurrence of n is replaced by "frost," v is replaced by "forms," m is replaced by "lacy," and the second occurrence of n is replaced by "patterns." The final replacement of these letters by words in the English language yields our sentence. This procedure of forming a sentence is abstracted in the concept of a phrase structure grammar. Let S be any set. Recall that S^* is the set of all finite sequences of elements in S, including the empty sequence e. We can think of the sequences as finite strings of elements in S.

Definition A phrase structure grammar G consists of a finite set N of elements called nonterminals, a finite nonempty set T of elements called terminals, with $N \cap T = \varnothing$, a finite set $P \subset ((N \cup T)^* \backslash T^*) \times (N \cup T)^*$ called the set of productions, and an element σ of N called the starting symbol. We denote G by (N, T, P, σ).

We customarily write $(u, v) \in P$ as $u \rightarrow v$, even though P is not a function. The set T^* is called the set of terminal sentences. The left-hand side u of any production $u \rightarrow v$ in P is not in T^*, hence must contain some nonterminal.

The grammar used in the analysis of "The frost formed lacy patterns" is $G_1 = (\{s, p, q, a, n, m, v\}, \{the, frost, formed, lacy, patterns\}, \{(s, pq), (p, an), (p, mn), (q, vp), (a, the), (n, frost), (n, patterns), (v, formed), (m, lacy)\}, s)$. The sentence is generated by the sequence $s \rightarrow pq \rightarrow anq \rightarrow anvp \rightarrow anvmn \rightarrow$ the $nvmn \rightarrow$ the frost $vmn \rightarrow$ the frost formed $mn \rightarrow$ the frost formed lacy $n \rightarrow$ the frost formed lacy patterns. In general, if $(\alpha, \beta) \in P$ and $w = f\alpha g$ is in $(N \cup T)^*$, we say $w_1 = f\beta g$ is *directly derived* from $w = f\alpha g$ and write $w \to w_1$. An element y in $(N \cup T)^*$ is *derived* from x in $(N \cup T)^*$ if there exists a sequence $x_1, x_2, \ldots, x_k$ for some k such that $x = x_1$, $y = x_k$, and x_{i+1} is directly derived from x_i, $i = 1, 2, \ldots, k - 1$. The sequence $x_1, x_2, \ldots, x_k$ is called a *derivation* of y from x. If y is derived from x, we write $x \Rightarrow y$. Thus the sentence, "The frost formed lacy patterns," is derived from s in the grammar G_1. If G is a grammar, the set of all elements in T^* that can be derived from σ is called the *language generated by the grammar* and is denoted by $L(G)$. The elements in $L(G)$ are called the *sentences* in the language. For example, the grammar $G_2 = (\{\sigma, x, y\}, \{a, b\}, \{(\sigma, xyx), (yx, xa), (xy, bx), (xx, bab)\}, \sigma)$ has the derivation $\sigma \to xyx \to xxa \to baba$ and also the derivation $\sigma \to xyx \to bxx \to bbab$. These are the only possible derivations of an element in T^* from σ, and thus $L(G_2) = \{baba, bbab\}$.

Natural language serves as a guiding example in the definitions of grammar and language, but unfortunately there is no known set of productions that adequately describe any natural language. However, we have already at our disposal the construction of Boolean expressions from Chapter 4, and the set of Boolean expressions can indeed be described as a language resulting from a grammar. The terminal symbols are $(,), \vee, \wedge, x_1,$ $\ldots, x_n, '$, where $'$ is the symbol used to mean complementation. The nonterminal symbols can be taken as σ, and the productions are $\sigma \to x_1, \sigma \to x_2,$ $\ldots, \sigma \to x_n, \sigma \to (\sigma) \vee (\sigma), \sigma \to (\sigma) \wedge (\sigma), \sigma \to (\sigma)'$. Thus the Boolean expression $(((x_1) \vee (x_2))') \wedge (x_3)$ has the derivation $\sigma \to (\sigma) \wedge (\sigma) \to (\sigma) \wedge (x_3) \to$ $((\sigma)') \wedge (x_3) \to (((\sigma) \vee (\sigma))') \wedge (x_3) \to (((x_1) \vee (\sigma))') \wedge (x_3) \to (((x_1) \vee (x_2))') \wedge$ (x_3). This is an example of a special type of phrase structure grammar called a context-free grammar.

Definition A grammar $G = (N, T, P, \sigma)$ is a context-free grammar if $(\alpha, \beta) \in P$ implies $\alpha \in N$, $\beta \in (N \cup T)^*$, and β is not the empty string.

If G is a context-free grammar, then $L(G)$ is called a *context-free language*. Context-free languages and their relationship to programming language are investigated in Section 6.2.

The simplest type of languages we study is regular languages. These languages are closely related to finite machines, as shown in Section 6.3.

Definition A grammar $G = (N, T, P, \sigma)$ is a regular grammar if $(\alpha, \beta) \in P$ implies $\alpha \in N$, $\beta = tn$, where $t \in T$, and $n \in N$ or $n = e$, the empty sequence.

If G is a regular grammar, then $L(G)$ is called a *regular language*. Recall that the empty sequence is denoted by e, so that $ew = w = we$, and e is an identity for $(N \cup T)^*$. Furthermore, for any element w in $(N \cup T)^*$, and a non-negative integer n, define w^n to be the string $ww \cdots w$, where w occurs n times. The grammar $G_3 = (\{\sigma\}, \{x, y\}, \{(\sigma, y\sigma), (\sigma, x)\}, \sigma)$ is a regular grammar, and $L(G_3) = \{y^n x : n$ is a non-negative integer$\}$. Furthermore, each $y^n x$ has a unique derivation $\sigma \to y\sigma \to y^2\sigma \to \cdots \to y^n\sigma \to y^n x$. An element in a language $L(G)$ commonly does not have a unique derivation in the grammar G.

Exercises

6-1   Determine $L(G)$ for the grammar $G = (\{\sigma, n, v\}, \{$dog, eats, mouse$\}, \{(\sigma, nvn), (v,$ eats$), (n,$ dog$), (n,$ mouse$)\}, \sigma)$.

6-2   Give two distinct derivations in the English language for the sentence, "Computers are flying machines."

6-3   Determine a grammar G such that $L(G) = \{x^n y^n : n$ is a non-negative integer$\}$.

6-4   Determine a grammar G such that

$$L(G) = \{ww : w \in \{0, 1\}^*, w \neq e\}.$$

*6.2   CONTEXT-FREE LANGUAGES

A derivation of a sentence in a context-free language can be described in terms of special rooted trees. For example, the derivation $\sigma \to (\sigma) \vee (\sigma) \to (x_1) \vee (\sigma) \to (x_1) \vee ((\sigma)') \to (x_1) \vee ((x_2)')$ in the grammar for Boolean expressions can be described by a rooted tree with nodes labeled by terminals or nonterminals in the following manner. Label the root σ. Since the production $\sigma \to (\sigma) \vee (\sigma)$ has seven symbols on the right, connect seven new vertices to the root node and label these vertices left to right with $($, σ, $)$, $\vee$, and $($, σ, $)$, respectively. The second step in the derivation replaces the first σ in $(\sigma) \vee (\sigma)$ with x_1, so connect the rightmost node labeled σ with a new node labeled x_1. The third step in the derivation replaces the σ in $(x_1) \vee (\sigma)$ with $(\sigma)'$, so connect the remaining node labeled σ to four new nodes labeled from left to right by $($, σ, $)$, and $'$, respectively. Finally, the last step of the derivation replaces σ by x_2, so that a new node labeled x_2 is connected to the remaining node labeled σ. The resulting tree is given in Figure 6.1. The nodes of out-degree 0 (often called *leaves*) are labeled with exactly the symbols of the sentence $(x_1) \vee ((x_2)')$ and, furthermore, if the labels of the leaves are ordered beginning with the upper left leaf and

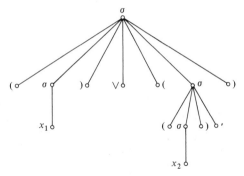

Figure 6.1

continuing counterclockwise around the periphery of the tree, we obtain
exactly the sequence $(x_1) \vee ((x_2)')$.

Thus we make the following definition.

Definition   A *derivation tree* for the grammar $G = (N, T, P, \sigma)$ is a
labeled tree with a function λ from the nodes to $N \cup T$, such that

i λ (root) $= \sigma$.

ii λ (node of outdegree 0) $\in T$.

iii   For any node v, if the set of immediate successors of v is nonempty and ordered
$v_1, v_2, \ldots, v_k$, then $\lambda(v) \to \lambda(v_1)\lambda(v_2) \cdots \lambda(v_k)$ is a production of G.

Since a derivation tree is a labeled tree, the nodes are totally ordered.
Suppose that x and y are distinct nodes with $\overrightarrow{vv_1}, \overrightarrow{v_1v_2}, \ldots, \overrightarrow{v_{i-1}v_i}, \overrightarrow{v_iw_1},$
$\overrightarrow{w_1w_2}, \ldots, \overrightarrow{w_kx}$, and $\overrightarrow{vv_1}, \overrightarrow{v_1v_2}, \ldots, \overrightarrow{v_{i-1}v_i}, \overrightarrow{v_iu_1}, \overrightarrow{u_1u_2}, \ldots, \overrightarrow{u_ly}$ being the
unique tree paths from the root v to the nodes x and y, respectively, with
$u_1 \neq w_1$. The node v_i is called the *branching point* of the two paths. The node
x is greater than y if the address of x is greater than the address of y. In other
words, $x > y$ if w_1 occurs before u_1 in the sequence given by the ordering of
the immediate successors of v_i, or if $v_i = x$. Since the set of all nodes of a
labeled tree is totally ordered, the subset of nodes of out-degree 0 (the leaves)
is also totally ordered. Suppose $x_1, x_2, \ldots, x_n$ are the nodes of out-degree 0
and that $x_1 > x_2 > \cdots > x_n$. The sequence $\lambda(x_1)\lambda(x_2) \cdots \lambda(x_n)$ is defined to
be the *result* of the derivation tree. For example, the grammar $G = (\{\sigma\},$
$\{a, b\}, \{(\sigma, a\sigma), (\sigma, \sigma b), (\sigma, b)\}, \sigma)$ has the derivation tree given in Figure 6.2.
The ordering of the nodes is $1 > 2 > 4 > 5 > 6 > 7 > 8 > 10 > 11 > 12 >$
$9 > 3$, so that the ordering of the nodes of out-degree 0 is $4 > 6 > 10 >$
$12 > 9 > 3$. Thus the result of the derivation tree is *aaabbb*.

A *subderivation tree* S_1 of a derivation tree S is a rooted subtree such
that, if v is a node of S_1, the set of immediate successors of v in S_1 is either

Node	λ (node)
1	σ
2	σ
3	b
4	a
5	σ
6	a
7	σ
8	σ
9	b
10	a
11	σ
12	b

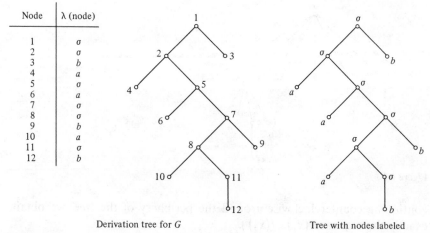

Derivation tree for G   Tree with nodes labeled

Figure 6.2

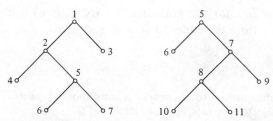

Figure 6.3 Subderivation trees.

empty or equals the set of immediate successors of v in S. Furthermore, the subderivation tree inherits the ordering in S of immediate successors of a node in S_1 and inherits the function λ. Thus λ restricted to S_1 still satisfies condition (iii) in the definition of a derivation tree. If $y_1 > y_2 > \cdots > y_k$ are the nodes of out-degree 0 in a subderivation tree, then $\lambda(y_1)\lambda(y_2) \cdots \lambda(y_k)$ is called the *result* of the subderivation tree. The two rooted trees in Figure 6.3 are subderivation trees of the derivation tree in Figure 6.2 and have the results $aa\sigma b$ and $aa\sigma b$, respectively.

The derivation of a sentence in the language of some context-free grammar is related to derivation trees by Theorem 6.1.

Theorem 6.1 Let $G = (N, T, P, \sigma)$ be a context-free grammar. Then $w \in L(G)$ if and only if there is a derivation tree in G with result w.

Proof Let $w \in L(G)$. Thus there exists a derivation $\sigma = w_0 \to w_1 \to w_2 \to \cdots \to w_k = w$ of w. We prove by induction that there exists a derivation tree with result w. Suppose T_i is a labeled tree with a function λ_i from the nodes of T_i to $N \cup T$ such that

i λ_i (root) $= \sigma$.

ii For any node v, if the immediate successors of v are ordered $v_1, v_2, \ldots, v_l$, then $\lambda_i(v) \to \lambda_i(v_1) \cdots \lambda_i(v_l)$ is a production of G.

iii If the nodes of out-degree 0 are ordered $x_1, x_2, \ldots, x_n$, then $w_i = \lambda_i(x_1)\lambda_i(x_2) \cdots \lambda_i(x_n)$.

Such a tree T_i certainly exists when $i = 0$. Suppose T_i exists for some i, $0 \le i < k$. Since $w_i \to w_{i+1}$, there exists f, y, and g such that $y \in N$, $f, g \in (N \cup T)^*$, $w_i = fyg$ and $w_{i+1} = fzg$, where $(y, z) \in P$, $z = s_1 \cdots s_d$, $s_b \in N \cup T$, for $1 \le b \le d$.

Suppose $\lambda_i(x_j) = y$. Define a new tree T_{i+1} which contains all the nodes, arcs, and orderings of immediate successors as T_i plus d new nodes, ordered, say, $x'_1, x'_2, \ldots, x'_d$ with arcs $\overrightarrow{x_j x'_m}$ for $1 \le m \le d$. Define $\lambda_{i+1}(x'_m) = s_m$ and for all nodes in T_i, $\lambda_i = \lambda_{i+1}$. The immediate successors of x_j thus satisfy $y = \lambda_{i+1}(x_j) \to \lambda_{i+1}(x'_1) \cdots \lambda_{i+1}(x'_d) = z$, which is a production in P. Thus T_{i+1} is a labeled tree satisfying (i) and (ii) above. The nodes of out-degree 0 now consist of $x_1, x_2, \ldots, x_{j-1}, x'_1, x'_2, \ldots, x'_d, x_{j+1}, \ldots, x_n$, and

$$w_{i+1} = fzg$$
$$= \lambda_{i+1}(x_1) \cdots \lambda_{i+1}(x_{j-1})\lambda_{i+1}(x'_1) \cdots \lambda_{i+1}(x'_d)\lambda_{i+1}(x_{j+1}) \cdots \lambda_{i+1}(x_n),$$

so that (iii) is satisfied. Hence T_i exists for all $0 \le i \le k$. The tree T_k is a derivation tree since, if the nodes of out-degree 0 are ordered $x_1, \ldots, x_n$, with $w_k = \lambda(x_1) \cdots \lambda(x_n) \in T^*$, then $\lambda(x_i) \in T$.

To prove the converse, assume that w is the result of a derivation tree S. We construct by induction a sequence $T_0, T_1, \ldots, T_k$ of subderivation trees with the same root as S such that w_i is the result of T_i, $i = 0$, 1, ..., k, $w_0 = \sigma$, $w_k = w$, and w_{i+1} is directly derived from w_i, $0 \le i < k$. Thus w is in $L(G)$. The tree T_0 consists of only the root node of the derivation tree S. Suppose $T_0, T_1, \ldots, T_j$ have been constructed, $0 \le j$, such that w_i is the result of T_i, $i = 0, 1, \ldots, j$, $w_0 = \sigma$, and w_{i+1} is directly derived from w_i, $i = 0$, 1, ..., $j - 1$. If T_j contains some node v of out-degree 0 and $\lambda(v) \notin T$, then define T_{j+1} to be the subderivation tree of S containing T_j plus all the immediate successors of v. The string w_j equals $\lambda(u_1) \cdots \lambda(u_l)\lambda(v)\lambda(z_1) \cdots \lambda(z_m)$. Since $\lambda(v) \to \lambda(v_1)\lambda(v_2) \cdots \lambda(v_p)$ is a production in which $v_1 > v_2 > \cdots > v_p$ are the immediate successors of v, and since the nodes of degree 0 in T_{j+1} are $u_1 > u_2 > \cdots > u_l > v_1 > v_2 > \cdots > v_p > z_1 > \cdots > z_m$, then

$$w_j = \lambda(u_1) \cdots \lambda(u_l)\lambda(v)\lambda(z_1) \cdots \lambda(z_m) \to$$
$$\lambda(u_1) \cdots \lambda(u_l)\lambda(v_1) \cdots \lambda(v_p)\lambda(z_1) \cdots \lambda(z_m) = w_{j+1}$$

is a direct derivation. Since T_{j+1} contains more nodes than T_j, the sequence terminates and all nodes y of out-degree 0 then satisfy $\lambda(y) \in T$. However, since the left-hand side of any production is not in T, no node y of S of out-degree $\neq 0$ has $\lambda(y) \in T$. Thus the process terminates at $T_k = S$.

The theory of context-free languages is important in the description of many programming languages. In particular, the Backus Naur form (BNF) is a system used in describing many programming languages, and this system can be interpreted as a context-free language. Specifically, decimal-number representations in Algol are generated by the following rules, where a vertical stroke denotes "or," brackets are used to denote an element in a class of elements, and $::=$ means "is defined to be."

i   ⟨digit⟩ $::=$ 0|1|2|3|4|5|6|7|8|9. Thus 4 is a digit, as is 5 or 8.

ii ⟨unsigned integer⟩ $::=$ ⟨digit⟩|⟨unsigned integer⟩⟨digit⟩. Since 4, 5, and 8 are digits, they are also unsigned integers. Since 4 is an unsigned integer and 6 is a digit, 46 is an unsigned integer. Likewise, 85 is an unsigned integer, as is 85 followed by the digit 1, namely, 851.

iii ⟨decimal fraction⟩ $::=$. ⟨unsigned integer⟩. Thus .851 is a decimal fraction.

iv ⟨integer⟩ $::=$ ⟨unsigned integer⟩ $|$ $+$⟨unsigned integer⟩ $|$ $-$⟨unsigned integer⟩. Since 851, 5, and 46 are all unsigned integers, 851, $+5$, and -46 are all integers.

v   ⟨number⟩ $::=$ ⟨integer⟩|⟨decimal fraction⟩|⟨integer⟩⟨decimal fraction⟩. Since -46 is an integer and .851 is a decimal fraction, -46.851 is a number.

The BNF above can be expressed as a context-free language. The set of terminals is $\{0, 1, 2, 3, 4, 5, 6, 7, 8, 9, \cdot, +, -\}$. The set of nonterminals can be $\{D, U, F, I, N\}$, where D indicates digit, U indicates unsigned integer, F indicates decimal fraction, I indicates integer, and N indicates number. The productions corresponding to (i), (ii), (iii), (iv), and (v), respectively, in BNF are as follows.

i $D \to 0, D \to 1, D \to 2$
       $D \to 3, D \to 4, D \to 5$
       $D \to 6, D \to 7, D \to 8$
       and $D \to 9$

ii $U \to D$ and $U \to UD$

iii $F \to .U$

iv $I \to U, I \to +U$, and $I \to -U$

v $N \to I, N \to F$, and $N \to IF$

Thus any number is a sentence in the context-free grammar ($\{D, U, F, I, N\}$, $\{0, 1, 2, 3, 4, 5, 6, 7, 8, 9, \cdot, +, -\}$, $\{(D, 0), (D, 1), (D, 2), (D, 3), (D, 4), (D, 5), (D, 6), (D, 7), (D, 8), (D, 9), (U, D), (U, UD), (F, \cdot U), (I, U), (I, +U),$

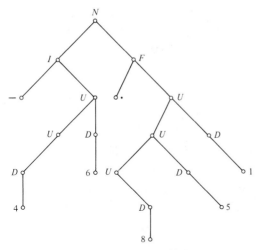

Figure 6.4 Derivation tree for −46.851.

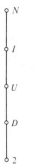

Figure 6.5 Derivation tree for 2.

$(I, -U), (N, I), (N, F), (N, IF)\}, N)$. By Theorem 6.1, any number can thus be described by a derivation tree as −46.851 is in Figure 6.4. The function $\lambda(v)$ is written beside each node v, and the immediate successors of v are ordered from right to left. Figure 6.5 shows a derivation tree for the number 2.

The context-free grammar describing the BNF has an apparently special form, that is, each production is of the form $\beta \to \gamma\delta$ or $\beta \to \delta$, where $\beta \in N$, δ, $\gamma \in N \cup T$. The intimate connection between context-free languages and programming languages is based on the fact that any context-free language is equal to the language determined by some context-free grammar having its productions in this special form. To make this notion precise, we introduce the following two definitions.

Definition A grammar G_1 is equivalent to a grammar G_2 if $L(G_1) = L(G_2)$.

Definition A grammar $G = (N, T, P, \sigma)$ is in Chomsky normal form if each production of G equals $(\beta, \alpha\gamma)$ or (β, t) for $\beta \in N$, γ, $\alpha \in N \cup T$, and $t \in T$.

The language $L(G)$ of the grammar

$$G_1 = (\{\sigma, \alpha, \beta\}, \{a, b\}, \{(\sigma, a\alpha b), (\alpha, \beta), (\alpha, \alpha b), (\sigma, a\beta), (\beta, a\beta), (\beta, a)\}, \sigma)$$

contains $a^j b^k$, j and k integers, $j \geq 2$, $k \geq 0$, as the derivations $\sigma \to a\alpha b \to a\alpha b^2 \to \cdots \to a\alpha b^k \to a\beta b^k \to a^2\beta b^k \to \cdots \to a^{j-1}\beta b^k \to a^j b^k$ for $k \geq 1$, $j \geq 2$, and $\sigma \to a\beta \to a^2\beta \to \cdots \to a^{j-1}\beta \to a^j$, $j \geq 2$, show. In fact, every derivation of a sentence is composed of a sequence of strings where each string is of the form $a\alpha b^m$, $m \geq 1$, $a^i\beta b^n$, $i \geq 1$, $n \geq 0$, or $a^j b^k$, $j \geq 2$, $k \geq 0$. Hence $L(G_1) = \{a^j b^k : j \geq 2, k \geq 0\}$. The language $L(G_2)$ of the grammar

$$G_2 = (\{\sigma, \delta, \gamma, \beta, \alpha\}, \{a, b\}, \{(\alpha, a), (\alpha, a\beta), (\alpha, \alpha b), (\sigma, a\beta),$$
$$(\beta, a\beta), (\beta, a), (\sigma, \delta\gamma), (\delta, a), (\gamma, \alpha b)\}, \sigma)$$

also contains $\{a^j b^k : j \geq 2, k \geq 0\}$, since $\sigma \to \delta\gamma \to a\gamma \to a\alpha b \Rightarrow a^j b^k$, $j \geq 2$, $k \geq 1$, and $\sigma \to a\beta \Rightarrow a^j$, $j \geq 2$. Furthermore, it is not difficult to see that $L(G_2) = \{a^j b^k : j \geq 2, k \geq 0\}$. Thus $L(G_1) = L(G_2)$ and the grammars are equivalent.

The grammar G_2 is, furthermore, in Chomsky normal form, since each production is of the required form. In fact, G_2 is obtained from G_1 by the following procedure. The production $\alpha \to \beta$ in G_1 can be deleted as long as the final string w in the sequence $\alpha \to \beta \to w$ can still be derived. Thus add $(\alpha, a\beta)$ and (α, a) to the productions of G_2 and delete (α, β). The production $(\sigma, a\alpha b)$ can also be deleted from G_1 as long as there is a derivation in G_2 beginning with σ and ending with $a\alpha b$. Thus $a(\alpha b)$ can be obtained from the product $\delta\gamma$ of two new variables δ and γ with productions (δ, a) and $(\gamma, \alpha b)$ and derivation $\delta\gamma \to a\gamma \to a\alpha b$. The product $\delta\gamma$ can be obtained by a new production $(\sigma, \delta\gamma)$.

The example above contains the essential ideas in showing that a context-free grammar is equivalent to a grammar in Chomsky normal form. Each grammar in Chomsky normal form is of course a context-free grammar, since the left-hand side of each production is a nonterminal. In order to prove that each context-free grammar is equivalent to a grammar in Chomsky normal form, we first prove Theorem 6.2.

Theorem 6.2 A context-free grammar G_1 is equivalent to a context-free grammar G_2 where G_2 contains no productions of the form (α, β), where α and β are nonterminals.

Proof We prove the theorem by induction of the number n of productions in G_1 of the form (δ, γ), where δ and γ are nonterminals. The theorem stands for $n = 0$ by choosing $G_2 = G_1$. Suppose the theorem holds for any G with n

productions of the form (δ, γ) and suppose $G_1 = (N, T, P_1, \sigma)$ has $n + 1$ such productions. Let (α, β) be one such production. We wish to eliminate this production and add necessary new productions to obtain a grammar $G = (N, T, P, \sigma)$ such that $L(G_1) = L(G)$ and yet the number of productions of the form (δ, γ) is n. If any nonterminal η can be derived from α and (η, c) is a production with $c \notin N$, then we add the production (α, c). Thus $P = P_1 \cup \{(\alpha, c) : c \notin N$ and there exists $\eta \in N$ such that $(\eta, c) \in P_1$ and $\alpha \Rightarrow \eta$ in $G_1\}\setminus\{(\alpha, \beta)\}$. The grammar G is a context-free grammar, and there are only n productions of the form (δ, γ). Thus by induction G is equivalent to a grammar G_2 which has no productions of the form (δ, γ). It remains only to show that $L(G_1) = L(G)$, since we then have $L(G_1) = L(G_2)$ and G_1 is equivalent to G_2. Suppose $w \in L(G_1)$. Let $G' = (N, T, P', \sigma)$, where $P' = P \cup \{(\alpha, \beta)\}$. Thus $P' \supseteq P_1$ and $w \in L(G')$. Suppose $\sigma \to w_1 \to w_2 \to \cdots \to w_k = w$ is a derivation of shortest length for w in $L(G')$, (i.e., k is minimal). If (α, β) is used in any step, say i, then we have $w_i = f\alpha g \to f\beta g = w_{i+1}$. Since $\beta \notin T$, the sequence must continue $w_i \to w_{i+1} \to \cdots \to w_j = f_j \beta g_j \to f_j v g_j = w_{j+1}$. If $v \notin N$, fine, but if $v \in N$ then the sequence continues until some production of the form (v, v_1) is used. Eventually, there exists a nonterminal γ with $\alpha \Rightarrow \gamma$, $w_l = f_l \gamma g_l$, $f \Rightarrow f_l$, $g \Rightarrow g_l$, and $w_{l+1} = f_l x g_l$ with $(\gamma, x) \in P_1$, $x \notin N$. Thus, since $\alpha \Rightarrow \gamma$ and $(\gamma, x) \in P_1$, $(\alpha, x) \in P$. Hence the derivation $w_i = f\alpha g \to fxg \to \cdots \to f_l x g_l$ has length one less than the derivation $w_i = f\alpha g \to f\beta g \to \cdots \to f_l \gamma g_l \to f_l x g_l$ in G', and w has a derivation of smaller length in G', which contradicts the minimality of k. Thus this derivation does not use the production (α, β), so that $w \in L(G)$. This shows that $L(G_1) \subseteq L(G)$.

Suppose now that $y \in L(G)$ and let $\sigma \to y_1 \to y_2 \to \cdots \to y_k = y$ be a derivation in G' with the fewest number of steps of the form $f\Psi g \to fzg$, where $(\Psi, z) \in P\setminus P_1$.

Suppose $y_i = f\Psi g \to fzg = y_{i+1}$ with $(\Psi, z) \in P\setminus P_1$. Since $(\Psi, z) \in P\setminus P_1$, there exists $\eta \in N$ with $\Psi \Rightarrow \eta$ in G_1 and $(\eta, z) \in P_1$. We may furthermore assume that $\Psi \Rightarrow \eta$ is given by the derivation $\Psi = \Psi_1 \to \Psi_2 \to \cdots \to \Psi_k = \eta$, so that $f\Psi g \to f\Psi_2 g \to \cdots \to f\Psi_k g = f\eta g \to fzg$ is a derivation $f\Psi g \to fzg$ in G_1. Hence $\sigma \to y_1 \to \cdots \to y_i \to f\Psi_2 g \to \cdots \to f\eta g \to y_{i+1} \to \cdots \to y_k = y$ is a derivation of y in G', which uses fewer productions $(\Psi, z) \in P\setminus P_1$. Hence by induction there exists a derivation of y in G' that uses no production in P not in P_1. Thus $y \in L(G_1)$ and $L(G_1) \supseteq L(G)$, proving the theorem.

Exercises

6-5 Determine a context-free grammar G such that $L(G) = \{0^i 1^{2j} 0^{3k} : i, j, \text{ and } k \text{ are positive integers}\}$.

6-6 Determine a context-free grammar G such that $L(G) = \{w \in \{0, 1\}^* : w \text{ con-}$

tains an equal number of 1's and 0's, $w \neq e$}. *Hint:* Try $G = (\{\sigma\}, \{0, 1\},$
$\{(\sigma, \sigma\sigma), (\sigma, 10), (\sigma, 01), (\sigma, 1\sigma 0), (\sigma, 0\sigma 1)\}, \sigma)$.

6-7   Determine the derivation trees for the sentences 0011000 and 0001111000 in the grammar of Exercise 6-5.

6-8   Determine the derivation tree for the sentence 00011011 in the grammar of Exercise 6-6.

6-9   Determine the Chomsky normal form for the grammar of Exercise 6-5.

6-10   Determine the Chomsky normal form for the grammar $G = (\{\sigma, \alpha, \beta\}, \{0, 1\},$
$\{(\sigma, 0\alpha\beta), (\alpha, \beta), (\alpha, 1), (\beta, \beta\sigma), (\beta, 0)\}, \sigma)$.

6-11   Describe the derivation tree for a sentence contained in a regular language.

6-12   Prove that if w is derived from a nonterminal α in a regular grammar, then $w = u\beta$, where β is a nonterminal or the empty word and $u \in T^* \backslash \{$empty word$\}$, where T is the set of terminals of the regular grammar.

6-13   Let G be a context-free grammar. Suppose T_1 is a derivation tree for a sentence in $L(G)$. Choose some longest path C in T_1 and suppose that any other path in T_1 that does not intersect C has length $\leq k$, where k is a fixed integer for all T_1. Prove that $L(G)$ is a regular language.

6-14   Let G be a regular grammar with k nonterminals. Prove that, if $w \in L(G)$ and the length $l(w)$ of w is greater than k, then $w = w_1 u w_2$, with u not the empty string, such that $w_1 u^n w_2 \in L(G)$ for all non-negative integers n.

6-15   Let G be a context-free language. Prove that there exists an integer k such that for any $w \in L(G)$ with $l(w) > k$, $w = w_1 u w_2 v w_3$, with not both u and v the empty string, and $w_1 u^n w_2 v^n w_2 \in L(G)$ for all non-negative integers n. (*Hint:* Put in Chomsky normal form and investigate the derivation tree.)

6-16   Prove that $\{w \in \{0, 1\}^* : w = 0^i 1^i, i > 0\}$ is not a regular language.

---

*6.3   REGULAR LANGUAGE AND FINITE STATE MACHINES

One of the simplest types of language is a regular language. An example is the set of all sequences in $\{0, 1\}^*$ that contain an odd number of 1's. If the nonterminal α (respectively, β) is used to indicate the fact that there is an even (respectively, odd) number of occurrences of 1 in the present string, then the grammar

$$G = (\{\alpha, \beta\}, \{0, 1\}, \{(\alpha, 1), (\alpha, 0\alpha), (\alpha, 1\beta), (\beta, 0\beta), (\beta, 1\alpha), (\beta, 0)\}, \alpha)$$

has the language

$$L(G) = \{w \in \{0, 1\}^* : w \text{ contains an odd number of 1's}\}.$$

The proof that this is indeed the case is left for the exercises.

If the set of terminals of a language is a subset of the input alphabet of a finite machine, then the sentences of the language are also input strings of the machine. A language is accepted by a machine if the machine somehow indicates whether an input string belongs to the language or not. For example, the parity-check machine in Section 5.2 can indicate any input string containing an odd number of 1's by having 1 as the last output wherever the machine begins in state even.

Let $\mathscr{I}$ and $\mathscr{O}$ be nonempty sets and let f be any function from $\mathscr{I}^*$ to $\mathscr{O}$.

Definition   A subset L of $\mathscr{I}^*$ is *acceptable* by $f : \mathscr{I}^* \to \mathscr{O}$ if there exists z in $\mathscr{O}$ such that, for any w in $\mathscr{I}^*$, $w \in L$ if and only if $f(w) = z$.

The functions of particular interest to us are the behavior functions determined by an i/o machine as defined in Section 5.5. A subset L of $\mathscr{I}^*$ is *acceptable* by an i/o machine if there exists a machine $M = (\mathscr{S}, \mathscr{I}, \mathscr{O}, \delta, \theta)$ and $s \in \mathscr{S}$ such that L is acceptable by β_s. The regular languages, as we will prove, are exactly those acceptable by finite machines.

Theorem 6.3   Let $M = (\mathscr{S}, \mathscr{I}, \mathscr{O}, \delta, \theta)$ be an i/o machine, s an element of $\mathscr{S}$, and z an element of $\mathscr{O}$. Then the set $\beta_s^{-1}(z) = \{w \in \mathscr{I}^* : \beta_s(w) = z\}$ is a regular language.

Proof   We must determine a regular grammar G such that $L(G) = \beta_s^{-1}(z)$. If $\beta_s^{-1}(z) = \varnothing$, choose any regular language with $L(G) = \varnothing$. Otherwise, let the set of terminals be $\mathscr{I}$ and the set of nonterminals be $\{\alpha_t\}$, one α_t for each state t of M. If $\delta(t, a) = t_1$, $t, t_1 \in \mathscr{S}$, $a \in \mathscr{I}$, then let $\alpha_t \to a\alpha_{t_1}$ be in the set P of productions of G. If in addition $\theta(t, a) = z$, let $\alpha_t \to a$ be in P. Thus

$$G = (\{\alpha_t : t \in \mathscr{S}\}, \mathscr{I}, P, \alpha_s),$$

is a regular grammar. We show that $L(G) = \beta_s^{-1}(z)$. Suppose we can prove that, for $w_1 \in \mathscr{I}^*$, $\alpha \Rightarrow w_1 \alpha_{\delta*(s, w_1)}$. If $w \in \beta_s^{-1}(z)$, w is not the empty word, so $w = w_1 a$, $a \in \mathscr{I}$, $w_1 \in \mathscr{I}^*$. Thus

$$z = \beta_s(w) = \theta(\delta^*(s, w_1), a),$$

so that $\alpha_{\delta*(s, w_1)} \to a$ is in P. However, $\alpha_s \Rightarrow w_1 \alpha_{\delta*(s, w_1)}$, so that $\alpha_s \Rightarrow w_1 a = w$ and $w \in L(G)$. Hence $\beta_s^{-1}(z) \subset L(G)$ will be shown, once we know that $\alpha_s \Rightarrow w_1 \alpha_{\delta*(s, w_1)}$ for all $w_1 \in \mathscr{I}^*$. This we prove by induction on the length $l(w_1)$ of w_1. If $l(w_1) = 1$, then $w_1 \in \mathscr{I}$ and $\alpha_s \to w_1 \alpha_{\delta(s, w_1)}$ is in P. Suppose $\alpha_s \Rightarrow w_1 \alpha_{\delta*(s, w_1)}$ for all w_1, with $l(w_1) \le k$, and suppose $l(v) = k + 1$. Thus $v = w_1 a$ for some $a \in \mathscr{I}$, $w_1 \in \mathscr{I}^*$, with $l(w_1) = k$. Thus by the induction hypothesis $\alpha_s \Rightarrow w_1 \alpha_{\delta*(s, w_1)}$. However,

$$\delta^*(s, v) = \delta^*(s, w_1 a) = \delta(\delta^*(s, w_1), a),$$

so that $\alpha_{\delta*(s,\,w_1)} \to a\alpha_{\delta*(s,\,v)}$ is in P. Hence $\alpha_s \Rightarrow w_1\alpha_{\delta*(s,\,w_1)} \to$ $w_1 a\alpha_{\delta*(s,\,v)} = v\alpha_{\delta*(s,\,v)}$, so the result follows for arbitrary v by induction. Hence $\beta_s^{-1}(z) \subset L(G)$.

It remains to show that $L(G) \subset \beta_s^{-1}(z)$. This result follows directly from the definition of G and is left as an exercise.

The converse of Theorem 6.3 is also true. The proof is slightly more involved, but the idea is still simple. If G is a regular grammar, we could attempt to construct a state output machine with states corresponding to the nonterminal of G plus one final state z_1. The inputs would be the set of terminals, and the productions $\alpha \to b\beta$ and $\alpha \to a$ could determine the next-state functions $\delta(\alpha, b) = \beta$ and $\delta(\alpha, a) = z_1$, respectively. If $w \in L(G)$, then w has a derivation $\sigma \to a_1 \alpha_1 \to a_1 a_2 \alpha_2 \to \cdots \to a_1 a_2 \cdots a_{n-1} a_n = w$, where $a_i \in T$, $\alpha_i \in N$, and $\alpha_i \to a_{i+1}\alpha_{i+1}$, $i = 1, 2, \ldots, n-2$, $\sigma \to a_1\alpha_1$, and $\alpha_{n-1} \to a_n$ are all productions.

The machine just described satisfies $\delta^*(\sigma, a_1 a_2 \cdots a_n) = z_1$ and, if $\rho(t) = z$ exactly for $t = z_1$, then $a_1 a_2 \cdots a_n \in \beta_\sigma^{-1}(z)$. The problem is that we have not described a finite state machine, since there may be several productions of the form $\alpha \to b\beta$ and $\alpha \to b\gamma$, which would mean that $\delta(\alpha, b)$ is not a single state. Furthermore, if there are no productions of the form $\alpha \to b\beta$, for any nonterminal β, then $\delta(\alpha, b)$ is not even defined. We can overcome this obstacle by keeping track, for a nonterminal α and a terminal b, of all possible nonterminals β with $\alpha \to b\beta$ a production. For example,

$$G = (\{\sigma, \alpha\}, \{0, 1\}, \{(\sigma, 0\alpha), (\sigma, 0\sigma), (\alpha, 1\alpha), (\alpha, 1)\}, \sigma)$$

is a regular grammar with the language

$$L(G) = \{0^i 1^j : i \text{ and } j \text{ are positive integers}\}.$$

The element 0 can carry σ to either α or σ and does not carry α to anything. The element 1 carries α to either α or the final state and does not carry σ to anything. Thus define $M = (\mathscr{S}, \mathscr{I}, \mathscr{O}, \delta, \rho)$ by

$$\mathscr{S} = \{\varnothing, \{\sigma\}, \{\alpha\}, \{z_1\}, \{\sigma, \alpha\}, \{\sigma, z_1\}, \{\alpha, z_1\}, \{\alpha, \sigma, z_1\}\}$$

$$\mathscr{I} = \{0, 1\}, \qquad \mathscr{O} = \{z, z'\},$$

where δ is given by Figure 6.6 and $\rho(s) = z$ if and only if $z_1 \in s$. The function δ is determined by $\delta(s, a) = \{\beta : \beta \in \{\sigma, \alpha\}$, and there exists $\gamma \in s$ with $\gamma \to a\beta$ a production of G or $\beta = z_1$, and $\gamma \to a$ is a production of $G\}$.

The machine M satisfies $\beta_{\{\sigma\}}^{-1}(z) = L(G)$. Since 0^i maps $\{\sigma\}$ to $\{\sigma, \alpha\}$ and 1^j maps $\{\sigma, \alpha\}$ to $\{\alpha, z_1\}$, we certainly have

$$L(G) \subset \beta_{\{\sigma\}}^{-1}(z).$$

Also, the only sequences that from starting state $\{\sigma\}$ eventually reach some

State	δ		ρ
	0	1	
$\emptyset$	$\emptyset$	$\emptyset$	z'
$\{\sigma\}$	$\{\alpha, \sigma\}$	$\emptyset$	z'
$\{\alpha\}$	$\emptyset$	$\{\alpha, z_1\}$	z'
$\{z_1\}$	$\emptyset$	$\emptyset$	z
$\{\sigma, \alpha\}$	$\{\alpha, \sigma\}$	$\{\alpha, z_1\}$	z'
$\{\sigma, z_1\}$	$\{\alpha, \sigma\}$	$\emptyset$	z
$\{\alpha, z_1\}$	$\emptyset$	$\{\alpha, z_1\}$	z
$\{\sigma, \alpha, z_1\}$	$\{\alpha, \sigma\}$	$\{\alpha, z_1\}$	z

Figure 6.6

state containing $\{\alpha, z_1\}$ are of the form $0^i 1^j$, where i and j are positive integers.

In the above example, the states ϕ, $\{\sigma\}$, $\{\alpha, \sigma\}$, and $\{\alpha, z_1\}$ are the only states that are accessible from $\{\sigma\}$. Thus the behavior function of M with starting state $\{\sigma\}$ is the same as the behavior function of M_2 with starting state $\{\sigma\}$, where $M_2 = (\mathscr{S}_2, \mathscr{I}, \mathscr{O}, \delta_2, \rho_2)$, $\mathscr{S}_2 = \{\phi, \{\sigma\}, \{\alpha, \sigma\}, \{\alpha, z_1\}\}$, $\delta_2(s, a) = \delta(s, a)$, for all $s \in \mathscr{S}_2$ and $a \in \mathscr{I}$, and $\rho_2(s) = \rho(s)$ for all $s \in \mathscr{S}_2$. This gives a much smaller machine with $\beta_s^{-1}(z) = L(G)$, but for simplicity we use the larger model in the proof of the next theorem.

Theorem 6.4 Let G be a regular grammar. Then there exists a finite state machine M with state s and output z such that

$$L(G) = \{w : \beta_s(w) = z\}.$$

Proof Suppose $G = (N, T, P, \sigma)$ and define

$$M = (\mathscr{P}(N \cup \{z_1\}), T, \{z', z\}, \delta, \rho),$$

where $\delta(\{\alpha_1, \ldots, \alpha_k\}, t) = \{\beta \in N \cup \{z_1\} : \alpha_i \to t\beta \in P$ for some i or $\beta = z_1$ and $\alpha_i \to t \in P$ for some $i\}$ and $\rho(S) = z$ if $z_1 \in S$ and $\rho(S) = z'$ if $z_1 \notin S$. Suppose now that $w \in L(G)$. Thus there is a derivation $\sigma \to a_1 \alpha_1 \to \cdots \to a_1 \cdots a_{n-1} \alpha_{n-1} \to a_1 \cdots a_n = w$ of w, where $\sigma \to a_1 \alpha_1$, $\alpha_{n-1} \to a_n$, and $\alpha_i \to a_{i+1} \alpha_{i+1}$ are in P for $i = 1, \ldots, n-2$. Thus $\{\sigma\} = s_1, \alpha_1 \in \delta(\{\sigma\}, a_1) = s_2$ and $\alpha_i \in \delta(s_i, a_i) = s_{i+1}$, $i = 2, \ldots, n-1$. However, $\alpha_{n-1} \to a_n \in P$ shows that $z_1 \in \delta(s_n, a_n) = s_{n+1}$ and that $\rho(s_{n+1}) = z$. Thus $\beta_{\{\sigma\}}(a_1 \cdots a_n) = z$, showing that $L(G) \subset \beta_{\{\sigma\}}^{-1}\{z\}$.

Suppose now that $w \in \beta_{\{\sigma\}}^{-1}(z)$ and that $w = a_1 a_2 \cdots a_n$. Thus there exists a sequence $s_1 = \{\sigma\}, s_2, \ldots, s_{n+1}$ such that $s_{i+1} = \delta(s_i, a_i)$, $i = 1, \ldots, n$, and $\rho(s_{n+1}) = z$. However, $\rho(s_{n+1}) = z$ if and only if $z_1 \in s_{n+1}$. Thus there exists a production $\alpha_{n-1} \to a_n$ for some nonterminal $\alpha_{n-1} \in s_n$. Continuing (or more formally by induction), we find that $\alpha_i \in s_{i+1}$ implies that there exists a production $\alpha_{i-1} \to a_i \alpha_i$ in P with $\alpha_{i-1} \in s_i$. Thus we have the productions $\sigma \to a_1 \alpha_1$, $\alpha_1 \to a_2 \alpha_2$, $\ldots$, $\alpha_{n-2} \to a_{n-1} \alpha_{n-1}$, $\alpha_{n-1} \to a_n$, so that $\sigma \to a_1 \alpha_1 \to \cdots \to a_1 \cdots a_{n-1} \alpha_{n-1} \to a_1 \cdots a_n = w$ is a derivation of w in G and $\beta_{\{\sigma\}}^{-1}(z) \subseteq L(G)$, proving the theorem for $s = \{\sigma\}$.

Corollary $L(G)$ is a regular language if and only if $L(G)$ is acceptable by some finite machine.

Exercises

6-17 If $G = (\{\alpha, \beta\}, \{0, 1\}, \{(\alpha, 1), (\alpha, 0\alpha), (\alpha, 1\beta), (\beta, 0\beta), (\beta, 1\alpha), (\beta, 0)\}, \alpha)$, prove that $L(G) = \{w \in \{0, 1\}^* : w \text{ contains an odd number of 1's}\}$.

6-18 Complete the proof of Theorem 6.3 by showing $L(G) \subset \beta_s^{-1}(z)$.

Chapter 7

Groups

7.1 INTRODUCTION

Groups and their generalization, semigroups, arise in many different areas of mathematics. The fundamental studies by Galois and Abel during the early nineteenth century show that the concept of group is essential in understanding the solvability of an equation and the form the roots of an equation can take. The more general concept of semigroup arose later and is fundamental in the study of transformations of sets. In Section 7.2, the concept of semigroup is explored. One important example of a semigroup is the transformations of the set of states of a finite machine by input sequences. Section 7.8 shows the relationships between semigroups and machines. Section 7.3 introduces the concept of group and gives some elementary properties which follow from the definition. Section 7.4 defines subgroup and coset and proves Lagrange's theorem, the proof of which gives, for each subgroup, a partition of the elements of the group—a partition that turns out to be useful in both the theory of finite machines and in the binary codes discussed in Chapter 9. A special class of transformations is the symmetries of objects, which is studied in the more general setting of permutation groups in Section 7.5. This subject matter is then applied in Section 7.7 to certain counting principles which give explicit formulas for the number of sets of similar objects in certain classes. Section 7.6 introduces the concept of homomorphism, and Section 7.9 shows how homomorphisms are obtained in terms of quotient groups.

7.2 SEMIGROUPS

Definition   A semigroup is a nonempty set S with a binary operation $\circ$ such that $x \circ (y \circ z) = (x \circ y) \circ z$ for all x, y, and z in S.

The binary operation is often called multiplication or product, regardless of whether there is any relationship to the usual multiplication of real numbers.

You may recall from Section 1.5 that, if $x \circ (y \circ z) = (x \circ y) \circ z$, for all x, y, and z, then the binary operation is said to be associative. A semigroup is thus just a set with an associative binary operation. If the underlying set S of the semigroup needs emphasis, then we will write $G = (S, \circ)$. Otherwise, we let G stand for both the underlying set S and the semigroup. If S is finite, then G is called a *finite* semigroup.

The defining properties of a semigroup are simple enough to ensure a wide variety of examples. The set of real numbers with the associative binary operation of addition is a semigroup. The real numbers with the associative binary operation of multiplication form a semigroup. Thus the same set may have several associative binary operations. The set of positive integers with the associative binary operation of greatest common divisor is a semigroup. The set $\mathscr{P}(X)$ of subsets of a given set X with the associative binary operation of set union is a semigroup. The set $\mathscr{P}(X)$ is also a semigroup under set intersection. The set Z of integers has the operation $\max\{a, b\}$, which takes the maximum of the integers a and b. Since $\max\{x, \max\{y, z\}\}$ and $\max\{\max\{x, y\}, z\}$ are both equal to the largest element in $\{x, y, z\}$, where x, y, and z are integers, the operation is associative. Thus Z, with the binary operation max, is a semigroup.

One might be tempted to think that any set with a binary operation is a semigroup, but this idea is dispelled by the example of the set of integers under the binary operation of subtraction, since $(a - b) - c \neq a - (b - c)$ unless c is zero. Also, the set of positive real numbers with the binary operation of division (and also of exponentiation) is not a semigroup.

The product of the integers 2, 3, 4, and 5 is commonly written $2 \cdot 3 \cdot 4 \cdot 5$ without regard for parentheses. This product may be interpreted as $((2 \cdot 3) \cdot 4) \cdot 5 = (6 \cdot 4) \cdot 5 = 24 \cdot 5 = 120$, $2 \cdot (3 \cdot (4 \cdot 5)) = 2 \cdot (3 \cdot 20) = 2 \cdot 60 = 120$, $(2 \cdot 3) \cdot (4 \cdot 5) = 6 \cdot 20 = 120$, $(2 \cdot (3 \cdot 4)) \cdot 5 = (2 \cdot 12) \cdot 5 =$

$24 \cdot 5 = 120$, or $2 \cdot ((3 \cdot 4) \cdot 5) = 2 \cdot (12 \cdot 5) = 2 \cdot 60 = 120$. The fact that these different ways of finding the product all result in the same answer, 120, is a result of the fact that multiplication of integers is associative. In general, if G is a semigroup and w, x, y, and z are elements of G, then by using associativity for each equality, we have $((w \circ x) \circ y) \circ z = (w \circ x) \circ (y \circ z) = w \circ (x \circ (y \circ z)) = w \circ ((x \circ y) \circ z) = (w \circ (x \circ y)) \circ z$. Since all the resulting products are equal in G, we denote the product by $w \circ x \circ y \circ z$.

To show that the parentheses can always be omitted in a product of elements from a semigroup, we must know how to build up expressions representing products. Let a_1, a_2 be a sequence of two elements in G. A product of this sequence is $a_1 \circ a_2 \in G$. Suppose now that products of sequences of length less than n, $n > 2$, have been defined, and that all such products are elements of G. If $a_1, a_2, \ldots, a_n$ is a sequence of elements from G, and x is any product of the sequence $a_1, a_2, \ldots, a_k$, and y is any product of the sequence $a_{k+1}, \ldots, a_n$, $1 \le k < n$, then $(x \circ y)$ is a product of the sequence $a_1, a_2, \ldots, a_n$.

Theorem 7.1 Let $a_1, a_2, \ldots, a_n$ be a sequence of elements in the semigroup G, $n \ge 2$. Then all products of $a_1, a_2, \ldots, a_n$ are equal.

Proof The proof is by induction on n, the number of elements in the sequence. If $n = 2$, there is only one product, namely, $a_1 \circ a_2$, so the theorem is true. Suppose the theorem is true for all sequences of at most $n - 1$ elements, $n \ge 3$. Denote the unique product of $b_1, b_2, \ldots, b_l$, $b_i \in G$, $1 \le i \le l \le n - 1$, by $b_1 \circ b_2 \circ \cdots \circ b_l$. Thus any two products of $a_1, a_2, \ldots, a_n$ have the form $(a_1 \circ a_2 \circ \cdots \circ a_j) \circ (a_{j+1} \circ \cdots \circ a_n)$, $1 \le j < n$, and $(a_1 \circ a_2 \circ \cdots \circ a_k) \circ (a_{k+1} \circ \cdots \circ a_n)$, $1 \le k < n$, respectively. If $k = j$, then these products are identical, hence equal. Thus assume $j < k$. By induction,

$$(a_{j+1} \circ \cdots \circ a_n) = (a_{j+1} \circ \cdots \circ a_k) \circ (a_{k+1} \circ \cdots \circ a_n),$$

so that

$$(a_1 \circ \cdots \circ a_j) \circ (a_{j+1} \circ \cdots \circ a_n)$$
$$= (a_1 \circ \cdots \circ a_j) \circ ((a_{j+1} \circ \cdots \circ a_k) \circ (a_{k+1} \circ \cdots \circ a_n))$$
$$= ((a_1 \circ \cdots \circ a_j) \circ (a_{j+1} \circ \cdots \circ a_k)) \circ (a_{k+1} \circ \cdots \circ a_n),$$

by associativity. However, again by induction,

$$(a_1 \circ \cdots \circ a_j) \circ (a_{j+1} \circ \cdots \circ a_k) = a_1 \circ \cdots \circ a_k,$$

so that

$$(a_1 \circ \cdots \circ a_j) \circ (a_{j+1} \circ \cdots \circ a_n) = (a_1 \circ \cdots \circ a_k) \circ (a_{k+1} \circ \cdots \circ a_n),$$

proving the theorem.

We denote the unique semigroup product of a_1, a_2, ..., a_n, in that order, by $a_1 \circ a_2 \circ \cdots \circ a_n$. The type of semigroup in which we are most interested consists of a set of functions from a given set X to X with the operation composition of functions.

Recall from Section 1.5 that, for functions f and g from X to X, the composition $f \circ g$ of f and g is the function that maps x to $f(g(x))$ for all x in X. Composition of functions from X to X is an associative binary operation on the set of all functions from X to X, as observed in Section 1.5. A subset H of the set G with a binary operation is said to be *closed* under the binary operation of G if the product of any two elements of H is again in H. If H is closed, the binary operation on G can also be considered a binary operation on H. Thus a set F of functions is a semigroup under composition if and only if F is closed under composition, so that we really have a binary operation on F and not just an operation from F to the set of all functions. As an example, let G_2 be the set $\{f_1, f_2\}$, where f_1 and f_2 are the functions from $\{1, 2, 3\}$ to $\{1, 2, 3\}$ given by

$$f_1 = \begin{pmatrix} 1 & 2 & 3 \\ 1 & 1 & 1 \end{pmatrix}, \qquad f_2 = \begin{pmatrix} 1 & 2 & 3 \\ 1 & 3 & 2 \end{pmatrix}.$$

Recall that the notation

$$f = \begin{pmatrix} \cdots & x & \cdots \\ \cdots & y & \cdots \end{pmatrix}$$

means $f(x) = y$, so that $f_1(1) = 1$, $f_1(2) = 1$, and $f_1(3) = 1$. The composition $f_1 \circ f_2$ is calculated as follows:

$$(f_1 \circ f_2)(1) = f_1(f_2(1)) = f_1(1) = 1$$
$$(f_1 \circ f_2)(2) = f_1(f_2(2)) = f_1(3) = 1$$
$$(f_1 \circ f_2)(3) = f_1(f_2(3)) = f_1(2) = 1,$$

so that $f_1 \circ f_2 = f_1$. Likewise, we find $f_1 \circ f_1 = f_1$, $f_2 \circ f_1 = f_1$, but

$$f_2 \circ f_2 = \begin{pmatrix} 1 & 2 & 3 \\ 1 & 2 & 3 \end{pmatrix},$$

which is not in G_2. Thus composition of functions is not a binary operation on the set G_2, since $f_2 \circ f_2$ is not a function in G_2. However, if we take

$$G_1 = \left\{ f_1, f_2, f_3 = \begin{pmatrix} 1 & 2 & 3 \\ 1 & 2 & 3 \end{pmatrix} \right\},$$

	f_1	f_2	f_3
f_1	f_1	f_1	f_1
f_2	f_1	f_3	f_2
f_3	f_1	f_2	f_3

Figure 7.1 Multiplication table for G_1.

then we have

$$f_1 \circ f_1 = f_1, \qquad f_1 \circ f_2 = f_1, \qquad f_1 \circ f_3 = f_1$$
$$f_2 \circ f_1 = f_1, \qquad f_2 \circ f_2 = f_3, \qquad f_2 \circ f_3 = f_2$$
$$f_3 \circ f_1 = f_1, \qquad f_3 \circ f_2 = f_2, \qquad f_3 \circ f_3 = f_3.$$

Thus the composition of any two functions in G_1 is again in G_1, so that G_1 is closed and composition is actually a binary operation on G_1. Since we already know that composition of functions is associative, G_1 thus forms a semigroup.

The information showing the composition of the pairs of elements in a finite semigroup can be conveniently displayed by means of a multiplication table (sometimes called a Cayley table). First totally order the elements in the semigroup, say, $g_1, g_2, \ldots, g_n$. A multiplication table is then defined to be the $n \times n$ table with $g_i \circ g_j$ the entry in the ith row and jth column. Thus a multiplication table for the semigroup G_1 is given in Figure 7.1. Of course, there are as many multiplication tables for G_1 as there are ways of ordering the elements of G_1, but all of them give the essential information about the product $g \circ g'$ for g and g' in G_1.

Recall that an element e is an *identity* for a set with a binary operation if $e \circ s = s \circ e = s$ for all s in the set. A semigroup containing an identity element is called a *monoid*. The set $\mathscr{P}(X)$ of all subsets of a given set X with the operation $\cap$ of set intersection is a monoid. $\mathscr{P}(X)$ with $\cap$ is certainly a semigroup, and X itself acts as an identity, since $X \cap S = S \cap X = S$ for any subset S of X. The set of real numbers under addition is a monoid with 0 an identity since $0 + r = r + 0 = r$ for any real number r. Not all semigroups are monoids, however. In the set z of integers with the binary operation $\max\{a, b\}$ for a, b in Z, there is no integer e satisfying $\max\{e, n\} = \max\{n, e\} = n$ for every n in Z.

The following is a simple property that holds for any monoid.

Proposition 7.1 Let G be a monoid. Then the identity element of G is unique.

Proof   Suppose e and e_1 are identity elements for G. Thus $e \circ e_1 = e_1$ since e is an identity, and $e \circ e_1 = e$ since e_1 is an identity. Hence $e = e \circ e_1 = e_1$, showing that the identity is unique.

Exercises

7-1   Let f be the function from $X = \{0, 1, 2, \ldots, n-1\}, 0 \le i \le n-1$, such that $f_i(j)$ is the remainder obtained after dividing $i + j$ by n. Use the division algorithm to show that $\{f_i : 0 \le i \le n-1\}$ forms a semigroup under composition of functions.

7-2   Let f_i be the functions defined in Exercise 7-1. Prove that $\{f_i : 0 \le i \le n-1\}$ is a monoid.

7-3   Prove that the set of all functions from the set of integers to the set of integers that map even integers into even integers forms a monoid under composition of functions.

7-4   Prove that the set of functions

$$\left\{\begin{pmatrix} 1 & 2 & 3 & 4 \\ 1 & 1 & 3 & 4 \end{pmatrix}, \begin{pmatrix} 1 & 2 & 3 & 4 \\ 1 & 2 & 3 & 3 \end{pmatrix}, \begin{pmatrix} 1 & 2 & 3 & 4 \\ 1 & 1 & 3 & 3 \end{pmatrix}, \begin{pmatrix} 1 & 2 & 3 & 4 \\ 1 & 1 & 1 & 1 \end{pmatrix}\right\}$$

forms a semigroup under composition of mappings. Write out a multiplication table for this set of mappings.

7-5   Show that

$$S = \left\{\begin{pmatrix} 1 & 2 & 3 & 4 \\ 1 & 1 & 3 & 4 \end{pmatrix}, \begin{pmatrix} 1 & 2 & 3 & 4 \\ 1 & 2 & 3 & 3 \end{pmatrix}, \begin{pmatrix} 1 & 2 & 3 & 4 \\ 1 & 1 & 1 & 1 \end{pmatrix}, \begin{pmatrix} 1 & 2 & 3 & 4 \\ 2 & 1 & 3 & 4 \end{pmatrix}, \begin{pmatrix} 1 & 2 & 3 & 4 \\ 2 & 2 & 3 & 4 \end{pmatrix}\right\}$$

is not a semigroup under composition of mappings. Determine a semigroup G of nine functions from $\{1, 2, 3, 4\}$ to $\{1, 2, 3, 4\}$ that contains the set S and whose binary operation is composition of functions.

7-6   Determine if the semigroup in Exercise 7-4 and the semigroup G in Exercise 7-5 are monoids. Find a monoid of ten functions from $\{1, 2, 3, 4\}$ to $\{1, 2, 3, 4\}$ that contains G and whose binary operation is composition of functions.

7.3   GROUPS

Definition   A *group* G is a monoid such that for each g in G there exists an element h (depending on g) such that $g \circ h = h \circ g = e$, where e is the identity of G.

The element h in the definition is called an *inverse* of g. Thus a group G is a nonempty set with an associative binary operation such that G contains an identity element and each element of G has an inverse.

The set of integers under addition forms a group with the additive identity 0, and the inverse of the integer n is $-n$ [since $n + (-n) = (-n) + n = 0$]. The set of positive rational numbers under multiplication forms a group with the multiplicative identity 1; the inverse of the positive rational r is $1/r$.

The most important type of group is a transformation group. If S is a set, then the set of one-to-one mappings of S onto S forms a group under the binary operation of composition of mappings. Composition of mappings of S onto S is certainly a binary operation, which by Proposition 1.1 is associative. An identity mapping certainly exists, namely, $i(s) = s$ for every $s \in S$. Furthermore, since each mapping is one-to-one and onto, the inverse exists and the set of all such mappings is a group.

Another example of a group closely related to the above group, when S is the real plane, is the set of isometries of the plane. An isometry of the plane is a one-to-one map T of the plane onto the plane that preserves distances. In other words, the Euclidean distance between $T(P)$ and $T(Q)$, where P and Q are any two points in the plane, is exactly the distance between P and Q. The set of isometries is closed under composition, contains the identity mapping $I(P) = P$, and contains the inverse of each isometry. Thus since composition of mappings is associative, the set of isometries is a group. This group contains translations [mappings for fixed c and d that take (x, y) to $(x + c, y + d)$], reflections about a fixed line, and rotations with a given center and through a given angle. In fact, the exercises show that any isometry can be viewed as a translation, followed by a rotation, followed by a reflection. Since translations and rotations are isometries, the number of elements in the group of all isometries is infinite.

An example of a finite set of isometries that forms a group is the set of isometries that map a given equilateral triangle onto itself. This set is called the rigid motions of the equilateral triangle and contains the six elements shown in Figure 7.2. That the set contains no more than these six elements follows from the fact that an isometry is determined by the images of three points (not all on the same line). This is shown in the exercises. Since the isometries are thus determined by the images of A, B, and C, and A, B, and C, being corners, must be mapped to corners, there are exactly six possible maps, and these are shown in Figure 7.2.

To see that the set G of rigid motions of the equilateral triangle actually forms a group under composition of mappings, we must first show that composition is a binary operation on G. For example, the mapping $R \circ V$ takes A to B, B to A, and C to C, so that $R \circ V = D_1$. Similarly, $D_1 \circ D_2$ takes A to C, B to A, and C to B, so that $D_1 \circ D_2 = R^2$. Figure 7.3 gives the

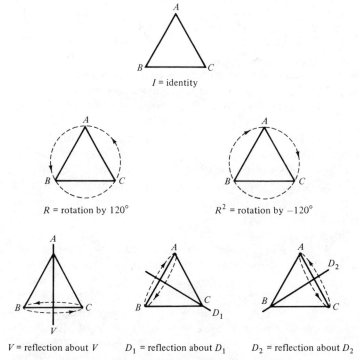

V = reflection about V D_1 = reflection about D_1 D_2 = reflection about D_2

Figure 7.2   The rigid motions of the equilateral triangle.

	I	R	R^2	V	D_1	D_2
I	I	R	R^2	V	D_1	D_2
R	R	R^2	I	D_1	D_2	V
R^2	R^2	I	R	D_2	V	D_1
V	V	D_2	D_1	I	R^2	R
D_1	D_1	V	D_2	R	I	R^2
D_2	D_2	D_1	V	R^2	R	I

Figure 7.3   Composition of rigid motions.

composition of the mappings. The entry in the row corresponding to g and the column corresponding to h is $g \circ h$ for the rigid motions g and h in G. Thus composition of rigid motions of an equilateral triangle is a binary operation. Since composition of mappings is associative and the identity I is in G, G forms a monoid under composition of mappings. The multiplication table in Figure 7.3 furthermore shows that $I \circ I = I$, $R \circ R^2 = I = R^2 \circ R$, $V \circ V = I$, $D_1 \circ D_1 = I$, and $D_2 \circ D_2 = I$, so that each element in G has a unique inverse. Thus G forms a group under composition of mappings.

Since a group satisfies the axioms for both a semigroup and a monoid, theorems that hold true for semigroups or monoids also hold true for groups. Thus we can omit parentheses from products, and the identity of a group is unique. There are several more elementary properties that hold true for groups.

Proposition 7.2 Let G be a group. If $g \in G$, then the inverse of g is unique.

Proof Suppose h and h_1 are in G, with $g \circ h = h \circ g = e$ and $g \circ h_1 = h_1 \circ g = e$, where e is the identity of G. Thus $h_1 = h_1 \circ e = h_1 \circ (g \circ h) = (h_1 \circ g) \circ h = e \circ h = h$, and the inverse of g is unique.

The unique inverse of an element g in the group G is denoted by g^{-1}.

One further simple consequence of the axioms for a group is right and left cancellation. *Right* (left) *cancellation* holds for a semigroup G if $a \circ b = a \circ c$ $(b \circ a = c \circ a)$ implies $b = c$ for all a, b, and c in G.

Proposition 7.3 Right and left cancellation holds for any group G.

Proof Suppose $a \circ b = a \circ c$ for a, b, and c in the group G. Then

$$a^{-1} \circ (a \circ b) = a^{-1} \circ (a \circ c) \qquad \text{(closure of } \circ\text{)}$$

$$(a^{-1} \circ a) \circ b = (a^{-1} \circ a) \circ c \qquad \text{(associativity)}$$

$$e \circ b = e \circ c \qquad \text{(inverse)}$$

$$b = c \qquad \text{(identity).}$$

If $b \circ a = c \circ a$, simply multiply on the right by a^{-1} and make the analogous argument.

Often we write ab for $a \circ b$ when it is clear that we are talking about the group product of two elements.

The product of an element g in the group G multiplied by itself m times is denoted by g^m, m a positive integer. By Theorem 7.1, we need not be concerned with the arrangement of the parentheses, so that $g^m = g \circ g \circ g \circ \cdots \circ g$ (m times) is well defined. This fact should convince us that the laws of exponents, namely, $g^n \circ g^m = g^{n+m}$ and $(g^n)^m = g^{n \circ m}$, hold. If we further define $g^0 = e$, and $g^{-m} = (g^{-1})^m$ for a positive integer m, the laws still apply, as we now show.

Theorem 7.2 Let g be an element in the group G. Then $g^n \circ g^m = g^{n+m}$ and $(g^n)^m = g^{nm}$ for integers n and m.

Proof   If n and m are both non-negative, then the result follows by Theorem 7.1. If both n and m are nonpositive, then $g^n \circ g^m = g^{n+m}$ again follows by Theorem 7.1. To complete the proof that $g^n \circ g^m = g^{n+m}$, consider the case in which one of n and m is positive and the other is negative. Assume $n > 0$ and $m < 0$. We show that $g^n \circ g^m = g^{n+m}$ by induction on n. If $n = 1$, then $g \circ g^m = (g \circ g^{-1}) \circ g^{1+m}$ by associativity and Theorem 7.1. Thus $g \circ g^m = e \circ g^{1+m} = g^{1+m}$. Suppose $g^n \circ g^m = g^{n+m}$ for all m. Thus $g^{n+1} \circ g^m = g^n \circ g \circ g^{-1} \circ g^{1+m} = g^n \circ e \circ g^{1+m} = g^n \circ g^{1+m}$. By induction, $g^n \circ g^{1+m} = g^{n+(1+m)} = g^{(n+1)+m}$, proving that $g^{n+1} \circ g^m = g^{(n+1)+m}$ for all m. The case of n negative and m positive follows similarly. It remains to show that $(g^n)^m = g^{nm}$, where one of n or m is negative. If n is negative and m is positive, Theorem 7.1 guarantees the result. To complete the cases in which m is negative, we first observe that $(h^k)^{-1} = h^{-k}$, where $h \in G$ and k is an integer. This follows from the first law of exponents, since $(h^k) \circ (h^{-k}) = h^{k-k} = h^0 = e$ implies $(h^k)^{-1} = h^{-k}$.

Thus for m negative we have $(g^n)^m = (g^n)^{-1} \circ (g^n)^{-1} \circ \cdots \circ (g^n)^{-1}$ taken $-m$ times, by Theorem 7.1. However, we have just seen that $(g^n)^{-1} = g^{-n}$, so that $(g^n)^m = g^{-n} \circ g^{-n} \circ \cdots \circ g^{-n}$ taken $-m$ times, which again by Theorem 7.1 is just $g^{(-n)(-m)} = g^{nm}$.

If G is a group containing only a finite number of elements, and $g \in G$, then the sequence $e = g^0, g^1, g^2, g^3, \ldots$ must eventually repeat an element, since otherwise there would be an infinite number of distinct elements in G. Suppose the first repetition is $g^i = g^j, i < j$. If $i > 0$, then $g^{-1} \circ g^i = g^{-1} \circ g^j$, and we obtain $g^{i-1} = g^{j-1}$. This contradicts the fact that $g^i = g^j$ is the first repetition. Thus $i = 0$ and $g^j = e$. A group of the form $\{e, g, g^2, \ldots, g^{n-1}\}$, where $g^n = e$ and no smaller positive power of g is e, or of the form $\{\ldots, g^{-2}, g^{-1}, e, g, g^2, \ldots\}$, where no nonzero power of g is e, is called a *cyclic group*. If $g^n = e$ for some $n > 0$ and $g^j \neq e$ for $0 < j < n$, then n is called the *order* of g.

Exercises

7-7   Prove that $\{1, -1, \sqrt{-1}, -\sqrt{-1}\}$ is a group under multiplication of complex numbers.

7-8   If $g \in G$, where G is a group, prove that $(g^{-1})^{-1} = g$.

7-9   Let X be a finite set and G a monoid of one-to-one functions from X onto X. Prove that each element of G has an inverse contained in G.

7-10   Prove that the monoid of functions in Exercise 7-9 is a group.

7-11   Let G be a group. For a and b in G, prove that $(a \circ b)^{-1} = b^{-1} \circ a^{-1}$.

7-12 A group is defined to be an *Abelian group* if $ab = ba$ for all a and b in G. If $a^2 = e$ for all a in a group G with identity e, prove that G is abelian. Prove that a group G is abelian if and only if $(ab)^2 = a^2b^2$ for all a and b in G.

7-13 Prove that the composition of isometries is an isometry and that the inverse of an isometry is an isometry.

7-14 Let T be an isometry and suppose A, B, and C are three distinct points not all on the same line. Determine an isometry T' consisting of a translation, followed by a rotation, followed by a reflection, such that $T'(A) = T(A)$, $T'(B) = T(B)$, and $T'(C) = T(C)$.

7-15 Prove that $T = T'$, where T and T' are the isometries in Exercise 7-14. (*Hint*: Show that the three distances from a point X to A, B, and C, respectively, determine X completely.)

7-16 Let P be a regular polygon with n edges. Show that the rigid motions of P (i.e., the isometries that map P into P) form a group. Describe the rigid motions in terms of rotations and reflections and determine the number of elements in the group.

7-17 Let G_1 and G_2 be groups. Define $G_1 \times G_2 = \{(a, b) : a \in G_1, b \in G_2\}$ and $(a, b) \circ (c, d) = (a \circ c, b \circ d)$, where (a, b) and (c, d) are in $G_1 \times G_2$. Prove that $G_1 \times G_2$ is a group with the given operation.

7-18 Prove $|G_1 \times G_2| = |G_1| \cdot |G_2|$ if G_1 and G_2 are finite groups, where $|G|$ is the number of elements in the group G (see Exercise 7-17).

7-19 Let S be a set and $\circ$ a binary operation on S satisfying $x \circ x = x, (x \circ y) \circ z = (y \circ z) \circ x$ for all x, y, and z in S. Prove that $\circ$ is associative and commutative.

7.4 SUBGROUPS

This section investigates the relationship between a group and certain subsets of that group which themselves form a group, and shows that this relationship gives rise to a natural partition of the elements in the group.

Definition A nonempty subset H of a group G is a subgroup of G if H is a group under the binary operation of G.

The group of rigid motions of an equilateral triangle contains several subgroups. The set $\{I, R, R^2\}$ forms a subgroup, since it contains an identity I, has inverses to each element $(R \circ R^2 = R^2 \circ R = I)$, and the multiplication is closed $(R \circ R = R^2, R^2 \circ R^2 = R)$. In fact, the subgroup $\{I, R, R^2\}$ is a cyclic group containing three elements. The number of elements in a group G is called the *order* of G and is written $|G|$.

If g is an element in the group G, the set $\langle g \rangle$ of all powers, both negative, zero, and positive, forms a subgroup of G, since $g^0 = e \in G$, the law of exponents $g^n \circ g^m = g^{n+m}$ implies that $\langle g \rangle$ is closed under the group operation of G, and finally, for each g^n, the inverse g^{-n} is again in $\langle g \rangle$. The subgroup $\langle g \rangle$ is called the cyclic subgroup generated by g and, by the observation in Section 7.3, the order of $\langle g \rangle$ is the same as the order of g.

From the definition, we see that a subset H is a subgroup of the group G if and only if e is in H, for a in H, a^{-1} is in H, and finally, for a, b in H, $a \circ b$ is in H. The property of associativity does not have to be listed, since the binary operation in G is associative. The criteria for a subset to be a subgroup can be shortened even further by the following statement which we present as a proposition.

Proposition 7.4 A nonempty subset H of a group G is a subgroup of G if and only if, for each a, b in H, $a \circ b^{-1}$ is in H.

Proof Suppose H is a subgroup of G. If b is in H, then b^{-1} is in H and $a \circ b^{-1}$ is also in H. Thus the "only if" part of the proposition is proven. Suppose now that H is a nonempty subset of G such that $a \circ b^{-1}$ is in H for all a and b in H. Since H is nonempty, there exists an element a in H. Thus $a \circ a^{-1} = e$ in H. Since e and a are in H, then $e \circ a^{-1} = a^{-1}$ is in H. To complete the proof that H is a subgroup we need only show that H is closed under the binary operation $\circ$. Since the inverse of an element is unique, $(b^{-1})^{-1} = b$. We have already shown for b in H that b^{-1} is in H. Hence for a and b in H, a and b^{-1} are in H, and thus $a \circ (b^{-1})^{-1} = a \circ b$ is in H. Closure is proven, hence H is indeed a subgroup of G.

We have the following theorem, which shows that the subgroups of a cyclic group are quite special.

Theorem 7.3 A subgroup of a cyclic group is a cyclic group.

Proof Let $G = \langle g \rangle = \{g^i : i \text{ is an integer}\}$ be a cyclic group generated by g and let H be a subgroup of G. The subgroup $\{e\}$, where e is the identity of G, is certainly cyclic so suppose that $H \neq \{e\}$. If $g^k \in H$, then $(g^k)^{-1} = g^{-k} \in H$, for k an integer, so $S = \{n : n \text{ is a positive integer and } g^n \in H\}$ is nonempty. By the well ordering of the positive integers, S contains a smallest positive integer, say m. We claim that $H = \langle g^m \rangle$. Since a product of elements in H is again in H, and the inverse of an element in H is in H, H certainly contains $\langle g^m \rangle$. Suppose $g^a \in H$ for some integer a. By the division algorithm, there exist integers q and r such that $a = qm + r$, where $0 \le r < m$. Thus $g^a = g^{qm+r} = (g^m)^q \circ g^r$ by the laws of exponents. Since $g^m \in H$, we have $(g^m)^q \in H$ and $((g^m)^q)^{-1} \in H$. Thus $((g^m)^q)^{-1} \circ g^a = ((g^m)^q)^{-1} \circ ((g^m)^q \circ g^r) =$

$(((g^m)^q)^{-1} \circ (g^m)^q) \circ g^r = e \circ g^r = g^r$ is in H, where e is the identity of G. Since m is the smallest positive integer in S, r must be 0, so that $g^a = (g^m)^q \circ g^0 = (g^m)^q$ and H is a cyclic group.

We have already remarked that the set of all one-to-one mappings from a set S onto a set S is an example of a group. Proposition 7.4 gives an easy criterion for deciding when a subset of the set of all mappings from S onto S is again a group. For example, if S is the positive integers and we look at all one-to-one mappings of the positive integers onto the positive integers that leave each even positive integer unchanged, then the inverse of such a mapping again fixes (leaves unchanged) each positive even integer, and the product of two such mappings fixes the even positive integers. Thus we obtain a subgroup of the group of all one-to-one mappings of the positive integers onto the positive integers.

The subgroup $H = \{I, R, R^2\}$ of the group of rigid motions of an equilateral triangle has order 3, which divides 6, the order of the group of rigid motions. In fact $G = \{I, R, R^2\} \cup \{V, D_2, D_1\}$. This second set $\{V, D_2, D_1\}$ equals $\{V \circ I, \quad V \circ R, \quad V \circ R^2\}$, which we write as $V \circ H$. Thus $G = H \cup V \circ H$ and $H \cap V \circ H = \varnothing$, so that we have a partition of G. The set $V \circ H$ is an example of a left coset, which we now define.

Definition A left coset of the subgroup H in the group G is a set of the form $\{gh : h \in H\}$, where g is a fixed element of G.

The left coset is denoted by gH, and the element g is called a coset representative. Thus a left coset is the set of all left multiples of elements of H by the fixed element g. We note that the subgroup H is itself a left coset, since $e \circ H = H$. The right coset is defined analogously but with multiplication from the right by the coset representative. Thus $Hg = \{hg : h \in H\}$ is a right coset of the subgroup H.

Proposition 7.5 The set of distinct left cosets of a subgroup H of the group G partitions G.

Proof If g is in G, the left coset $g \circ H$ contains the element $g \circ e = g$, so every element in G is in some left coset. To complete the proof that the left cosets of H partition the group G, it is sufficient to show that two left cosets with nonempty intersection are in fact identical. Suppose the left cosets gH and kH contain a common element x. Thus there exist h_1 and h_2 in H with $gh_1 = x = kh_2$. Thus $g = (kh_2)h_1^{-1}$. If $y = gh$ is an element of gH, then $y = k(h_2(h_1^{-1}h))$. Since $h_2(h_1^{-1}h)$ is an element of H, y is in kH. Thus the left coset gH is contained in kH. Similarly, we can prove kH is contained in gH, so the left cosets are identical, and we have shown that the distinct left cosets partition the group.

The partition of a group by left cosets is called coset decomposition. Results involving left cosets also apply to right cosets, and the proofs are analogous.

The left coset $\{V, D_1, D_2\}$ contains the same number of elements as the subgroup $\{I, R, R^2\}$. This fact is true in general.

Lemma 7.1 If H is a finite subgroup of a group G, the left coset gH contains the same number of elements as H.

Proof The mapping $h \to gh$ from H to gH is one-to-one and onto. It is one-to-one, since $gh_1 = gh_2$ implies $(g^{-1}g)h_1 = (g^{-1}g)h_2$, which in turn implies $h_1 = eh_1 = eh_2 = h_2$. The map is clearly onto.

The main theorem of this section now follows.

Theorem 7.4 (*Lagrange's Theorem*) The order of a subgroup of a group divides the order of the group.

Proof The left cosets of the subgroup partition the group, and each left coset contains the same number of elements as the subgroup. Hence the number of distinct cosets multiplied by the order of the subgroup is the order of the group.

The number of distinct left cosets of a subgroup H in a group G is called the index of the subgroup H in the group G and is denoted by $[G : H]$. If we denote the order of a group G by $|G|$, then Lagrange's theorem states that $[G : H]|H| = |G|$ for H a subgroup of G.

An immediate result of Theorem 7.4 is the following. A *prime* is a positive integer p, $p > 1$, such that $p = ab$, with a and b positive, implies that one of a or b is p and the other is 1.

Corollary 7.1 A group of prime order p is cyclic.

Proof Pick an element g, $g \neq e$, in the group. The order of the cyclic subgroup $\langle g \rangle$ generated by g, $|\langle g \rangle|$, is larger than 1 and divides p. Hence $|\langle g \rangle| = p$, and the group is cyclic.

Exercises

7-20 Write out explicitly a coset decomposition for the subgroup {identity, reflection about the main diagonal} of the group of rigid motions of a square.

7-21 Let G be the group of rigid motions of a regular polygon with n sides, n a positive integer (a regular polygon has n equal sides, with adjacent sides making an angle of $360°/n$). Let H be the subgroup of G consisting of rotations about the center of the polygon by angles of $k(360°/n)$, k any integer. Prove that H is a cyclic group of order n.

7-22   Determine the order of the group of rigid motions of a regular polygon with n sides, n a positive integer. Give a coset decomposition for the subgroup of rotations about the center.

7-23   Let G be a finite group. If H is a nonempty subset of G that is closed under the binary operation of G, prove that H is a subgroup of G.

7-24   Prove that the subgroups of a cyclic group $G = \langle g \rangle$ of order n are the cyclic groups of the form $\langle g^m \rangle$, where m divides n.

7.5   PERMUTATION GROUPS

A permutation of a nonempty set X is defined to be a one-to-one function from X onto X. Composition of functions from X into X is a well-defined binary operation on the set of functions from X into X. From Section 1.5, we know that composition of functions is associative. The identity function $\iota(x) = x$ for x in X is a permutation, and $\iota \circ \pi = \pi \circ \iota = \pi$ for any other permutation π of X. Thus the set S_X of all permutations of X has an identity element. If π is in S_X, there is exactly one x in X, with $\pi(x) = y$, for y chosen in Y. Thus $\pi^{-1}(y) = \{x\}$, and $\pi^{-1}(y) = x$ is a well-defined function which is actually a permutation. The permutation $\pi^{-1}(\pi(x)) = \pi^{-1}(y) = x$ maps each element x in X back to itself. Thus $\pi^{-1} \circ \pi$ is the identity permutation ι, and the set S_X of all permutations of X forms a group under the binary operation of composition of functions.

A permutation group acting on the (nonempty) set X is defined to be a subgroup of S_X. Most commonly we look at finite sets X and in fact usually identify X with $\{1, 2, 3, \ldots, n\}$, in which case S_X is denoted by S_n.

In general, the image of each element under a permutation π must be specified separately. This can be realized by the description,

$$\pi := \begin{pmatrix} x_1 & x_2 & \cdots & x_n \\ \pi(x_1) & \pi(x_2) & \cdots & \pi(x_n) \end{pmatrix}.$$

Since a permutation is a function, we can describe a permutation as we do a function. For example, the permutation γ in S_4 defined by $\gamma(1) = 2$, $\gamma(2) = 3$, $\gamma(3) = 1$, and $\gamma(4) = 4$ is written

$$\gamma = \begin{pmatrix} 1 & 2 & 3 & 4 \\ 2 & 3 & 1 & 4 \end{pmatrix}.$$

Multiplication of permutations is composition of functions and, since it is standard usage for the function $f \circ g$ to map x to $f(g(x))$, we thus apply the rightmost permutation first, which is then followed by the leftmost permutation. For example, suppose

$$\gamma = \begin{pmatrix} 1 & 2 & 3 & 4 \\ 2 & 3 & 1 & 4 \end{pmatrix} \quad \text{and} \quad \beta = \begin{pmatrix} 1 & 2 & 3 & 4 \\ 1 & 3 & 4 & 2 \end{pmatrix}$$

are permutations in S_4. The product

$$\gamma \circ \beta = \begin{pmatrix} 1 & 2 & 3 & 4 \\ 2 & 3 & 1 & 4 \end{pmatrix} \circ \begin{pmatrix} 1 & 2 & 3 & 4 \\ 1 & 3 & 4 & 2 \end{pmatrix}$$

is calculated by determining the images of 1, 2, 3, and 4:

$$\gamma(\beta(1)) = \gamma(1) = 2$$
$$\gamma(\beta(2)) = \gamma(3) = 1$$
$$\gamma(\beta(3)) = \gamma(4) = 4$$
$$\gamma(\beta(4)) = \gamma(2) = 3,$$

so that the product is

$$\gamma \circ \beta = \begin{pmatrix} 1 & 2 & 3 & 4 \\ 2 & 1 & 4 & 3 \end{pmatrix}.$$

Although the above notation for a permutation gives the mapping, there is a more concise notation called the cycle decomposition which also describes the mapping. Suppose γ is a permutation of a finite set X. Begin with any x in X and write $(x \; \gamma(x) \; \gamma^2(x) \cdots \gamma^{k-1}(x))$, where $\gamma^k(x)$ is the first repetition of x. This is called a cycle. Since X is finite, some $\gamma^i(x)$ must eventually repeat, $i \geq 0$, and this must first be x, since $\gamma^i(x) = \gamma^j(x)$ for $i \geq 1$, $j \geq 1$ implies $\gamma^{i-1}(x) = \gamma^{j-1}(x)$. Next choose some y in X that is not in the previous cycles and write $(y \; \gamma(y) \; \gamma^2(y) \cdots \gamma^{l-1}(y))$, where $\gamma^l(y)$ is the first repetition of y. Continue in this manner until all elements of X occur in cycles with different cycles disjoint. An element cannot occur in two different cycles, since this would imply that two different elements are mapped by the permutation to the same element. For example,

$$\gamma = \begin{pmatrix} 1 & 2 & 3 & 4 & 5 & 6 & 7 & 8 \\ 6 & 8 & 5 & 3 & 4 & 2 & 7 & 1 \end{pmatrix}$$

is written $\gamma = (1 \; 6 \; 2 \; 8)(3 \; 5 \; 4)(7)$. If we indicate the mappings by arrows, γ is

$$(1 \; 6 \; 2 \; 8)(3 \; 5 \; 4)(7).$$

The identity element in S_n, for a positive integer n, has cycle decomposition $(1)(2) \cdots (n)$. The cycle decomposition specifies the permutation completely. Often in writing the cycle decomposition, we omit cycles of the form (x). Thus if an element x does not appear in the cycle decomposition of π, then $\pi(x) = x$.

The number of elements in a cycle is called the *length* of the cycle. Theorem 7.5 gives the relationship between the lengths of the cycles in a permutation and the order of that permutation.

Theorem 7.5   The order of a permutation is the least common multiple of the lengths of the cycles.

Proof   In the cycle decomposition of a permutation γ of the set X, the cycles partition X. Furthermore, the permutation maps the set of elements contained in a cycle onto that same set of elements. Hence γ^k is the identity map on the elements of that cycle if and only if k is a multiple of that cycle length. The permutation γ^k is thus the identity on X if and only if k is a multiple of each one of the cycle lengths. Hence the smallest such positive k is the least common multiple of the cycle lengths.

A permutation group is a group of functions, hence is concerned not only with group structure but also with the functional aspect of each permutation. The latter aspect is of primary importance in studying the symmetries of a group of permutations.

Definition   Let G be a permutation group on the set X. An element x in X is said to be *G-equivalent* to y in X if there exists g in G such that $g(x) = y$. We write this $x \underset{G}{\sim} y$.

The relation G-equivalent is an equivalence relation on X. Since G contains the identity e and $e(x) = x$, for all x in X, $x \underset{G}{\sim} x$, so that G-equivalent is a reflexive relation. Likewise, $x \underset{G}{\sim} y$ implies that there exists a g with $g(x) = y$ but, since G is a group, g^{-1} exists and

$$g^{-1}(y) = g^{-1}(g(x)) = e(x) = x,$$

so that $\underset{G}{\sim}$ is symmetric. Finally, if $x \underset{G}{\sim} y$ and $y \underset{G}{\sim} z$, then there exist g and h in G such that $g(x) = y$ and $h(y) = z$. Thus

$$(h \circ g)(x) = h(g(x)) = h(y) = z.$$

Since $h \circ g \in G$, this implies that $\underset{\widetilde{G}}{\sim}$ is transitive. By Theorem 1.1, the equivalence relation $\underset{\widetilde{G}}{\sim}$ partitions X into equivalence classes. A class is called an *orbit* of G. For example, the group

$$G = \{e, (1 \quad 2)(3 \quad 4)(5 \quad 6)(7 \quad 8), (1 \quad 3)(2 \quad 4)(5 \quad 7)(6 \quad 8),$$

$$(1 \quad 4)(2 \quad 3)(5 \quad 8)(6 \quad 7)\}$$

has orbits $\{1, 2, 3, 4\}$ and $\{5, 6, 7, 8\}$.

We examine G-equivalent in more detail and give examples in Section 7.7. If G is a permutation group on X, then the element g in G *fixes* x if $g(x) = x$. The set of all fixed points of g is denoted by $F(g)$. Thus

$$F(g) = \{x \in X : g(x) = x\}.$$

Sometimes different group elements have the same number of fixed points. Thus in the group S_3, $(2 \quad 3)$ and $(1 \quad 2)$ have one fixed point each. In fact,

$$(2 \quad 3) = (1 \quad 2 \quad 3) \circ (1 \quad 2) \circ (1 \quad 3 \quad 2)$$

$$= (1 \quad 3 \quad 2)^{-1} \circ (1 \quad 2) \circ (1 \quad 3 \quad 2).$$

Definition   Let G be a group. The element g in G is *conjugate* to g_1 in G if there exists h in G with $g = h^{-1} \circ g_1 \circ h$.

Proposition 7.6   Let g be a permutation of the finite set X. If g is conjugate to g_1 in S_X, then $|F(g)| = |F(g_1)|$.

Proof   If $x \in F(g)$, then $x = g(x) = (h^{-1} \circ g_1 \circ h)(x)$, where $g = h^{-1} \circ g_1 \circ h$, $h \in G$. Thus $h(x) = (h \circ h^{-1} \circ g_1)(h(x)) = e \circ g_1(h(x)) = g_1(h(x))$, so that $h(x) \in F(g_1)$. Since h is a one-to-one mapping, $|F(g)| \leq |F(g_1)|$.

Since we also have $g_1 = (h^{-1})^{-1} \circ g \circ h^{-1}$, the same argument as above shows that $|F(g_1)| \leq |F(g)|$, so equality holds and the proposition follows.

Proposition 7.6 is a special case of a more general property of conjugate elements in a permutation group. The key observation is actually that, if $g = h^{-1} \circ g_1 \circ h$ in S_X, with $g(x) = y$, then $y = g(x) = h^{-1}(g_1(h(x)))$, so that $h(y) = g_1(h(x))$ and g_1 maps $h(x)$ to $h(y)$. Thus if the cycle decomposition of g is known, then the cycle decomposition of $g_1 = h \circ g \circ h^{-1}$ just has $h(x)$ in place of x for each x appearing in the cycle decomposition of g. For example, if $g = (1 \quad 2 \quad 3)(4 \quad 5)(6)$ in S_6 and $h = (1 \quad 5 \quad 3)(2 \quad 4 \quad 6)$, then

$$hgh^{-1} = (h(1)h(2)h(3))(h(4)h(5))(h(6)) = (5 \quad 4 \quad 1)(6 \quad 3)(2).$$

Thus not only do conjugate elements in a permutation group have the same number of fixed points, but they also have the same number of cycles of fixed length in their cycle decompositions. This fact is presented as a theorem.

Theorem 7.6 Let X be a finite set. If g_1 in S_X is conjugate to g_2 in S_X, then g_1 has the same number of cycles of length l, $l > 0$, in its cycle decomposition as g_2.

The converse of Theorem 7.6 is also true, so that two elements in S_X are conjugate if and only if they have the same number of cycles of length l, for each integer l, in their cycle decompositions. The proof of this is left as an exercise.

A permutation π of S_n is a *transposition* if π interchanges two elements and leaves all others fixed. In other words, the cycle structure of π consists of (ij) with all other elements fixed. With the convention that elements fixed by a permutation are deleted when writing the cycle decomposition, the transpositions in S_3 are $(1\ 2)$, $(1\ 3)$, and $(2\ 3)$. Any permutation can be obtained as a product of transpositions. We simply note that $(1\ 2\ \cdots\ n) = (1\ n)(1\ n-1)\ \cdots\ (1\ 3)(1\ 2)$. Thus by suitable relabeling, any cycle of the cycle decomposition of a permutation is a product of transpositions, so that the permutation itself, being a product of the cycles of its cycle decomposition, is a product of transpositions. For example, $(1\ 2\ 3)(4\ 5\ 6\ 7) = (1\ 3)(1\ 2)(4\ 7)(4\ 6)(4\ 5)$ in S_7. If the length of a cycle is odd, then the cycle can be written as a product of an even number of transpositions; and if the length is even, then the cycle can be written as a product of an odd number of transpositions. Thus any permutation with an even number of cycles of even length can be written as a product of an even number of transpositions. Since the sum of two even numbers is again even, the set of all permutations of S_n that can be written as a product of an even number of transpositions is a subgroup A_n of S_n. It not yet clear that A_n is different from S_n, since it may be possible to express every permutation as a product of an even number of transpositions. In fact, this is not the case.

Theorem 7.7 The subgroup A_n has index 2 in S_n.

Proof We show that $S_n = A_n \cup (1\ 2)A_n$, where $A_n \cap (1\ 2)A_n = \varnothing$. Since all permutations that are a product of an even number of transpositions are in A_n, and a permutation π which equals a product of an odd number of transpositions also equals $(1\ 2)(1\ 2)\pi$, where $(1\ 2)\pi$ is now in A_n, then $S_n = A_n \cup (1\ 2)A_n$. It remains to show that $A_n \cap (1\ 2)A_n = \varnothing$. To do this, define the permutation π to be *even* if there is an even number of cycles of even length in the cycle decomposition of π and define π to be *odd* if there is an odd number of cycles of even length in the cycle decomposition of π. Thus, if $E = \{\text{even permutations}\}$ and $\theta = \{\text{odd permutations}\}$, then $S_n = E \cup \theta$ and $E \cap \theta = \varnothing$. Suppose γ is in S_n, and we multiply $\gamma \circ (ij)$. If i and j occur in the same cycle of the cycle decomposition of γ, say $(ii_2 \cdots i_{r-1}ji_{r+1} \cdots i_t)$, then $\gamma(ij)$ results in $(ji_2 \cdots i_{r-1})(ii_{r+1} \cdots i_t)$, so that if t is even then both resulting new cycles in the product are even or both are odd. Thus the number of even cycles in $\gamma(ij)$ is changed by one. If i and j occur in different cycles of the cycle decomposition of γ, say $(ii_2 \cdots i_r)(jj_2 \cdots j_s)$, then $\gamma(ij)$ results in new cycles $(ji_2 \cdots i_r ij_2 \cdots j_s)$. If r and s are both even or both odd, then the new cycle is even. If exactly one of r or s is odd, then the new cycle is odd. Both of the above cases thus show that, if γ is even then $\gamma(ij)$ is odd, and if γ is odd then $\gamma(ij)$ is even. Suppose now that an even permutation τ can be written as a product of an odd number of transpositions; say, $\tau = (i_1 i_2) \cdots (i_{2k-1} i_{2k})$, where k is odd. Thus $\tau(i_{2k-1} i_{2k}) = (i_1 i_2) \cdots (i_{2k-3} i_{2k-2})$, and the left-hand side is now an odd permutation. Continuing this way, we see that $\tau(i_{2k-1} i_{2k}) \cdots (i_1 i_2) = e$, the identity, is an odd permutation which is impossible, since e has no cycles of even length. Thus $A_n = E$ and $A_n \cap (1 \ \ 2)A_n = \varnothing$.

Exercises

7-25 Calculate the following products of permutations:
   a $(1 \ \ 2 \ \ 3)(4 \ \ 5 \ \ 6 \ \ 7) \circ (1 \ \ 2)(3 \ \ 4)(5)(6)(7)$

   b $\begin{pmatrix} 1 & 2 & 3 & 4 \\ 2 & 3 & 1 & 4 \end{pmatrix} \circ \begin{pmatrix} 1 & 2 & 3 & 4 \\ 3 & 1 & 4 & 2 \end{pmatrix}$.

7-26 Determine the order of the following group elements:
   a $(1 \ \ 2 \ \ 3)(4 \ \ 5 \ \ 6)(7 \ \ 8 \ \ 9)(10 \ \ 11 \ \ 12)$
   b $(1 \ \ 2)(3 \ \ 4 \ \ 5)(6 \ \ 7 \ \ 8 \ \ 9 \ \ 10)(11)(12)$.

7-27 Compute $[(1 \ \ 2 \ \ 3)(4 \ \ 5)] \circ [(1 \ \ 2)(3 \ \ 4 \ \ 5)] \circ [(1 \ \ 2 \ \ 3 \ \ 4)(5)]$.

7-28 Write (ij) as a product of transpositions where each transposition is either $(1i)$ or $(1j)$.

7-29 Prove that every element of S_n can be written as a product of transpositions of the form $(1k)$, $k = 2, \ldots, n$.

7-30 Prove the converse of Theorem 7.6.

7.6 HOMOMORPHISMS

Two different semigroups may be quite alike in some aspects. Figure 7.4 gives the multiplication table for the semigroup

$$G_1 = \left\{ f_1 = \begin{pmatrix} 1 & 2 & 3 \\ 1 & 1 & 1 \end{pmatrix}, f_2 = \begin{pmatrix} 1 & 2 & 3 \\ 1 & 3 & 2 \end{pmatrix}, f_3 = \begin{pmatrix} 1 & 2 & 3 \\ 1 & 2 & 3 \end{pmatrix} \right\}$$

	f_1	f_2	f_3
f_1	f_1	f_1	f_1
f_2	f_1	f_3	f_2
f_3	f_1	f_2	f_3

Figure 7.4 Multiplication table for G.

$\circ$	0	1	-1
0	0	0	0
1	0	1	-1
-1	0	-1	1

Figure 7.5 Multiplication table for H_1.

	0	-1	1
0	0	0	0
-1	0	1	-1
1	0	-1	1

Figure 7.6 ϕ (Multiplication table for G_1).

of certain functions from $\{1, 2, 3\}$ to $\{1, 2, 3\}$, where the semigroup operation is composition of mappings. Figure 7.5 gives the multiplication table for the semigroup $H_1 = \{0, 1, -1\}$ of certain real integers under multiplication of real numbers. In the semigroups G_1 and H_1, the elements f_1 and 0 act alike in the sense that for any g in G_1, $g \circ f_1 = f_1 \circ g = f_1$, and for any h in H_1, $h \circ 0 = 0 \circ h = 0$. Likewise, $g \circ f_3 = f_3 \circ g = g$ for any g in G_1, and $h \circ 1 = 1 \circ h = h$ for any h in H_1, so that f_3 and 1 act alike. Finally f_2 and -1 act alike. In fact, if we relabel the elements of G by the function

$$\phi = \begin{pmatrix} f_1 & f_2 & f_3 \\ 0 & -1 & 1 \end{pmatrix}$$

from G_1 onto H_1, then ϕ applied to the multiplication table for G_1 in Figure 7.4 results in the table in Figure 7.6.

The table is just a multiplication table for H_1 with the elements of H_1 ordered 0, -1, 1. Thus H_1 is just a disguise for G_1 if our only concern is the binary operations on H_1 and G_1. The property that ϕ applied to a multiplication table for G_1 yields a multiplication table for H_1 can be expressed succinctly by $\phi(g \circ h) = \phi(g) \circ \phi(h)$ for g and h in G_1. Thus, if we order the elements of H_1 by $\phi(f_1) = 0$, $\phi(f_2) = -1$, $\phi(f_3) = 1$, then ϕ of the entry in the x-row and y-column of the table for G_1 is $\phi(x \circ y)$, which is the same as the entry $\phi(x) \circ \phi(y)$ in the $\phi(x)$-row and $\phi(y)$-column for the table for H_1, x and y in G_1.

	a	b	c	d
a	a	a	a	a
b	a	b	c	c
c	a	c	b	b
d	a	c	b	b

Figure 7.7 Table for H_2.

Definition A semigroup G is *isomorphic* to a semigroup H if there exists a one-to-one mapping ϕ from G onto H such that $\phi(g \circ g') = \phi(g) \circ \phi(g')$ for all g and g' in G. The mapping ϕ is called an *isomorphism* from G onto H and, as illustrated with the example above, means that G and H are the same semigroups except that the elements have different names.

A concept more general and more important than isomorphism is the idea of homomorphism.

Definition The mapping ϕ from the semigroup G to the semigroup H is a *homomorphism* if $\phi(g \circ g') = \phi(g) \circ \phi(g')$ for all g and g' in G.

If ϕ maps G onto H, then ϕ is said to be a *homomorphism from G onto H* and H is said to be the *homomorphic image* of G.

The set $H_2 = \{a, b, c, d\}$, with binary operation given by the table in Figure 7.7, is actually a semigroup. In general, for an arbitrary table, it is tedious to check whether or not the multiplication given by the table is actually associative. This checking involves computing $(x \circ y) \circ z$ and $x \circ (y \circ z)$ for all choices of x, y, and z and then comparing the two results to see if they are equal. In Figure 7.7 we are saved some labor if we note that the subset $\{a, b, c\}$ is closed under the multiplication in Figure 7.7, and in fact $\{a, b, c\}$ is isomorphic to G_1. Thus the binary operation on $\{a, b, c\}$ is associative. Since d multiplies exactly like c, we can replace d by c in any occurrence of d in the expressions $(x \circ y) \circ z$ and $x \circ (y \circ z)$ and, since there are now only elements from $\{a, b, c\}$ in $(x \circ y) \circ z$ and $x \circ (y \circ z)$, the binary operation on $\{a, b, c, d\}$ is associative.

The mapping

$$\phi = \begin{pmatrix} a & b & c & d \\ f_1 & f_3 & f_2 & f_2 \end{pmatrix}$$

is a homomorphism from H_2 onto H_1. To check this, note that ϕ is certainly a function, and ϕ applied to each entry in Figure 7.7 yields Figure 7.8, which has the entry $h \circ h'$ for any row labeled h and column labeled h'. Of the three explicit examples of semigroups given so far, only the first is a semigroup of

	f_1	f_3	f_2	f_2
f_1	f_1	f_1	f_1	f_1
f_3	f_1	f_3	f_2	f_2
f_2	f_1	f_2	f_3	f_3
f_2	f_1	f_2	f_3	f_3

Figure 7.8 ϕ (Table for H_2).

functions. However, the second example is isomorphic to a semigroup of functions, and the third example has a homomorphic image which is a semigroup of functions. This phenomenon is always the case.

Let G be a semigroup and let $\mathcal{F}_G$ be the set of functions

$$\{f_g : g \in G \text{ and } f_g(h) = g \circ h \text{ for all } h \in G\}$$

from G to G. $\mathcal{F}_G$ is actually a semigroup, since

$$(f_g \circ f_{g'})(h) = f_g(f_{g'}(h)) = f_g(g' \circ h) = g \circ (g' \circ h),$$

which by associativity in G equals $(g \circ g') \circ h = f_{g \circ g'}(h)$. The mapping $g \to f_g$ from G onto F_G is called the *left regular representation* of G, and in fact is a homomorphism, as we now show.

Theorem 7.8 Let G be a semigroup. The function ϕ such that $\phi(g) = f_g$ is a homomorphism from G onto $\mathcal{F}_G$.

Proof We need only check that $\phi(g \circ g') = \phi(g) \circ \phi(g')$ for g and g' in G. However, $\phi(g \circ g') = f_{g \circ g'}$ and $\phi(g) \circ \phi(g') = f_g \circ f_{g'}$. The function $f_{g \circ g'}$ maps h to $f_{g \circ g'}(h) = (g \circ g') \circ h$, and the function $f_g \circ f_{g'}$ maps h to $(f_g \circ f_{g'})(h) = f_g(f_{g'}(h)) = f_g(g' \circ h) = g \circ (g' \circ h)$. Since G is associative, $(g \circ g') \circ h = g \circ (g' \circ h)$ and $f_{g \circ g'}(h) = (f_g \circ f_{g'})(h)$ for any h. Thus $f_{g \circ g'} = f_g \circ f_{g'}$, and ϕ is a homomorphism.

In the left regular representation of $H_1 = \{0, 1, -1\}$,

$$f_0 = \begin{pmatrix} 0 & 1 & -1 \\ 0 \circ 0 & 0 \circ 1 & 0 \circ (-1) \end{pmatrix} = \begin{pmatrix} 0 & 1 & -1 \\ 0 & 0 & 0 \end{pmatrix}$$

$$f_1 = \begin{pmatrix} 0 & 1 & -1 \\ 1 \circ 0 & 1 \circ 1 & 1 \circ (-1) \end{pmatrix} = \begin{pmatrix} 0 & 1 & -1 \\ 0 & 1 & -1 \end{pmatrix}$$

$$f_{-1} = \begin{pmatrix} 0 & 1 & -1 \\ (-1) \circ 0 & (-1) \circ 1 & (-1) \circ (1) \end{pmatrix} = \begin{pmatrix} 0 & 1 & -1 \\ 0 & -1 & 1 \end{pmatrix},$$

so that the mapping $0 \to f_0$, $1 \to f_1$, and $-1 \to f_{-1}$ is actually an isomorphism.

However, the left regular representation of $H_2 = \{a, b, c, d\}$, with multiplication as in Figure 7.7,

maps a to

$$\begin{pmatrix} a & b & c & d \\ a \circ a & a \circ b & a \circ c & a \circ d \end{pmatrix} = \begin{pmatrix} a & b & c & d \\ a & a & a & a \end{pmatrix},$$

b to

$$\begin{pmatrix} a & b & c & d \\ b \circ a & b \circ b & b \circ c & b \circ d \end{pmatrix} = \begin{pmatrix} a & b & c & d \\ a & b & c & c \end{pmatrix},$$

c to

$$\begin{pmatrix} a & b & c & d \\ c \circ a & c \circ b & c \circ c & c \circ d \end{pmatrix} = \begin{pmatrix} a & b & c & d \\ a & c & b & b \end{pmatrix},$$

and d to

$$\begin{pmatrix} a & b & c & d \\ d \circ a & d \circ b & d \circ c & d \circ d \end{pmatrix} = \begin{pmatrix} a & b & c & d \\ a & c & b & b \end{pmatrix},$$

so that the image $\mathscr{F}_G$ contains only the three functions

$$\begin{pmatrix} a & b & c & d \\ a & a & a & a \end{pmatrix}, \quad \begin{pmatrix} a & b & c & d \\ a & b & c & c \end{pmatrix}, \quad \begin{pmatrix} a & b & c & d \\ a & c & b & b \end{pmatrix}.$$

Thus this mapping is not an isomorphism.

The left regular representation will be an isomorphism if it is a one-to-one map, that is, if each g in G maps to a distinct function. This will happen as long as, for any distinct g and g' in G, there exists at least one h (depending on g and g') such that $g \circ h \neq g' \circ h$, so that $f_g(h) \neq f_{g'}(h)$. We rephase this in the following definition.

Definition The semigroup G is weakly cancellative if $g \circ h = g' \circ h$, for all $h \in G$, implies $g = g'$.

Theorem 7.9 The left regular representation of the semigroup G is an isomorphism if and only if G is weakly cancellative.

Proof If G is weakly cancellative, then for g and g' distinct, there exists h with $g \circ h \neq g' \circ h$. Thus $f_g(h) \neq f_{g'}(h)$, and $f_g \neq f_{g'}$. The left regular representation is a one-to-one homomorphism from G onto $\mathscr{F}_G$, hence is an isomorphism. Conversely, if the map $g \to f_g$ is an isomorphism and if $g \circ h = g' \circ h$ for all h in G, then $f_g(h) = f_{g'}(h)$, for all h in G, showing that $f_g = f_{g'}$. Since $g \to f_g$ is one-to-one, $g = g'$ and G is weakly cancellative.

The simple fact that an identity exists means that a monoid G is weakly cancellative, since for g and g' distinct in G, $g \circ e = g \neq g' = g' \circ e$. Thus a direct result of Theorem 7.9 is the following.

Theorem 7.10 Let G be a monoid. The left regular representation of G is an isomorphism.

Hence every monoid G can be thought of as a monoid of functions from the set G into G. Since a group H is also a monoid, the left regular representation of H is an isomorphism. In fact, for h in H, the image f_h of h under the regular representation is a one-to-one function from H onto H. The proof of this is left as an exercise. Thus f_h is a permutation in S_H, and H is isomorphic (by the left regular representation) to a group of permutations. The concept of permutation group therefore includes the seemingly more general concept of group.

Let G be a group and let $g \to f_g \in S_G$, for g in G, be the left regular representation of G. We denote the image of G in S_G by $\mathscr{F}_G$, so that $\mathscr{F}_G$ is a group of functions which permute the elements of G. Since $f_{h \circ g^{-1}}(g) = (h \circ g^{-1}) \circ g = h \circ (g^{-1} \circ g) = h \circ e = h$, for g and h in G, we have that g is $\mathscr{F}_G$-equivalent to h, that is, $g \underset{\mathscr{F}_G}{\sim} h$. Thus there is exactly one orbit of $\mathscr{F}_G$. Suppose now that H is a subgroup of G, and we map H into S_G by $h \to f_h$, where $f_h \in \mathscr{F}_G$. As in the left regular representation, the mapping $h \to f_h$ is an isomorphism from H into S_G. We denote the image of H in S_G by $\mathscr{F}_1$. There exists an h in H with $f_h(g_1) = h \circ g_1 = g_2$ if and only if $g_1 \underset{\mathscr{F}_1}{\sim} g_2$. That is, $g_1 \underset{\mathscr{F}_1}{\sim} g_2$ if and only if $g_2 \in Hg_1$. Thus the $\mathscr{F}_1$-equivalent classes are just the right cosets of H in G.

Exercises

7-31 Prove that the logarithmic function to the base 10 is an isomorphism from the group of positive real numbers under multiplication to the group of all real numbers under addition.

7-32 Let ϕ be a homomorphism from a monoid G onto a semigroup H. Prove that H is a monoid.

7-33 Let ϕ be a homomorphism from a group G onto a semigroup H. Prove that H is a group.

7-34 Determine the groups (up to isomorphism) of order 6.

7-35 Let G be a group and $g \to f_g$ be the left regular representation of G, where $g \in G$ and $f_g \in S_G$. Prove that f is a permutation of G.

7-36   Let Z be the group of integers under $+$, and let $\phi(n) = 2n$ for $n \in Z$. Prove or disprove that ϕ is a homomorphism.

7-37   Let ϕ be a homomorphism from a group G into a group H. Prove that $\{\phi(g) : g \in G\}$ is a subgroup of H. Let e_H be the identity of H. Prove that $\{g \in G : \phi(g) = e_H\}$ is a subgroup of G.

7-38   Prove that the composition of homomorphisms of semigroups is a homomorphism of semigroups.

7.7 COUNTING SYMMETRIES

Symmetry is a fundamental aspect of life and of mathematics. Many sets have symmetries associated with the elements of the set, and often it is not the individual element we are concerned with, but sets of similar elements. In chemistry, the orientation of a molecule is not of concern in studying the intrinsic properties of the molecule. Thus transformation of the molecule by rigid motions or reflections gives an equivalent molecule. Likewise, there are many symmetries associated with Boolean functions. In determining different Boolean functions, the permutations of the labels of the variables are not important, since it is an easy matter to change the input wiring to obtain the new function. For example, if a device is constructed corresponding to $x_1 x_2 \vee x_3 \bar{x}_2$, then this device is easily changed to one corresponding to $x_2 x_1 \vee x_3 \bar{x}_1$ by simply interchanging the lead-in wires corresponding to x_1 and x_2 (see Figure 7.9). Thus the permutations of the variables reduce the number of devices to be considered.

Often the symmetries or permutations of a class of objects form a group, and in this case the combinatorial aspects of the group are important in studying the classes of similar elements. As an example, suppose we examine the number of distinct ways that men and women can be seated at a bridge table. The set of distinct seatings is illustrated in Figure 7.10, where M stands for man and W stands for woman. These seating arrangements are all distinct, but the positioning of the table in the room may not be of interest to us, in which case seatings 1, 2, 3, and 4 are the same. Likewise, 5, 7, 8, and 10 are the same, 6 and 9 are the same, and 11, 12, 13, and 14 are the same. Hence the number of distinct seating arrangements is 6 instead of 16.

Although the notion of seating arrangement is intuitively clear, we formalize it by defining a seating arrangement to be a function from 1, 2, 3, 4 (representing the north, south, east, and west sides of the table, respectively) into m, w (representing man and woman, respectively). Thus the function

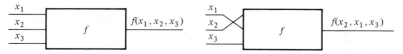

Figure 7.9 The function $f(x_2, x_1, x_3)$ obtained from $f(x_1, x_2, x_3)$ by interchanging input wires.

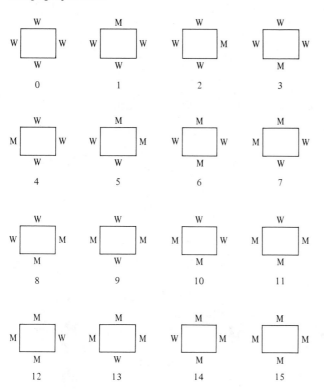

Figure 7.10 Seatings of men and women at a bridge table.

$$f_0 = \begin{pmatrix} 1 & 2 & 3 & 4 \\ w & w & w & w \end{pmatrix} \quad \text{is the arrangement}$$

$$f_4 = \begin{pmatrix} 1 & 2 & 3 & 4 \\ w & w & w & m \end{pmatrix} \quad \text{is the arrangement}$$

$$f_8 = \begin{pmatrix} 1 & 2 & 3 & 4 \\ w & m & m & w \end{pmatrix} \quad \text{is the arrangement}$$

$$\text{and} \quad f_{12} = \begin{pmatrix} 1 & 2 & 3 & 4 \\ m & m & w & m \end{pmatrix} \quad \text{is the arrangement}$$

Rotations of the square are represented by the permutations $e = (1)(2)(3)(4)$, $\rho_{90°} = (1 \ 3 \ 2 \ 4)$, $\rho_{180°} = (1 \ 2)(3 \ 4)$, and $\rho_{270°} = (1 \ 4 \ 2 \ 3)$, and we denote this group by G.

These rotations can also be thought of as operating on the seating arrangements. Thus the rotation $(1 \ 3 \ 2 \ 4)$ applied to

That is, f_4 is mapped to f_1.

Since $f_4 = f_1 \circ \rho_{90°}$ and $f_1 = f_4 \circ \rho_{90°}^{-1}$, the rotation ρ by 90° takes f_4 to $f_4 \circ \rho^{-1}$. In general, if ρ is a permutation on X, then we define a permutation ρ' on the set of functions from X to Y by $\rho'(f) = f \circ \rho^{-1}$ for f a function from X to Y. The function ρ' is onto, since $\rho'(f \circ \rho) = (f \circ \rho) \circ \rho^{-1} = f \circ (\rho \circ \rho^{-1}) = f \circ e = f$. ρ' is one-to-one, since $f_1 \circ \rho^{-1} = \rho'(f_1) = \rho'(f_2) = f_2 \circ \rho^{-1}$, and for x in X, there exists x_1 with $\rho^{-1}(x_1) = x$, so that

$$f_1(x) = f_1(\rho^{-1}(x_1)) = (f_1 \circ \rho^{-1})(x_1) = (f_2 \circ \rho^{-1})(x_1) = f_2(\rho^{-1}(x_1))$$

$$= f_2(x) \qquad \text{(for all } x \in X).$$

Thus $f_1 = f_2$ and ρ' is one-to-one and onto.

If $\mathscr{F}$ is a set of functions from X to Y, $|Y| \geq 2$, G a permutation group on X, and $f \circ \rho^{-1} \in \mathscr{F}$, for all $\rho \in G$, then $G_{\mathscr{F}} = \{\rho' : \rho \in G$ and $\rho'(f) = f \circ \rho^{-1}$ for all $f \in \mathscr{F}\}$ is a permutation group on $\mathscr{F}$. In fact, the mapping $\rho \to \rho'$ is a homomorphism from G onto $G_{\mathscr{F}}$.

Theorem 7.11 Let G be a permutation group on a finite set X and let $\mathscr{F}$ be a set of functions from X to Y. If $\rho'(f) = f \circ \rho^{-1}$ is in $\mathscr{F}$, for all $\rho \in G$, $f \in \mathscr{F}$, then $G_{\mathscr{F}} = \{\rho' : \rho'(f) = f \circ \rho^{-1}, \rho \in G\}$ is a group of permutations on $\mathscr{F}$ and the mapping $\rho \to \rho'$ is a homomorphism from G onto $G_{\mathscr{F}}$.

Proof We have already shown that ρ' is one-to-one and onto. Since $\rho'(f) \in \mathcal{F}$, for all $f \in \mathcal{F}$, then ρ' is a permutation of $\mathcal{F}$. To see that $G_{\mathcal{F}}$ is a group, let $\gamma, \rho \in G$. The permutation γ' of $G_{\mathcal{F}}$ maps f to $f \circ \gamma^{-1}$, so that $(\gamma')^{-1}$ maps $f \circ \gamma^{-1}$ to f. Also, for $f_1 \in \mathcal{F}$, $f = f_1 \circ \gamma$ satisfies $f_1 = f \circ \gamma^{-1}$. Hence

$$(\rho' \circ (\gamma')^{-1})(f_1) = \rho'((\gamma')^{-1}(f_1)) = \rho'((\gamma')^{-1}(f \circ \gamma^{-1}))$$
$$= \rho'(f) = f \circ \rho^{-1} = (f_1 \circ \gamma) \circ \rho^{-1}$$
$$= f_1 \circ (\gamma \circ \rho^{-1}) = (\rho \circ \gamma^{-1})'(f_1).$$

Since $\rho \circ \gamma^{-1} \in G$, $\rho' \circ (\gamma')^{-1} \in G_{\mathcal{F}}$ and $G_{\mathcal{F}}$ is a group. That $\rho \to \rho'$ is a homomorphism follows from the fact that

$$(\rho \circ \gamma)'(f) = f \circ (\rho \circ \gamma)^{-1} = f \circ \gamma^{-1} \circ \rho^{-1}$$
$$= \rho'(f \circ \gamma^{-1}) = \rho'(\gamma'(f)) = (\rho' \circ \gamma')(f).$$

Not only is the map from G to $G_{\mathcal{F}}$ always a homomorphism but, in the cases of interest to us, it is an isomorphism.

Theorem 7.12 Let G be a permutation group on a finite set X and let $\mathcal{F}$ be a set of functions from X to Y such that for $x_1 \neq x_2$ in X there exists $f \in \mathcal{F}$ with $f(x_1) \neq f(x_2)$. If $\rho'(f) = f \circ \rho^{-1}$ is in $\mathcal{F}$ for all ρ in G and f in $\mathcal{F}$, then the mapping $\rho \to \rho'$ is an isomorphism from G onto $G_{\mathcal{F}}$.

Proof Theorem 7.11 guarantees that this mapping is a homomorphism from G onto $G_{\mathcal{F}}$. It remains only to show that $\rho \to \rho'$ is one-to-one. Suppose that $\rho' = \gamma'$. If there exists x with $\rho^{-1}(x) \neq \gamma^{-1}(x)$, then by hypothesis there exists $f \in \mathcal{F}$ with $f(\rho^{-1}(x)) \neq f(\gamma^{-1}(x))$. Thus $\rho'(f) = f \circ \rho^{-1} \neq f \circ \gamma^{-1} = \gamma'(f)$, so that $\rho' \neq \gamma'$. Since we are assuming $\rho' = \gamma'$, there cannot exist x with $\rho^{-1}(x) \neq \gamma^{-1}(x)$. Thus $\rho^{-1} = \gamma^{-1}$ and $\rho = (\rho^{-1})^{-1} = (\gamma^{-1})^{-1} = \gamma$, which proves the theorem.

Theorem 7.12 shows that, if $\mathcal{F}$ is the set of all functions from X to Y and $|Y| \geq 2$, then G is isomorphic to $G_{\mathcal{F}}$.

In the example involving seating arrangements $G = \{e, (1\ \ 3\ \ 2\ \ 4), (1\ \ 2)(3\ \ 4), (1\ \ 4\ \ 2\ \ 3)\}$, and, if the functions from $\{1, 2, 3, 4\}$ to m, w are f_i, $i = 0, 1, \ldots, 15$, corresponding to the arrangements $0, 1, \ldots, 15$ in Figure 7.10, then $G_{\mathcal{F}}$ contains e',

$$(1\ \ 3\ \ 2\ \ 4)' = (f_0)(f_1\ f_2\ f_3\ f_4)(f_5\ f_8\ f_{10}\ f_7)(f_6\ f_9)(f_{11}\ f_{12}\ f_{13}\ f_{14})(f_{15})$$
$$((1\ \ 2)(3\ \ 4))' = (f_0)(f_1\ f_3)(f_2\ f_4)(f_5\ f_{10})(f_7\ f_8)(f_6)(f_9)(f_{11}\ f_{13})(f_{12}\ f_{14})(f_{15})$$
$$(1\ \ 4\ \ 2\ \ 3)' = (f_0)(f_1\ f_4\ f_2\ f_3)(f_5\ f_7\ f_{10}\ f_8)(f_6\ f_9)(f_{11}\ f_{14}\ f_{13}\ f_{12})(f_{15}).$$

Furthermore, f_i is equivalent to f_j if there exists ρ' in $G_{\mathscr{F}}$ with $\rho'(f_i) = f_i \circ \rho^{-1} = f_j$. Thus f_i is $G_{\mathscr{F}}$-equivalent to f_j as defined in Section 7.5, and the number of equivalence classes under $G_{\mathscr{F}}$-equivalent in this instance is six.

If G is a permutation group on X, then the *stabilizer* of x in X is

$$G_x = \{g \in G : g(x) = x\}.$$

Thus the stabilizer is simply the set of elements in G that individually fix x. In the example involving seating arrangements, the stabilizer of seating arrangement f_9 is $\{e', \rho'_{180°}\}$, which is certainly a subgroup of the whole group $G_{\mathscr{F}}$. In fact, G_x is a subgroup of any permutation group G, since g, $h \in G_x$ implies $g(x) = x$, $h(x) = x$, so that $(g \circ h^{-1})(x) = g(h^{-1}(x)) = g(x) = x$ and $gh^{-1} \in G_x$. Thus G_x, being nonempty ($e \in G_x$), is a subgroup by Proposition 7.4.

Theorem 7.13 Let G be a permutation group on the finite set X. If $\mathscr{C}$ is a G-equivalent class in X, then $|G| = |\mathscr{C}||G_x|$, where $x \in \mathscr{C}$.

Proof The stabilizer of x is a subgroup of G and, by Lagrange's theorem,

$$|G| = [G : G_x]|G_x|,$$

where $[G : G_x]$ is the number of left cosets in G. If g and g_1 are in the same left coset, then $g = g_1 h$ for some h in G_x, so that

$$g(x) = g_1(h(x)) = g_1(x).$$

Thus all elements in the same left coset map x to the same place. Furthermore, if g and g_1 are in G, with $g(x) \neq g_1(x)$, then g and g_1 are in different left cosets. This shows that the number of left cosets of G_x in G equals the number of distinct images of x, which is just $|\mathscr{C}|$. Thus $|G| = |\mathscr{C}||G_x|$, proving the theorem.

If G is the permutation group on the set of seating arrangements in the previous example, then $|G| = 4$, $|G_{f_9}| = 2$, and the orbit of f_9 is $\{f_9, f_6\}$, which contains two elements.

Theorem 7.13 is the basis for showing that the number of G-equivalent classes equals the average number of fixed points. For g in the permutation group G on X, let the set of fixed points be $F(g)$. Thus

$$F(g) = \{x \in X : g(x) = x\}.$$

Theorem 7.14 (*Burnside's Theorem*) Let G be a permutation group on the finite set X. The number of G-equivalent classes in X is

$$\frac{1}{|G|}\left(\sum_{g \in G} |F(g)|\right).$$

Proof To count the total number of ways elements of X can be fixed, we can count the number of permutations that fix a given element and then sum over all the elements of the set, or we can determine the number of elements in X that are fixed by a particular permutation and then sum over all the permutations in the group. Concisely, this says

$$\sum_{x \in X} |G_x| = \sum_{g \in G} |F(g)|.$$

However, $X = \mathscr{P}_1 \cup \mathscr{P}_2 \cup \cdots \cup \mathscr{P}_k$, where $\mathscr{P}_i$ are the G-equivalent classes, so that

$$\sum_{x \in X} |G_x| = \sum_{i=1}^{k}\left(\sum_{x \in \mathscr{P}_i} |G_x|\right).$$

By Theorem 7.13, $|G_x| = |G|/|\mathscr{P}_i|$ for all x in $\mathscr{P}_i$. Thus

$$\sum_{i=1}^{k}\left(\sum_{x \in \mathscr{P}_i} |G_x|\right) = \sum_{i=1}^{k}\left(\sum_{x \in \mathscr{P}_i} \frac{|G|}{|\mathscr{P}_i|}\right) = \sum_{i=1}^{k} |\mathscr{P}_i| \frac{|G|}{|\mathscr{P}_i|} = \sum_{i=1}^{k} |G| = k|G|.$$

However this shows that

$$k = \frac{1}{|G|}\left(\sum_{g \in G} |F(g)|\right).$$

Since k is the number of G-equivalent classes, the theorem is proven.

In the example involving seating arrangements at a bridge table, if ρ equals $\rho_{90°}$, then $G_{\mathscr{F}} = \{e', \rho', (\rho')^2, (\rho')^3\}$, and $|F(e')| = 16$, $|F(\rho')| = 2$, $|F((\rho')^2)| = 4$, and $|F((\rho')^3)| = 2$. The number of equivalence classes by Burnside's theorem is $(16 + 2 + 4 + 2)/4$, which equals 6, agreeing with our previous calculation.

Let U be a given cube in space. We must take some care in defining the group of rigid motions of this cube, since, for example, a reflection of space about a plane going through diagonally opposite edges of the cube (for instance, the edges through 1 and 4 and the edge through 6 and 7 in Figure 7.11) is certainly an isometry of space that maps the cube into itself. However, we choose not to consider this isometry a rigid motion. Thus the rigid motions of the cube are defined to be that subgroup of isometries of space that map the cube onto itself and are generated by rotations. In Figure 7.11 there are rotations that map vertex 1 onto any other vertex. This gives eight choices and, once this is done, the image of vertex 2 can be rotated to any of the three vertices adjacent to the image of vertex 1. These are the only possibilities, so that the group of rigid motions contains $8 \cdot 3 = 24$ elements. In fact, let 1, 2, 3, 4, 5, and 6 represent the faces of the cube as pictured in Figure 7.12. The group of rigid motions is isomorphic to the permutation group G on $\{1, 2, 3, 4, 5, 6\}$, where G is given in Figure 7.13.

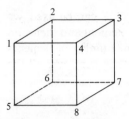

Figure 7.11

Figure 7.12

Suppose we now find the number of ways to color a cube, one different color on each face, with n colors, where n is an integer larger than 5. A colored cube that can be transformed into another colored cube by a product of rotations is considered equivalent. As in the case of the seating arrangements, a coloring is defined to be a function—in particular a function from $\{1, 2, 3, 4, 5, 6\}$, which corresponds to the six faces of the cube, into $\{r_1, r_2, \ldots, r_n\}$, which corresponds to the n colors. The hypotheses of Theorem 7.12 are satisfied, so that G is isomorphic to $G_{\mathscr{F}}$ and $|G| = |G_{\mathscr{F}}|$. Theorem 7.14 now shows that the number of equivalence classes is

$$k = \frac{1}{|G|} \sum_{g \in G_{\mathscr{F}}} |F(g)|.$$

However, since we require each face to be colored differently, $|F(g)| = 0$, for any $g \neq e$, and

$$|F(e)| = n(n - 1)(n - 2)(n - 3)(n - 4)(n - 5).$$

Thus the number of ways to color a cube, one different color on each face, with n different colors, is

$$\frac{n(n - 1)(n - 2)(n - 3)(n - 4)(n - 5)}{24}.$$

If G is taken to be the subgroup of isometries that map the cube onto the cube (allowing the reflections excluded from the group of rigid motions), then the number of ways to color a cube, one different color on each face, with n different colors, is

$$\frac{n(n - 1)(n - 2)(n - 3)(n - 4)(n - 5)}{48}.$$

Permutation	Degrees of rotation	Axis of rotation
e	0	
(1542)	90	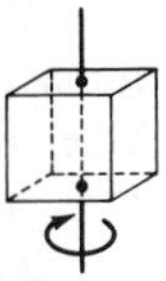
(14)(52)	180	
(1245)	270	
(2653)	90	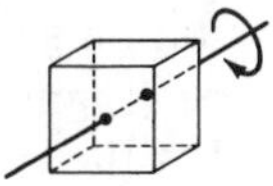
(25)(63)	180	
(2356)	270	
(1346)	90	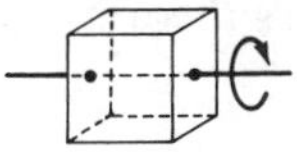
(14)(36)	180	
(1643)	270	
(35)(14)(26)	180	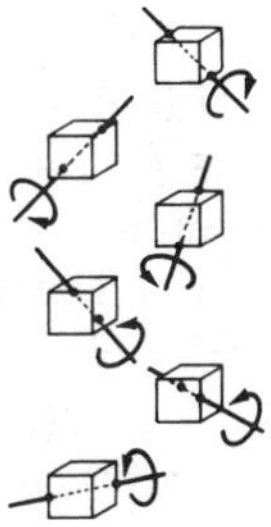
(23)(14)(56)	180	
(34)(16)(25)	180	
(13)(25)(46)	180	
(12)(45)(36)	180	
(15)(24)(36)	180	
(123)(456)	120	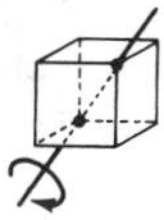
(132)(465)	240	
(243)(165)	120	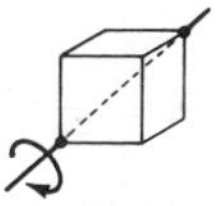
(234)(156)	240	
(345)(126)	120	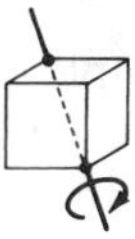
(354)(162)	240	
(135)(246)	120	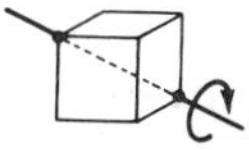
(153)(264)	240	

Figure 7.13 Correspondence between G and rigid motions.

As another example of Burnside's theorem, let X be the set $\{1, 2, 3, 4, 5, 6\}$ corresponding to the faces of a cube. Let $\mathscr{F}$ be the set of functions from $X = \{1, 2, 3, 4, 5, 6\}$ to $\{R, W, B\}$ such that each function maps exactly two elements of X to R, two elements to W, and two elements to B. This corresponds to coloring the faces of a cube such that two faces are colored red, two white, and two blue. There are $\binom{6}{2} = 15$ ways to choose the elements of X mapped to R and $\binom{4}{2} = 6$ ways to choose the elements of X mapped to W, and finally, the last 2 elements of X are mapped to B. Thus there are $15 \cdot 6 = 90$ functions from X to $\{R, W, B\}$ that correspond to our colorings. Let G be the permutation group on X that corresponds to the group of rigid motions of the cube (Figure 7.13). The set $\mathscr{F}$ satisfies the hypotheses of Theorem 7.12, so that the mapping from G onto $G_{\mathscr{F}}$ given by g goes to the permutation of $\mathscr{F}$, which takes f in $\mathscr{F}$ to $f \circ g^{-1}$, is an isomorphism.

By Burnside's theorem, the number of equivalence classes of coloring is

$$k = \frac{1}{|G_{\mathscr{F}}|} \sum_{g' \in G_{\mathscr{F}}} |F(g')|.$$

Since $|\mathscr{F}| = 90$, $|F(e')| = 90$. For $f \in \mathscr{F}$, $(1 \ \ 5 \ \ 4 \ \ 2)'(f) = f \circ (1 \ \ 5 \ \ 4 \ \ 2)^{-1} = f$ implies $f(1) = f(2) = f(4) = f(5)$. This means that four faces are colored the same color, which cannot happen if $f \in \mathscr{F}$. Thus $|F((1 \ \ 5 \ \ 4 \ \ 2)')| = 0$. The same type of argument shows that $|F(g')| = 0$ for $g' \in \{(1 \ \ 2 \ \ 4 \ \ 5), (2 \ \ 6 \ \ 5 \ \ 3), (2 \ \ 3 \ \ 5 \ \ 6), (1 \ \ 3 \ \ 4 \ \ 6), (1 \ \ 6 \ \ 4 \ \ 3)\}$. If $[(1 \ \ 2 \ \ 3)(4 \ \ 5 \ \ 6)]'(f) = f$, then $f(1) = f(3) = f(2)$, so that $|F([(1 \ \ 2 \ \ 3)(4 \ \ 5 \ \ 6)]')| = 0$. An analogous argument again shows that $|F(g')| = 0$ for the remaining seven elements in G that have a cycle of length 3. If $[(1 \ \ 4)(5 \ \ 2)]'(f) = f$, then $f \circ (1 \ \ 4)(5 \ \ 2) = f$, $f(1) = f(4)$, and $f(5) = f(2)$. There are then three choices in $\{R, W, B\}$ for $f(1) = f(4)$ and two choices for $f(5) = f(2)$, and the remaining color is chosen for $f(3) = f(6)$. Thus $|F([(1 \ \ 4)(5 \ \ 2)]')| = 6$. Likewise, the remaining eight permutations, which contain two cycles of length 2, also have exactly six fixed points each. Thus

$$k = \tfrac{1}{24}(1 \cdot 90 + 6.0 + 8.0 + 9.6) = 6,$$

and there are six ways to color a cube with two faces each red, white, and blue, respectively.

As another example of Theorem 7.14, let X again be the set $\{1, 2, 3, 4, 5, 6\}$ corresponding to the faces of a cube and let G be the permutation group on X corresponding to the rigid motions of the cube. Let F be the set of all possible colorings of the faces of the cube with n colors, $n \geq 2$. Thus F is the set of all functions from X to $\{r_1, r_2, \ldots, r_n\}$.

By Burnside's theorem, the number of equivalence classes of colorings is

$$k = \frac{1}{|G_{\mathscr{F}}|} \sum_{g' \in G_{\mathscr{F}}} |F(g')|.$$

Since there are n choices for each of the six faces of the cube, $|F(e')| = n^6$. For $f \in \mathscr{F}$, $(1 \ \ 5 \ \ 4 \ \ 2)' \circ f = f$ if and only if $f(1) = f(5) = f(4) = f(2)$. Thus we have n choices for $f(1) = f(5) = f(4) = f(2)$, n choices for $f(3)$, and n choices for $f(6)$, showing that $|F[(1 \ \ 5 \ \ 4 \ \ 2)']| = n^3$. The same type of argument shows that $|F(g')| = n^3$ for the remaining five cycles, with one cycle of length 4 and two cycles of length 1. Similarly, we conclude that $|F(g')| = n^2$ if g contains two cycles each of length 3, $|F(g')| = n^4$ if g contains two cycles of length 2 and two cycles of length 1, and $|F(g')| = n^3$ if g contains three cycles of length 2. Thus

$$k = \tfrac{1}{24}(1 \cdot n^6 + 6 \cdot n^3 + 8 \cdot n^2 + 3 \cdot n^4 + 6 \cdot n^3)$$

$$= \frac{n^2}{24}(n^4 + 3n^2 + 12n + 8).$$

The above example uses a special argument which is useful in the general case.

Lemma 7.2 Let G be a permutation group on the finite set X. Let $\mathscr{F}$ be the set of all functions from X to Y, $|Y| \geq 2$. Then $|F(g')| = |Y|^{c(g)}$ for $g \in G$, where $c(g)$ is the number of cycles in the cycle decomposition of g.

Proof An element f in $\mathscr{F}$ is in $F(g')$ if and only if $g'(f) = f \circ g^{-1} = f$. The number of cycles of g^{-1}, however, is the same as that of g, since $g^{-1} = \cdots (x_1 x_2 \cdots x_m) \cdots$ implies $g = \cdots (x_1 x_m x_{m-1} \cdots x_2) \cdots$. Furthermore, $f(x_1) = f(g^{-1}(x_1)) = f(x_2), f(x_2) = f(g^{-1}(x_2)) = f(x_3)$, and continuing we see that $f(x_1) = f(x_2) = \cdots = f(x_m)$. Thus f is constant on each cycle of g. Therefore $f \in F(g')$ if and only if f is constant on each cycle of g. However, the elements of a cycle have $|Y|$ possible images. Since there are $c(g)$ cycles, there are $|Y|^{c(g)}$ functions f in $F(g')$.

A direct result of Lemma 7.2 is the following theorem.

Theorem 7.15 Let G be a permutation group on the finite set X and let F be the set of all functions from X to Y, $|Y| \geq 2$. The number of $G_{\mathscr{F}}$-equivalent classes is

$$\frac{1}{|G|} \sum_{i=1} n_i |Y|^i,$$

where n_i is the number of elements in G with i cycles in their cycle decomposition.

Proof By Theorem 7.14, the number of $G_{\mathscr{F}}$-equivalent classes is

$$\frac{1}{|G_{\mathscr{F}}|} \sum_{g' \in G_{\mathscr{F}}} |F(g')|.$$

By Theorem 7.12, $G_{\mathscr{F}}$ is isomorphic to G, and by Lemma 7.2, $|F(g')| = |Y|^{c(g)}$. Combining these observations, we have the theorem.

If we again examine the number of colorings of a cube with n colors, Theorem 7.15 gives the answer:

$$\tfrac{1}{24}(1 \cdot n^6 + 12 \cdot n^3 + 3 \cdot n^4 + 8 \cdot n^2).$$

In the example involving seating arrangements of men and women at a bridge table, the group is $\{e, (1\ \ 3\ \ 2\ \ 4), (1\ \ 2)(3\ \ 4), (1\ \ 4\ \ 2\ \ 3)\}$, so that the number of equivalence classes of arrangements is

$$\tfrac{1}{4}(2^{c(e)} + 2^{c[(12)(34)]} + 2 \cdot 2^{c[(1324)]}) = \tfrac{1}{4}(2^4 + 2^2 + 2 \cdot 2) = 6,$$

and was previously computed.

As a more important example using Theorem 7.15 let $X = \{(x_1, x_2, x_3) : x_i \in \{0, 1\}\}$ and let $Y = \{0, 1\}$. Thus the set of $2^{2^3} = 256$ Boolean functions in three variables is exactly the set of functions from X into Y. The group acting on X is derived from the permutations of x_1, x_2, and x_3. If we assign 1 to 000, 2 to 001, 3 to 010, 4 to 011, 5 to 100, 6 to 101, 7 to 110, and 8 to 111, then the permutations on X that correspond, respectively, to $(x_1)(x_2)(x_3)$, $(x_1 x_2)(x_3)$, $(x_1)(x_2 x_3)$, $(x_1 x_3)(x_2)$, $(x_1 x_2 x_3)$, and $(x_1 x_3 x_2)$ are $(1)(2)(3)(4)(5)(6)(7)(8)$, $(1)(2)(3\ \ 5)(4\ \ 6)(7)(8)$, $(1)(2\ \ 3)(4)(5)(6\ \ 7)(8)$, $(1)(2\ \ 5)(3)(4\ \ 7)(6)(8)$, $(1)(2\ \ 3\ \ 5)(4\ \ 7\ \ 6)(8)$, and $(1)(2\ \ 5\ \ 3)(4\ \ 6\ \ 7)(8)$. Thus the number of $G_{\mathscr{F}}$-equivalent classes of Boolean functions is

$$\tfrac{1}{6}(2^8 + 3 \cdot 2^6 + 2 \cdot 2^4) = 80,$$

instead of 256.

Thus a stock list of 256 devices with 3 inputs really need consist of only 80 devices. If the circuit designer wishes to further reduce the number of switching functions, inputs of x and $\bar{x}$ can be considered equivalent. This is not unreasonable in many applications (in relay contacts), since the cost of making a switch x or a switch $\bar{x}$ is essentially the same. Considering only the permutations of X induced by S_3 as above and $x_1 x_2 x_3 \to \bar{x}_1 \bar{x}_2 \bar{x}_3$, the permutation group is thus enlarged to

$(1)(2)(3)(4)(5)(6)(7)(8)$, $(1)(2)(3\ \ 5)(4\ \ 6)(7)(8)$

$(1)(2\ \ 3)(4)(5)(6\ \ 7)(8)$, $(1)(2\ \ 5)(3)(4\ \ 7)(6)(8)$

$(1)(2\ \ 3\ \ 5)(4\ \ 7\ \ 6)(8)$, $(1)(2\ \ 5\ \ 3)(4\ \ 6\ \ 7)(8)$

$(1\ \ 8)(2\ \ 7)(3\ \ 6)(4\ \ 5)$, $(1\ \ 8)(2\ \ 7)(3\ \ 4)(5\ \ 6)$

$(1\ \ 8)(2\ \ 6)(3\ \ 7)(4\ \ 5)$, $(1\ \ 8)(2\ \ 4)(3\ \ 6)(5\ \ 7)$

$(1\ \ 8)(2\ \ 6\ \ 5\ \ 7\ \ 3\ \ 4)$, $(1\ \ 8)(2\ \ 4\ \ 3\ \ 7\ \ 5\ \ 6)$.

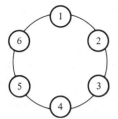

Figure 7.14 Necklace with 6 beads.

Thus the number of equivalence classes of Boolean functions is

$$\tfrac{1}{12}(2^8 + 3 \cdot 2^6 + 6 \cdot 2^4 + 2 \cdot 2^2) = 46.$$

Even this gives too many devices, and it is left to the exercises to calculate the number of equivalence classes under more general permutation groups.

As a final example of the use of Theorem 7.15 let us compute the number of distinct necklaces made of six beads, where each bead can be red, white, or blue. The necklace is represented in Figure 7.14.

Since the necklace is unchanged by rotation by a multiple of 60 or a reflection about any of the six symmetric axes, the set

$$X = \{1, 2, 3, 4, 5, 6\}$$

has the permutation group

$$G = \{(1)(2)(3)(4)(5)(6), (1 \quad 2 \quad 3 \quad 4 \quad 5 \quad 6), (1 \quad 3 \quad 5)(2 \quad 4 \quad 6),$$
$$(1 \quad 4)(2 \quad 5)(3 \quad 6), (1 \quad 5 \quad 3)(2 \quad 6 \quad 4), (1 \quad 6 \quad 5 \quad 4 \quad 3 \quad 2),$$
$$(1)(4)(2 \quad 6)(3 \quad 5), (1 \quad 2)(3 \quad 6)(4 \quad 5), (2)(1 \quad 3)(4 \quad 6)(5),$$
$$(2 \quad 3)(1 \quad 4)(5 \quad 6), (3)(2 \quad 4)(1 \quad 5)(6), (1 \quad 6)(2 \quad 5)(3 \quad 4)\}$$

acting on X, so that the number of distinct necklaces is

$$\tfrac{1}{12}(3^6 + 3 \cdot 3^4 + 4 \cdot 3^3 + 2 \cdot 3^2 + 2 \cdot 3) = 92.$$

Exercises

7-39 Let F be the set of all functions from $X = \{1, 2, 3\}$ to $\{0, 1\}$ and let $G = S_X$. Explicitly write out $G_{\mathscr{F}}$.

7-40 Let $\mathscr{F}$ be the set of functions f from $X = \{1, 2, 3\}$ to $\{0, 1\}$ such that $f(1) = f(3)$. Explicitly determine the homomorphism from $G = S_X$ onto $G_{\mathscr{F}}$.

7-41 Let G be a permutation group on X and let U be a nonempty subset of X. Prove that $\{g \in G : g(u) = u \text{ for all } u \text{ in } U\}$ is a subgroup of G.

7-42 If G is a permutation group on X and if U is a nonempty subset of X, prove that $\{g \in G : g(u) \in U$ for all u in $U\}$ is a subgroup of G.

7-43 Determine the number of distinct ways a 3×3 chessboard can have cells colored black or white. Assume that the back of the chessboard can be used and that the colors show through the cells.

7-44 Determine the number of distinct necklaces made from seven beads, each bead being one of four possible choices.

7-45 Determine the number of equivalence classes of Boolean functions on four variables where the group is the group induced by all permutations of the variables.

7-46 Determine the group G of permutations of $\{(x_1, x_2, x_3) : x_i = 0$ or $1\}$ induced by

$$
\begin{array}{lll}
x_1 \rightarrow \bar{x}_1 & x_1 \rightarrow x_1 & x_1 \rightarrow x_1 \\
x_2 \rightarrow x_2 & x_2 \rightarrow \bar{x}_2 & x_2 \rightarrow x_2 \\
x_3 \rightarrow x_3 & x_3 \rightarrow x_3 & x_3 \rightarrow \bar{x}_3 \\[2mm]
x_1 \rightarrow \bar{x}_1 & x_1 \rightarrow \bar{x}_1 & x_1 \rightarrow x_1 \\
x_2 \rightarrow \bar{x}_2 & x_2 \rightarrow x_2 & x_2 \rightarrow \bar{x}_2 \\
x_3 \rightarrow x_3 & x_3 \rightarrow \bar{x}_3 & x_3 \rightarrow \bar{x}_3 \\[2mm]
x_1 \rightarrow \bar{x}_1 & x_1 \rightarrow x_1 & \\
x_2 \rightarrow \bar{x}_2 & x_2 \rightarrow x_2 & \\
x_3 \rightarrow \bar{x}_3 & x_3 \rightarrow x_3. &
\end{array}
$$

7-47 Determine the number of equivalence classes of Boolean functions in three variables with group G in Exercise 7-46.

7-48 Let H be the smallest subgroup of S_D, where $D = \{(x_1, x_2, x_3) : x_i = 0, 1\}$ which contains the group G in Exercise 7-46 and the permutations induced by permuting the x_i's. Determine the number of equivalence classes of Boolean functions in three variables under H.

---

*7.8 MONOIDS AND MACHINES

Semigroups play an important role in the theory of finite machines. The simplest semigroup that arises is the set $\mathscr{I}^*$ of all finite sequences of elements from $\mathscr{I}$, the inputs, under the binary operation of concatenation. Thus if $\mathscr{I} = \{0, 1\}$, $\mathscr{I}^*$ contains the sequences 0110010 and 11100110, and their product $(0110010) \circ (11100110) = 011001011100110$. If $M = (\mathscr{S}, \mathscr{I}, \delta)$ is a state machine, then define $G_M = \{f_w : w \in \mathscr{I}^*$ and f_w is the function from $\mathscr{S}$

	δ	
	0	1
1	3	1
2	2	3
3	2	1

Figure 7.15

	f_0	f_1	f_{00}	f_{01}	f_{10}	f_{11}	f_{001}	f_e
1	3	1	2	1	3	1	3	1
2	2	3	2	3	2	1	3	2
3	2	1	2	3	3	1	3	3

Figure 7.16 Semigroups of the machine of Figure 7.15.

	δ		
	0	1	-1
0	0	0	0
1	0	1	-1
-1	0	-1	1

Figure 7.17 State table for M_G.

to $\mathscr{S}$ given by $f_w(s) = \delta^*(s, w)$ for all $s \in \mathscr{S}\}$. Composition of these functions satisfies

$$(f_{w_1} \circ f_{w_2})(s) = f_{w_1}(f_{w_2}(s)) = f_{w_1}(\delta^*(s, w_2))$$
$$= \delta^*(\delta^*(s, w_2), w_1) = \delta^*(s, w_2 w_1) = f_{w_2 w_1}(s),$$

so that G_M is actually a semigroup.

The machine given in Figure 7.15 has the semigroup given in Figure 7.16, where the i, j entry in the table is $f_j(i)$. That Figure 7.16 indeed gives the whole semigroup is shown in Section 5.4, which deals with the dynamics of state machines.

The empty sequence e in $\mathscr{I}^*$ induces the identity function f_e from $\mathscr{S}$ to $\mathscr{S}$ by $f_e(s) = \delta^*(s, e) = s$. Hence G_M is a monoid. By Theorem 7.10, every monoid G can be thought of as a monoid of functions from the set G into G. This is nearly like a machine already. In fact, define $M_G = (G, G, \delta)$, where $\delta(g_1, g_2) = g_2 \circ g_1$. Thus, if G is the monoid $\{0, 1, -1\}$ under multiplication of real numbers, the machine M_G has states $\{0, 1, -1\}$, inputs $\{0, 1, -1\}$, and the next-state function given in Figure 7.17.

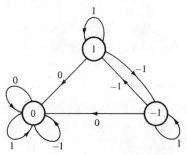

Figure 7.18 State diagram for M_G.

States	δ_1					
	0			**1**		
f_0	$f_0 \circ f_0$	$= f_{00}$		$f_1 \circ f_0$	$= f_{01}$	
f_1	$f_0 \circ f_1$	$= f_{10}$		$f_1 \circ f_1$	$= f_{11}$	
f_{00}	$f_0 \circ f_{00}$	$= f_{000}$	$= f_{00}$	$f_1 \circ f_{00}$	$= f_{001}$	
f_{10}	$f_0 \circ f_{10}$	$= f_{100}$	$= f_{00}$	$f_1 \circ f_{10}$	$= f_{101}$	$= f_1$
f_{01}	$f_0 \circ f_{01}$	$= f_{010}$	$= f_0$	$f_1 \circ f_{01}$	$= f_{011}$	$= f_{11}$
f_{11}	$f_0 \circ f_{11}$	$= f_{110}$	$= f_{001}$	$f_1 \circ f_{11}$	$= f_{111}$	$= f_{11}$
f_{001}	$f_0 \circ f_{001}$	$= f_{0010}$	$= f_{00}$	$f_1 \circ f_{001}$	$= f_{0011}$	$= f_{11}$
f_e	$f_0 \circ f_e$	$= f_e$		$f_1 \circ f_e$	$= f_1$	

Figure 7.19 Table for M_1.

The state diagram is given in Figure 7.18.

A more complex example is the machine of the monoid given in Figure 7.16. The set of states and the sets of inputs are each equal to $\{f_0, f_1, f_{00}, f_{01}, f_{10}, f_{11}, f_{001}, f_e\}$, and the next-state function is given by the transpose of the 8×8 multiplication table. Suppose now that $M = (\mathscr{S}, \mathscr{I}, \delta)$ is a state machine and let $G = G_M$ be the monoid of M. The machine $M_G = (G, G, \delta_1)$ has an input alphabet different from that of M but, since a can be mapped to $f_a \in G$, we can define

$$M_{G, \mathscr{I}} = (G, \mathscr{I}, \delta_1),$$

where $\delta_1(g, a) = f_a \circ g$. The monoid G_1 of the machine in Figure 7.15 thus yields the machine

$$M_1 = (\{f_0, f_1, f_{00}, f_{10}, f_{01}, f_{11}, f_{001}, f_e\}, \{0, 1\}, \delta_1),$$

where δ_1 is given in Figure 7.19.

The states G of the machine $M_{G, \mathscr{I}}$ are functions from S to S, and in general there may be no natural way to relate the functions in G to the elements of S. However, there is if M has a starting state.

Definition   Let $M = (\mathscr{S}, \mathscr{I}, \delta)$ be a state machine. The state s is a *starting state* for M if, for $t \in \mathscr{S}$, there exists $w \in \mathscr{I}^*$ (depending on t) such that $\delta^*(s, w) = t$.

The machine in Figure 7.15 satisfies $\delta(3, 0) = 2$, $\delta(3, 1) = 1$, and $\delta(3, 10) = 3$, so that 3 is a starting state. The machine in Figure 7.18 has -1 as a starting state.

If G_M is the monoid of the machine M with starting state s_0, then each element g of G can be mapped to the state $g(s_0)$.

Thus

$$
\begin{aligned}
f_0 &\longrightarrow f_0(3) &&= 2 \\
f_1 &\longrightarrow f_1(3) &&= 1 \\
f_{00} &\longrightarrow f_{00}(3) &&= 2 \\
f_{01} &\longrightarrow f_{01}(3) &&= 3 \\
f_{10} &\longrightarrow f_{10}(3) &&= 3 \\
f_{11} &\longrightarrow f_{11}(3) &&= 1 \\
f_{001} &\longrightarrow f_{001}(3) &&= 3 \\
f_e &\longrightarrow f_e(3) &&= 3
\end{aligned}
$$

for the machine in Figure 7.15.

Theorem 7.16   Let $M = (\mathscr{S}, \mathscr{I}, \delta)$ be a state machine and $G = G_M$ be the monoid of M. If M has a starting state, then there is a state homomorphism from $M_{G,\mathscr{I}} = (G, \mathscr{I}, \delta_1)$ onto M.

Proof   Let ϕ be the mapping $\phi(g) = g(s_0)$ from G into $\mathscr{S}$, where s_0 is a given starting state of M. For $t \in \mathscr{S}$, there exists $w \in \mathscr{I}^*$ with $\delta^*(s_0, w) = t$. Thus $f_w \in G$ and $f_w(s_0) = \delta^*(s_0, w) = t$, so that ϕ maps G onto $\mathscr{S}$. To check that ϕ is a state homomorphism now requires that

$$\phi(\delta_1(g, a)) = \delta(\phi(g), a)$$

for all g in G and a in $\mathscr{I}$. However,

$$\phi(\delta_1(g, a)) = \phi(f_a \circ g) = (f_a \circ g)(s_0) = f_a(g(s_0)) = \delta(g(s_0), a) = \delta(\phi(g), a),$$

so that ϕ is a state homomorphism.

The converse of Theorem 7.16, namely, if there is a state homomorphism from $M_{G,\mathscr{I}}$ onto M then M has a starting state, is also true. The proof, however, is left for the exercises.

If $M = (\mathscr{S}, \mathscr{I}, \mathscr{O}, \delta, \rho)$ is a state output machine with starting state s_0 and $G = G_M$ is the monoid of M, then $M_{G,\mathscr{I}} = (G, \mathscr{I}, \mathscr{O}, \delta_1, \rho_1)$ is a state output machine, where $\rho_1(g) = \rho(g(s_0))$. Thus $\rho_1(g) = \rho(\phi(g))$, where ϕ is the state homomorphism from $M_{G,\mathscr{I}}$ onto M, so that ϕ is actually a state output homomorphism. The relationship between M and $M_{G,\mathscr{I}}$ in this case is similar to that between an i/o machine M_1 and the state output machine M_2, as given in Theorem 5.3 and Exercise 5-17, in that there is a homomorphism from $M_{G,\mathscr{I}}$ onto M and there is a function ψ from M into $M_{G,\mathscr{I}}$ such that $\beta_s = \beta_{\psi(s)}$ for each $s \in \mathscr{S}$. The proof of this last fact is left as an exercise.

Theorem 7.16 shows that, starting with a machine $M = (\mathscr{S}, \mathscr{I}, \mathscr{O})$, we can construct a monoid G_M, hence a machine $M_{G_M,\mathscr{I}}$ that has input alphabet $\mathscr{I}$. Usually, the set $\mathscr{I}$ has considerably fewer elements than G_M. However, if G is an arbitrary monoid, then $M_G = (G, G, \delta_1)$, so that the input alphabet is quite large.

Definition   A semigroup G is *generated by* $\mathscr{I} \subset G$ if, for $g \in G$, there exists an integer k and elements $a_1, a_2, \ldots, a_k$, all in $\mathscr{I}$ (k and a_i depending on g) such that $g = a_1 \circ a_2 \circ \cdots \circ a_k$.

For example, the monoid $H_1 = \{0, 1, -1\}$ under multiplication contains the subset $\mathscr{I} = \{0, -1\}$, and we can write $0 = 0$, $-1 = -1$, and $1 = (-1) \circ (-1)$. If G is a monoid and G is generated by $\mathscr{I}$, then $(G, \mathscr{I}, \delta)$ is a machine where $\delta(g, a) = a \circ g$ for $a \in \mathscr{I}$. In fact, we can prove the following theorem.

Theorem 7.17   Let G be a monoid generated by $\mathscr{I}$. Then the monoid of the machine $(G, \mathscr{I}, \delta)$ is isomorphic to G.

Proof   The monoid of the machine $(G, \mathscr{I}, \delta)$ is the set of functions f_w, $w \in \mathscr{I}^*$, that map G into G by $f_w(g) = \delta^*(g, w)$. Since G is a monoid, G is isomorphic by the left regular representation ϕ to a set of functions $\mathscr{F}_G$. If we can show that the monoid of the machine is equal to $\mathscr{F}_G$, then we are finished. In fact, we prove that $f_w = \phi(a_k \circ a_{k-1} \circ \cdots \circ a_1)$, where $w \in \mathscr{I}^*$ is the string $a_1 a_2 \cdots a_k$. We have

$$f_w(h) = \delta^*(h, w) = \delta^*(h, a_1 a_2 \cdots a_k)$$
$$= \delta(\delta^*(h, a_1 \cdots a_{k-1}), a_k)$$
$$= a_k \circ \delta^*(h, a_1 \cdots a_{k-1}).$$

Continuing (or more formally by induction) we see that $f_w(h) = a_k \circ a_{k-1} \circ \cdots \circ a_1 \circ h = \phi(a_k \circ \cdots \circ a_1)(h)$. Thus f_w is indeed the function $\phi(a_k \circ a_{k-1} \circ \cdots \circ a_1)$, so that the monoid of the machine is contained in $\mathscr{F}_G$.

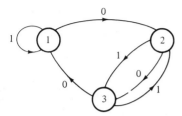

Figure 7.20

Since G is generated by $\mathcal{I}$, g in G implies that there exist $b_1, \ldots, b_n$ such that $g = b_1 \circ \cdots \circ b_n$. Hence $f_{w_1} = \phi(g)$, where w_1 is the sequence $b_n b_{n-1} \cdots b_1$. Thus the monoid actually equals $\mathcal{F}_G$, proving the theorem.

Since the set consisting of all elements of G generates the monoid G, Theorem 7.17 shows that the monoid of the machine (G, G, δ) is isomorphic to G.

If $(\mathcal{S}, \mathcal{I}, \delta)$ is a state machine with monoid G, then Theorem 7.17 shows that, if $\mathcal{I}_1$ is a generating set of G, then $(G, \mathcal{I}_1, \delta)$ has monoid G. It may be that $|\mathcal{I}_1|$ is properly smaller than $|\mathcal{I}|$ but, in most examples arising in practice, $|G|$ is larger than $|\mathcal{S}|$. Thus we have increased the number of states for a machine with monoid G. However, if X is some set and $\mathcal{F}$ is a monoid of functions from X to X, which is isomorphic to G, then $(X, \mathcal{I}, \delta_1)$ is a machine with monoid G. The problem of finding an efficient method for determining $\mathcal{I}_1$ and X with $|\mathcal{I}|_1$ minimal and $|X|$ minimal, where $\mathcal{I}_1$ is a generating set for G and G is isomorphic to a monoid of functions from X to X, has not been thoroughly studied.

The monoid of a state machine describes the transformations of the set of states under given inputs, and sometimes this monoid is actually a group. For example, the state machine in Figure 7.20 has the monoid described in Figure 7.21. The monoid in this example is actually a group, since

$$0^{-1} = 00$$
$$(00)^{-1} = 0$$
$$1^{-1} = 1$$
$$e = 11$$
$$(01)^{-1} = 01$$
$$(10)^{-1} = 10,$$

and each element has an inverse.

In this example, we actually compute the inverse of each element in the monoid. However, we need only observe that each element is a one-to-one

	Input string					
	011		111	∅		
	110	101	010	000	100	001
State	0	00	1	11	01	10
1	2	3	1	1	3	2
2	3	1	3	2	2	1
3	1	2	2	3	1	3

Figure 7.21 Monoid of machine in Figure 7.20.

mapping of the set of states onto the set of states. By Exercise 1-25, a one-to-one mapping of a set onto itself has an inverse. This inverse is actually in the monoid, a fact to be considered in an exercise. The partition of a group into a set of left cosets of a given subgroup has special importance to state machines. By Theorem 5.2, a state machine homomorphism is determined by a state machine congruence. In other words, if there is a homomorphism from $(\mathscr{S}, \mathscr{I}, \delta)$ onto $(\mathscr{S}_1, \mathscr{I}, \delta_1)$, then there is a partition $\mathscr{P}$ of $\mathscr{S}$ such that $\delta(P, a)$ is contained in a unique subset of the partition for each $P \in \mathscr{P}$ and $a \in \mathscr{I}$.

Furthermore, $(\mathscr{P}, \mathscr{I}, \bar{\delta})$ is isomorphic to $(\mathscr{S}_1, \mathscr{I}, \delta_1)$. If G is a group and $\mathscr{I}$ generates G, then $(G, \mathscr{I}, \delta)$ is a state machine where $\delta(g, a) = a \circ g$. If there is a homomorphism of $(G, \mathscr{I}, \delta)$ onto some other machine, then the partition of G is automatically determined by this homomorphism. For example, let G be the group of the machine in Figure 7.20. Thus $G = \{0, 00, 1, 11, 01, 10\}$ with multiplication table given in Figure 7.22. The identity of the group G is the function 11.

Since $\{0, 1\}$ is a generating set, $(G, \{0, 1\}, \delta_1)$ is a state machine. Furthermore, since G is actually the monoid of a machine with $\mathscr{I} = \{0, 1\}$, and this machine has a starting state (e.g., state 2), there is a homomorphism from $(G, \mathscr{I}, \delta_1)$ onto $(\{1, 2, 3\}, \{0, 1\}, \delta)$, with δ determined by Figure 7.21. Each state g of $(G, \mathscr{I}, \delta_1)$ is mapped to $g(2)$, so that we have

$$0 \longrightarrow (2)0 = 3$$
$$00 \longrightarrow (2)00 = 1$$
$$1 \longrightarrow (2)1 = 3$$
$$11 \longrightarrow (2)11 = 2$$
$$01 \longrightarrow (2)01 = 2$$
$$10 \longrightarrow (2)10 = 1.$$

	0	00	1	11	01	10
0	00	11	10	0	1	01
00	11	0	01	00	10	1
1	01	10	11	1	0	00
11	0	00	1	11	01	10
01	10	1	00	01	11	0
10	1	01	0	10	00	11

Figure 7.22 Multiplication table for G.

Thus the partition of G is

$$G = \{g : g \rightarrow 2\} \cup \{g : g \rightarrow 3\} \cup \{g : g \rightarrow 1\}$$
$$= \{01, 11\} \cup \{0, 1\} \cup \{00, 10\}$$
$$= \{01, 11\} \cup 1 \circ \{01, 11\} \cup 10 \circ \{01, 11\}.$$

This partition of G is a coset decomposition, since $\{01, 11\}$ is a subgroup H of G ($01 \circ 01 = 11$, $01 \circ 11 = 11 \circ 01 = 01$, $11 \circ 11 = 11$) and $G = H \cup 1 \circ H \cup 10 \circ H$. If G is a group and $\mathscr{P}$ is a partition of G that is a state machine congruence for $(G, \mathscr{I}, \delta_1)$, then $\mathscr{P}$ in fact must be a coset decomposition of G.

Theorem 7.18   Let G be a finite group and $\mathscr{I}$ a generating set for G. If $\mathscr{P}$ is a state machine congruence of $M = (G, \mathscr{I}, \delta)$, then each subset in $\mathscr{P}$ is a left coset.

Proof   Let H be the subset of $\mathscr{P}$ containing e, the identity of G. If $h \in H$, then there exists $w \in \mathscr{I}^*$ such that $\delta^*(e, w) = h \circ e = h \in H$. Thus $\delta^*(H, w) \subset H$, and $h \circ h_1 \in H$ for all $h_1 \in H$. Thus H is closed under multiplication. However, G is a finite group, hence H is a subgroup (this fact is left as an exercise) of G. If P is a subset in $\mathscr{P}$ and $g \in P$, then there exists $w_1 \in \mathscr{I}^*$ such that $\delta^*(s, w_1) = g^{-1} \circ s$. Thus $\delta^*(P, w_1) \supset g^{-1} \circ P$, and $g^{-1} \circ g = e \in g^{-1} \circ P$. Thus $H \supset g^{-1} \circ P$, and $g \circ H \supset g \circ g^{-1} \circ P = e \circ P = P$. Since $\delta^*(H, w) \supset g \circ H$ for some $w \in \mathscr{I}^*$, then $\delta^*(H, w) \supset g \circ H \supset P$. However, both $\delta^*(H, w)$ and P being in $\mathscr{P}$ implies $\delta^*(H, w) = P$ and $P = g \circ H$. Thus P is a left coset, and the theorem is proven.

The converse of Theorem 7.18 is also true and its proof is left as an exercise.

Exercises

7-49   Prove the converse of Theorem 7.16.

7-50   Let $M = (\mathscr{S}, \mathscr{I}, \mathcal{O}, \delta, \rho)$ be a state output machine with starting state s_0 and let $G = G_M$ be the monoid of this machine. Prove that there is a function ψ from M into $M_{G, \mathscr{I}} = (G, \mathscr{I}, \mathcal{O}, \delta_1, \rho_1)$, where $\rho_1(g) = \rho(g(s_0))$, such that $\beta_s = \beta_{\psi(s)}$.

7-51   Let G_M be the monoid of the finite machine M. If each element in G_M is a one-to-one function, prove that G_M is a group.

7-52   Prove that, if $\mathscr{P}$ is a coset decomposition of the group G with respect to the subgroup H and $\mathscr{I}$ is a generating set for G, then $\mathscr{P}$ is a state machine congruence for $(G, \mathscr{I}, \delta)$.

---

*7.9   QUOTIENT GROUPS

Homomorphism of semigroups is defined in Section 7.6, and Theorem 7.8 shows that there is a homomorphism from a semigroup onto a semigroup of functions. Furthermore, this homomorphism is actually an isomorphism if the semigroup is weakly cancelative, a condition that is satisfied by any group. In Section 7.7, we discovered that there is a homomorphism from a permutation group on X to a permutation group on a set $\mathscr{F}$ of functions from X to a set Y. This homomorphism is again an isomorphism if there are enough functions to ensure that, for $x_1, x_2 \in X$, there exists $f \in \mathscr{F}$ with $f(x_1) \neq f(x_2)$. As is the case with machine homomorphisms, semigroup homomorphisms are determined by certain special partitions. If the semigroup is, furthermore, a group, the partition is associated with a special subgroup. This section defines semigroup congruence, relates homomorphisms to these semigroup congruences, and shows how normal subgroups of a group correspond to homomorphisms of a group.

Definition   Let G be a semigroup. A partition $\mathscr{P}$ of G is a semigroup congruence if, for P and Q in $\mathscr{P}$, $PQ = \{pq : p \in P, q \in Q\}$ is contained in a unique class of $\mathscr{P}$.

If $\mathscr{P}$ is a semigroup congruence for the semigroup G, define, for $P \in \mathscr{P}$, $Q \in \mathscr{P}$, $P * Q$ to be the unique class of $\mathscr{P}$ containing $PQ = \{pq : p \in P$ and $q \in Q\}$, so that $*$ is thus a binary operation on $\mathscr{P}$. Denote $\mathscr{P}$ with the operation $*$ by $G/\mathscr{P}$.

Theorem 7.19 Let $\mathscr{P}$ be a semigroup congruence for the semigroup G. Then $G/\mathscr{P}$ is a semigroup, and the mapping $\phi(g) = [g]$, $g \in G$, is a semigroup homomorphism from G onto $G/\mathscr{P}$.

Proof For classes P, Q, and R in $\mathscr{P}$, $(PQ)R = \{(pq)r : p \in P,\ q \in Q,\ r \in R\} = \{p(qr) : p \in P,\ q \in Q,\ r \in R\} = P(QR)$. Thus both classes $(P * Q) * R$ and $P * (Q * R)$ contain $(PQ)R = P(QR)$. Hence $(P * Q) * R = P * (Q * R)$, and $G/\mathscr{P}$ is a semigroup. To show that ϕ is a homomorphism, observe that $[g_1] * [g_2] = [g_1 g_2]$. Thus $\phi(g_1 g_2) = [g_1 g_2] = [g_1] * [g_2] = \phi(g_1) * \phi(g_2)$, completing the proof.

Theorem 7.19 shows that semigroup congruences give rise to homomorphisms. Conversely, each homomorphism of a semigroup partitions the semigroup into classes of elements that have the same image. This partition is a semigroup congruence, as we now show.

Theorem 7.20 Let ϕ be a homomorphism from the semigroup G onto the semigroup G_1. Then there exists a semigroup congruence $\mathscr{P}$ for G such that $G/\mathscr{P}$ is isomorphic to G_1.

Proof For g_1 and g_2 in G, define $g_1 \sim g_2$ if $\phi(g_1) = \phi(g_2)$. It is easy to check that $\sim$ is an equivalence relation on G. Let $\mathscr{P}$ be the partition determined by $\sim$ and, as usual, let $[g]$ be the class containing g. If we show that $[g_1] \cdot [g_2] \subseteq [g_1 g_2]$, then $\mathscr{P}$ is a semigroup congruence. Suppose now that $h_1 \in [g_1]$ and $h_2 \in [g_2]$. Thus $\phi(h_1) = \phi(g_1)$, and $\phi(h_2) = \phi(g_2)$. Since ϕ is a homomorphism, $\phi(h_1 h_2) = \phi(h_1)\phi(h_2) = \phi(g_1)\phi(g_2) = \phi(g_1 g_2)$, so that $h_1 h_2 \in [g_1 g_2]$. Thus $[g_1][g_2] \subseteq [g_1 g_2]$, and $\mathscr{P}$ is a semigroup congruence. Suppose now that $x \in G_1$. Since ϕ is onto, there exists $a \in G$ with $\phi(a) = x$. Define $\psi(x) = [a]$. The relation ψ is a function from G_1 to $G/\mathscr{P}$, since $x = \phi(b)$, $b \in G$, implies $\phi(a) = \phi(b)$ and $[a] = [b]$. We see that ψ is onto and, to show that ψ is one-to-one, suppose that $\psi(y) = \psi(z)$, $y, z \in G_1$. There exists $c, d \in G$ with $\phi(c) = y$ and $\phi(d) = z$, so that $[c] = \psi(y) = \psi(z) = [d]$. Hence $\phi(c) = \phi(d)$, and $y = z$. Finally, it remains to show that $\psi(xy) = \psi(x)\psi(y)$. However, $xy = \phi(a)\phi(c) = \phi(ac)$, so that

$$\psi(xy) = [ac] = [a] * [c] = \psi(x)\psi(y),$$

completing the proof of the theorem.

Since a group is a semigroup, Theorems 7.19 and 7.20 apply to homomorphisms of groups. However, a semigroup congruence on a group has a special form. The class of the partition that contains the identity of the group is a special type of subgroup, and the remaining classes in the partition are left cosets of this subgroup. Since a semigroup congruence $\mathscr{P}$ of G determines a homomorphism from G onto $G/\mathscr{P}$, and since a homomorphism determines a semigroup congruence, we consider only homomorphisms. Let ϕ be a homomorphism from G to G_1. Suppose e is the identity of G and e_1 is the identity of G_1. Define the *kernel* of ϕ to be $H = \{g \in G : \phi(g) = e_1\}$. We claim that H is a subgroup of G. This follows since g and h in H implies $\phi(gh^{-1}) = \phi(g)\phi(h^{-1}) = \phi(g)(\phi(h))^{-1} = e_1 e_1^{-1} = e_1$ (see Exercise 7-37). By Proposition 7.4, H is thus a subgroup of G. The kernel of a homomorphism ϕ of a group G satisfies the additional property that each left coset equals a right coset. In fact, if H is the kernel of ϕ, then for g in G, $gH = Hg$. We leave the proof of this statement to the exercises.

Definition A subgroup H of a group G is called a normal subgroup if $gH = Hg$ for all g in G.

The group of rigid motions of an equilateral triangle contains the subgroup of rotations $\{I, R, R^2\}$ and the subgroup of reflections about the vertical $\{I, V\}$. The subgroup of rotations $\{I, R, R^2\}$ is a normal subgroup, but the subgroup $\{I, V\}$ has $R \circ \{I, V\} = \{R, D_1\} \neq \{R, D_2\} = \{I, V\} \circ R$ and so is not normal.

Theorem 7.21 Let ϕ be a homomorphism from a group G onto a group G_1. The semigroup congruence determined by ϕ consists of the cosets of the kernel of ϕ.

Proof Let e_1 be the identity of G_1. Then $H = \{g \in G : \phi(g) = e_1\}$ is the kernel of ϕ. If $g_1 \in G_1$, then $P = \{g \in G : \phi(g) = g_1\}$ is a set in the semigroup congruence $\mathscr{P}$ determined by ϕ. Suppose $x \in P$. If h is in H, then $\phi(xh) = \phi(x)\phi(h) = g_1 e_1 = g_1$, so $xh \in P$ and $xH \subseteq P$. If $p \in P$, $\phi(x^{-1}p) = (\phi(x))^{-1}\phi(p) = (g_1)^{-1}g_1 = e_1$, so that $x^{-1}p \in H$ and $p \in xH$. Thus $P \subseteq xH$, and $P = xH$, proving the theorem.

Theorem 7.21 shows that a homomorphism yields a congruence consisting of a normal subgroup and its cosets. The converse to this statement also holds.

Theorem 7.22 Let H be a normal subgroup of the group G. Then the set of cosets of H is a semigroup congruence on G.

Proof We need only show that, for x and y in G, $(xH)(yH) \subseteq xyH$. Let $h_1 \in H$, $h_2 \in H$. Since H is normal, $Hy = yH$, so that in particular there exists $h' \in H$ with $h_1 y = yh'$. Hence $(xh_1)(yh_2) = xyh'h \in xyH$, and $(xH)(yH) \subseteq xyH$, proving the theorem.

If H is a normal subgroup of G, and $\mathscr{P}$ is the set of cosets of H, the group $G/\mathscr{P}$ is denoted by G/H.

Exercises

7-53 Prove that, if H is the kernel of a homomorphism ϕ of the group G, then for any y in G, $yH = Hy$.

7-54 Let H be a subgroup of the group G. If $[G : H] = 2$, prove that H is a normal subgroup.

7-55 Prove that, if H_1 and H_2 are normal subgroups of the group G, then $H_1 H_2 = \{h_1 \circ h_2 \in G : h_1 \in H$ and $h_2 \in H\}$ is a subgroup of G which is again normal. If S is a subgroup of a finite group G, prove that S contains a subgroup normal in G which is largest among subgroups of S normal in G.

7-56 Let G be a group and let H_i be a normal subgroup of G for each i in a fixed set I. Prove that $\bigcap_{i \in I} H_i = \{h \in G : h \in H_i$ for each $i \in I\}$ is a subgroup normal in G. Prove that, if S is a subgroup of G, then there is a unique smallest normal subgroup of G in the set of all normal subgroups containing S.

7-57 Determine all normal subgroups of the group G of rigid motions of a regular hexagon, hence determine (up to isomorphism) all homomorphic images of G.

7-58 Let H be a subgroup of the group G and let $G = g_1 H \cup \cdots \cup g_n H$ be a coset decomposition of G with $g_i H \neq g_j H, i \neq j, 1 \leq i \leq n, 1 \leq j \leq n$. Prove that the mapping $g \rightarrow \pi_g$, where π_g is the permutation of the cosets given by $\pi_g(g_i H) = g \circ g_i H$, is a homomorphism. Prove that the kernel of this homomorphism is the largest normal subgroup of G contained in H.

Modular Arithmetic

8.1   INTRODUCTION

The set of integers is one of the most familiar mathematical objects. Counting and manipulating whole numbers is learned very early in life, and this knowledge is used extensively by every individual. Even though a child routinely learns to recite the sequence 1, 2, 3, 4, 5, 6, 7, 8, 9, 10, it requires somewhat more maturity to see that the property of twoness, for example, is a property of sets, and that the set $\{\square, \bigcirc\}$ is associated with the number 2. Slightly later in childhood, the realization occurs that $2 + 2 = 4$ corresponds to taking the union of two disjoint sets, each containing two elements. Furthermore, the child soon discovers that for any given integer there is always a larger one, so that counting can go on without end. All these arithmetic operations correspond to manipulations on finite sets, but the size of these finite sets must be unbounded.

In computing, there are practical bounds on the size of the sets (or integers) that can be considered, so that it may be desirable to have operations that give results which remain in the finite set under consideration. The shift register in a computer takes a string of 0's and 1's of length k, where k is a fixed positive integer, and produces another string of 0's and 1's of length k.

The algebra behind the operation of the shift register can be explained in terms of binary operations on finite sets, where the operations correspond to addition and multiplication. The basis for the algebraic structure of shift registers is given in the discussion of modular arithmetic and finite fields and is developed in Chapter 10. Many uses of computers involve arithmetic operations, and it is often advantageous to be able to obtain solutions of equations within the finite set under consideration. Thus the operations must have the necessary properties that permit equations to be solved.

This chapter first investigates the abstract properties satisfied by addition and multiplication of integers. Second, the algorithmic tools useful in dealing with the integers are investigated and applied to prove the Chinese remainder theorem, which yields a technique for representing integers that results in a fast method for exact multiplication of large integers. Third, the arithmetic operations of addition and multiplication of the elements of a finite set are defined, which yield solutions for certain linear equations. This is an important property which is used in Chapter 9 in the encoding and decoding of cryptographic codes.

8.2 THE INTEGERS

This section describes, first, the representation of integers and, second, some of the properties satisfied by the operations of addition and multiplication of integers. The abstract study of the integers is independent of the way we express or write a given integer. However, the actual mechanics of addition and multiplication depend heavily on the way an integer is expressed. The most common way of representing an integer is in positional notation, although we encounter another method in Section 8.4.

The integer in positional notation $(a_n a_{n-1} \cdots a_1 a_0)$ with radix b is defined to be

$$(a_n \cdots a_0) = a_n b^n + a_{n-1} b^{n-1} + \cdots + a_1 b + a_0.$$

We usually assume $0 \le a_i < b$ and that a_i, b are integers with b positive. The a_i's are called the digits of the representation. The usual representation is in decimal form, where the a_i's are chosen from $\{0, 1, 2, 3, 4, 5, 6, 7, 8, 9\}$ and b is 10. Internal computer representation is in binary, where the a_i's are chosen from $\{0, 1\}$ and b is 2. Section 8.3 shows us that every positive integer can be represented uniquely in positional notation with the radix a positive integer b and the a_i non-negative integers smaller than b.

We now turn from representation of an integer to properties satisfied by the operations of addition and multiplication of integers. It is apparent that the order in which the addition of the integers in a finite set of integers is made does not affect the outcome. The same is true for multiplication, and these facts follow from the properties that $a + b = b + a$, $a \cdot b = b \cdot a$, $a + (b + c) = (a + b) + c$, and $a \cdot (b \cdot c) = (a \cdot b) \cdot c$ for integers a, b, and c. However, when the two operations are mixed, the outcome depends on the order of performance. For example, adding 2 to 5 and then adding 8 is the same as adding 5 to 8 and then adding 2, but multiplying 2 and 5 and then adding 8 is quite different from multiplying 5 and 8 and then adding 2. There is a rule for mixing operations, however, since the addition of two integers followed by multiplying the result by a third integer yields the same result as multiplying each of the first two integers by the third and adding the resulting integers. This is expressed by $a(b + c) = ab + ac$ for any integers a, b, and c.

Not all linear equations with integer coefficients have integer solutions. However, the special equations $x + a = b$ and $cx = cb$ do, when a, b, and c are integers. In the latter case, the solution must be $x = b$ if c is not 0.

The above properties plus the special status of 1 and 0 are the essential aspects of the operations of addition and multiplication. An integral domain is any set (finite or infinite) that has operations satisfying these properties. Formally we make the following definition. Recall that a group G is *Abelian* if $a \circ b = b \circ a$ for all a and b in G (called commutativity).

Definition   Let D be a nonempty set with binary operations + and $\cdot$. D is an integral domain if the following conditions are satisfied for arbitrary a, b, and c in D.

i   The elements $a + b$ and $a \cdot b$ are uniquely defined elements of D (closure property).

ii D is an Abelian group under the binary operation + (called addition). The identity of D under + is denoted by 0, and the inverse of a in D under + is denoted by $-a$.

iii D is a monoid under the binary operation $\cdot$ (called multiplication). The identity of D under $\cdot$ is denoted by 1, and we assume $1 \neq 0$.

iv $a \cdot b = b \cdot a$ (commutativity of multiplication).

v $a \cdot (b + c) = a \cdot b + a \cdot c$ (distributivity).

vi If $c \neq 0$ and $c \cdot a = c \cdot b$, then $a = b$ (cancellation property).

The set of integers is clearly an integral domain, and there are many other examples of integral domains. In fact, any proposition we can prove using only properties (i) through (vi) of an integral domain will be proved not only for the integers but for any set with binary operations satisfying properties (i) through (vi). This method of abstraction gives algebra much of its power.

The set of integers has numerous other properties which are not listed in the definition of integral domain. Some of these are not listed because we wish to consider a general structure instead of just the integers. Others are not listed because they may be proved using (i) through (vi). It is clear that, in the set of integers, $a \cdot 0 = 0$ for any integer a, and this can be proved simply by using (i) through (vi); hence it is true in any integral domain.

Proposition 8.1   If D is an integral domain, then $a \cdot 0 = 0$ for all a in D.

Proof

$$0 = a + (-a) \qquad \text{(additive inverse)}$$
$$= (a \cdot 1) + (-a) \qquad \text{(multiplicative identity)}$$
$$= [a \cdot (1 + 0)] + (-a) \qquad \text{(additive identity)}$$
$$= (a \cdot 1 + a \cdot 0) + (-a) \qquad \text{(distributivity)}$$
$$= (a \cdot 0 + a \cdot 1) + (-a) \qquad \text{(commutativity of addition)}$$
$$= a \cdot 0 + [a \cdot 1 + (-a)] \qquad \text{(associativity)}$$
$$= a \cdot 0 + [a + (-a)] \qquad \text{(multiplicative identity)}$$
$$= a \cdot 0 + 0 \qquad \text{(additive inverse)}$$
$$= a \cdot 0 \qquad \text{(additive identity)}.$$

Hence $a \cdot 0 = 0$.

There are numerous simple properties, such as the one illustrated in Proposition 8.1, that are true not only for the integers but for any integral domain. Proposition 8.1 is given simply as an example of a proof of an elementary property of the integers which is true for general integral domains. Several more such proofs are left for the exercises.

When clear from the context, $a \cdot b$ is denoted by ab, a and b in an integral domain.

In addition to the integers being an integral domain, they are also a totally ordered set under the natural ordering $\cdots < -2 < -1 < 0 < 1 < \cdots$. This total ordering interacts with the binary operations of addition and multiplication in the following special way. Let a, b, c, and d be integers with $a < b, d > 0$. Then

1   $c + a < c + b$, and

2   $da < db$.

If the above two properties hold for elements a, b, c, and d in an integral domain D which is also a totally ordered set, then the integral domain is called an *ordered integral domain*. Just as we proved that certain properties of the integers are satisfied by any integral domain, we can show that certain properties of the total ordering on the integers are satisfied by any ordered integral domain.

Proposition 8.2   Let a and b be elements in an ordered integral domain D. If $a < 0$ and $b < 0$, then $ab > 0$.

Proof   If $a < 0$, then $-a > 0$ by Exercise 8-3. Likewise, $-b > 0$ and $(-a)(-b) > (-a)0 = 0$. But by Exercise 8-2, $(-a) = (-1)a$ and $(-b) = (-1)b$. Thus $[(-1)a][(-1)b] > 0$ and $[(-1)(-1)](ab) > 0$. Again by Exercise 8-2, $(-1)(-1) = 1$, so that

$$1(ab) = ab > 0.$$

If D is an ordered integral domain, an element $a > 0$ is called *positive*, and an element $b < 0$ is called *negative*.

Exercises

8-1   Express the numbers 2, 3, 4, 5, 6, 7, 8, and 9 in positional notation with radix b, where
   a $b = 2$
   b $b = 3$
   c $b = 7$
   d $b = -2$
   e $b = 2i$, where $i = \sqrt{-1}$.

8-2   Let D be an integral domain. Prove
   a $0 = -0$
   b $(-1)a = -a$
   c $-(-a) = a$
   d $(-1)(-1) = 1$.

8-3   Let D be an ordered integral domain. Prove
   a $a < 0$ implies $-a > 0$
   b $a < b$ implies $-a > -b$.

8-4   Prove that there is no integer m such that $0 < m < 1$ using only the fact that the set of integers is an ordered integral domain whose positive elements are well ordered.

8.3 THE EUCLIDEAN ALGORITHM

The division algorithm described in Section 1.6 has several important consequences. The first is that a non-negative integer can be represented uniquely in positional notation with integer radix $b > 1$. The proof requires induction, but we leave this as an exercise and simply give the following algorithm for determining positional notation with integer radix $b > 1$.

Step 1 Set positional notation p to be empty.

Step 2 Divide a by b to obtain quotient q and remainder r. Replace (p) by (r, p).

Step 3 If $q = 0$, terminate with (p) the positional notation. Otherwise replace a by q and return to step 2.

Since in step 2, $q < a$, the algorithm eventually terminates because there is only a finite number of integers (hence steps) less than a. As an example, take $b = 3$, $a = 35$, and we have the following results.

a	b	$a = qb + r$	p
35	3	$35 = 11 \cdot 3 + 2$	(2)
11	3	$11 = 3 \cdot 3 + 2$	(22)
3	3	$3 = 1 \cdot 3 + 0$	(022)
1	3	$1 = 0 \cdot 3 + 1$	(1022)

Thus the positional notation for 35 with radix 3 is (1022).

If the remainder is 0 in the division algorithm, then a can be written in the form $a = bq$, where b and q are integers. The integer q is said to be a *factor* of a and is also said to *divide a*. This is written $q \mid a$. The integer q is a *proper factor* of a if q is neither $\pm a$ nor ± 1. Along with the notion of a factor of an integer is the idea of a common factor of a pair of integers. If a and b are two integers and q divides both a and b, then q is said to be a *common factor* of a and b or, alternatively, q is called a *common divisor* of a and b. The division algorithm has a very important consequence which enables us to find the greatest common divisor (gcd) of any pair of integers. This consequence of the division algorithm is a procedure called the Euclidean algorithm and is fundamental in the study of modular arithmetic.

The main theorem of the section can now be stated and proven.

Theorem 8.1 For any nonzero integers a and b, there exist integers s and t such that $sa + tb$ is the gcd of a and b (written gcd$\{a, b\}$). Furthermore, any common divisor divides gcd$\{a, b\}$.

The proof of this theorem embodies an algorithm, called the Euclidean algorithm, which uses the division algorithm as a subroutine for computing $\gcd\{a, b\}$. Let a and b be integers with $b > 0$.

Step 1   Set $x = a$ and $y = b$.

Step 2   Divide x by y to obtain q and r.

Step 3   If $r = 0$, then terminate with $y = \gcd\{a, b\}$. If $r \neq 0$ then replace x by y, y by r, and return to step 2.

For example, if $a = 36$ and $b = 20$, we have

x	y	$x = q \cdot y + r$
36	20	$36 = 1 \cdot 20 + 16$
20	16	$20 = 1 \cdot 16 + 4$
16	4	$16 = 4 \cdot 4 + 0$

Hence $\gcd\{36, 20\} = 4$.

Proof of Theorem 8.1   Suppose the Euclidean algorithm gives the following sequence of computations.

$$a = bq_1 + r_1 \qquad (0 \le r_1 < b)$$
$$b = r_1 q_2 + r_2 \qquad (0 \le r_2 < r_1)$$
$$r_1 = r_2 q_3 + r_3 \qquad (0 \le r_3 < r_2)$$
$$\vdots \qquad \vdots \qquad \vdots$$
$$r_{n-2} = r_{n-1} q_n + r_n \qquad (0 \le r_n < r_{n-1})$$
$$r_{n-1} = r_n q_{n+1} + r_{n+1} \qquad (0 = r_{n+1} < r_n).$$

That $r_{n+1} = 0$, for some n, follows by the well ordering of the non-negative integers. Furthermore, if $r_1 = 0$, then b is the greatest common divisor of a and b. Otherwise, there is some nonzero r_n such that $r_{n+1} = 0$. The element r_n is the greatest common divisor of a and b. This can be proven by the following observations. Let $k, m, n, s,$ and t be integers with $k \mid m$ and $k \mid n$. Then the integer k divides $sm + tn$. Thus, in the algorithm, since r_n divides r_{n-1} and r_n divides r_n, then r_n divides r_{n-2}. Continuing with this procedure (or using formal mathematical induction) we see that r_n divides all r_i for $i = 1, \ldots, n$. Thus r_n divides b, hence r_n divides a. Thus r_n is a positive common divisor of both a and b. To see that r_n is the greatest common divisor, suppose the positive integer d divides both a and b. Thus d divides $a - bq_1 = r_1$. The integer d then also divides $b - r_1 q_2 = r_2$, and continuing with this procedure we see that d divides r_i for $i = 1, \ldots, n$. Thus d divides r_n, hence we must have $0 < d \le r_n$. Hence the integer r_n is the greatest common divisor, and any common divisor divides r_n.

Finally, we show that $r_n = sa + tb$. We have $r_n = r_{n-2} - r_{n-1} q_n$. Since $r_{n-1} = r_{n-3} - r_{n-2} q_{n-1}$, by substitution, $r_n = r_{n-2} - (r_{n-3} - r_{n-2} q_{n-1}) q_n = r_{n-3}(-q_n) + r_{n-2}(1 + q_{n-1} q_n)$. Thus r_n has the form $s_2 r_{n-3} + t_2 r_{n-2}$. Continuing in this manner (or more formally by mathematical induction) we see that $r_n = sa + tb$.

The computation of s and t in Theorem 8.1 can be accomplished simultaneously with the computation of gcd$\{a, b\}$, as opposed to the algorithm in the proof, which requires the computation of gcd$\{a, b\}$ along with the storage of q_i's and r_i's and then the calculation of s and t by going back up the sequence. The combined algorithm is as follows.

Step 1 Set $X = (1, 0, a)$, $Y = (0, 1, b)$, and $Z = (0, 0, 0)$.

Step 2 Divide the third component of X by the third component of Y to obtain q and r.

Step 3 If $r = 0$, terminate the algorithm with $Y = (s, t, \text{gcd}\{a, b\})$. If $r \ne 0$, replace Z by Y, Y by $X - q \cdot Y$, and X by Z, and repeat step 2.

As an example, let us determine both the gcd$\{207207, 17204\}$ and integers s and t satisfying gcd$\{207207, 17204\} = 207207 \cdot s + 17204 \cdot t$.

X	Y	q	r	$X - qY$
$(1, 0, 207207)$	$(0, 1, 17204)$	12	759	$(1, -12, 759)$
$(0, 1, 17204)$	$(1, -12, 759)$	22	506	$(-22, 265, 506)$
$(1, -12, 759)$	$(-22, 265, 506)$	1	253	$(23, -277, 253)$
$(-22, 265, 506)$	$(23, -277, 253)$	2	0	

Thus the gcd$\{207207, 17204\} = 253$, and $253 = 207207(23) + 17204(-277)$.

That this algorithm accomplishes what is claimed is not too difficult to see and is shown in the context of computing the greatest common divisor of polynomials in Section 8.6.

The greatest common divisor is closely related to the least common multiple. The integer m is a *common multiple* of nonzero integers a and b if $a \mid m$ and $b \mid m$. Since $\pm ab$ is a common multiple of a and b, positive common multiples always exist. By the well ordering of the integers, a smallest positive common multiple exists. The exercises show that the least common multiple (lcm) divides every common multiple and in fact equals $\pm a \cdot b/\text{gcd}\{a, b\}$, whichever is positive.

The last but very important theorem of the section is the fundamental theorem of arithmetic. It shows that every nonzero integer is a product of primes with certain uniqueness properties. A prime is a positive integer p, $p \neq 1$, whose only divisors are $\pm p$ and ± 1. The fundamental theorem is used whenever convenient, even though the proof, while not difficult, is postponed to the more general setting of Section 8.6.

Theorem 8.2 *Fundamental Theorem of Arithmetic* Let n be any integer $\neq 0, 1$. Then $n = \pm p_1^{\alpha_1} p_2^{\alpha_2} \cdots p_k^{\alpha_k}$, where p_i are primes with $p_1 < p_2 < \cdots < p_k$ and α_i are positive integers. Furthermore, this representation is unique.

Exercises

8-5 Prove that, if a is a positive integer and b is a positive integer, $b > 1$, then a can be written uniquely as $a_k b^k + a_{k-1} b^{k-1} + \cdots + a_1 b + a_0$, where $0 \leq a_i < b$.

8-6 Find the gcd of the following pairs of integers and express this gcd as $sa + tb$, where a and b are the given integers.
  a 234, 4535
  b 27144, 34452
  c 10230, 21212.

8-7 Extend the definition of gcd to arbitrary nonempty sets of integers. Prove that $\gcd\{a, b, c\}$ can be written in the form $la + mb + nc$, where l, m, and n are integers.

8-8 Give an example to show that the integers m and n are not unique in an expression of the form $\gcd\{a, b\} = ma + nb$.

8-9 Prove that, if $\gcd\{a, b\} = 1$ and $\gcd\{c, b\} = d$, then $\gcd\{ac, b\} = d$.

8-10 Prove that $\text{lcm}\{a, b\}$ divides each common multiple of a and b.

8-11 Prove that $\text{lcm}\{a, b\} = a \cdot b/\gcd\{a, b\}$.

8.4 THE CHINESE REMAINDER THEOREM

The division and Euclidean algorithms are basic tools in the study of the integers. This section shows how they are used to prove the Chinese remainder theorem, which yields a fast method for the multiplication of large integers.

If n divides $a - b$, for integers a and b, then a is defined to be *congruent* to b *modulo* n. We write a congruent to b modulo n as $a \equiv b$ mod n. By definition, $a \equiv b$ mod n if and only if $a - b = sn$ for some integer s. That is, $a = b + sn$ or, equivalently, a and b are a multiple of n units apart on the real line.

The first simple result is the following.

Theorem 8.3 Let a, b, c, d, x, y, and n be integers. If $a \equiv b$ mod n and $c \equiv d$ mod n, then $ax + cy \equiv bx + dy$ mod n, and $ac \equiv bd$ mod n.

The proof of Theorem 8.3 is a straightforward consequence of the definitions and is left for the exercises.

If "congruent modulo n" is thought of as "equals," then Theorem 8.3 says that equals added to equals are equal and that equals multiplied by equals are equal. It is tempting to suppose that equals divided by equals are equal, but at this point the analogy breaks down. However, the following can be proven. We say integers a and n are *relatively prime* if $\gcd\{a, n\} = 1$.

Theorem 8.4 Let a, b, c, and n be integers with a and n relatively prime. If $ab \equiv ac$ mod n, then $b \equiv c$ mod n.

Proof $ab \equiv ac$ mod n, so that $ab - ac = dn$ for some integer d. Thus $a(b - c) = dn$. Since $\gcd\{a, n\} = 1$, Theorem 8.1 shows that there exist integers s and t with $1 = sa + tn$. Therefore $sa = 1 - tn$, so that $sa(b - c) = (1 - tn)(b - c)$. This implies

$$sdn = (1 - tn)(b - c) = (b - c) - tn(b - c),$$

so that

$$b - c = n[sd + t(b - c)].$$

Thus $b \equiv c$ mod n.

Theorem 8.4 shows that integers a, which are relatively prime to n, can be canceled. The number of positive integers less than or equal to n that are relatively prime to n is denoted by $\phi(n)$. This function has special properties which enable us to prove the Chinese remainder theorem constructively. However, before this is done, $\phi(n)$ must be computed. If $n = p_1^{\alpha_1} \cdots p_k^{\alpha_k}$, where $p_1, p_2, \ldots, p_k$ are distinct prime integers, then it is shown in the exercises that

$$\phi(n) = (p_1^{\alpha_1} - p_1^{\alpha_1 - 1})(p_2^{\alpha_2} - p_2^{\alpha_2 - 1}) \cdots (p_k^{\alpha_k} - p_k^{\alpha_k - 1}) = n\left(1 - \frac{1}{p_1}\right) \cdots \left(1 - \frac{1}{p_k}\right),$$

which gives a simple method for computing $\phi(n)$ if a factorization of n as a product of distinct prime powers is known. However, the determination of a factorization of n for an arbitrary n into prime powers is difficult and time-consuming. Essentially, we need to know all the primes less than or equal to $\sqrt{n}$. This can be accomplished, among other ways, by using the sieve of Eratosthenes, which computes all primes less than or equal to a given integer N.

1   Store in S in natural order all odd numbers k with $1 < k \leq N$. Set $T = \{2\}$.
2   Let p be the first (necessarily prime) integer in S.
3   Store p in T, set x equal to p, and delete p from S.
4   If $px > N$, stop, and $T \cup S$ is the set of all primes $\leq N$.
5   Delete px from S and replace x by $x + 2$.
6   If $px > N$, then repeat (2), otherwise repeat (5).

Once the primes $\leq \sqrt{n}$ are determined, then n can be factored by the following algorithm. Let $p_1 < p_2 < p_3 < \cdots < p_k$ be the primes $\leq \sqrt{n}$.

1   Set $i = 1$ and $T = (\ )$.
2   If $n = 1$, then T is the prime factorization, so stop.
3   Divide n by p_i to obtain remainder r and quotient q.
4   If $r = 0$, replace n by q and set T to be (p_i, t), where previously $T = (t)$, and repeat (2).
5   Replace i by $i + 1$.
6   If $i \leq k$, repeat (3); otherwise, $T = (n, t)$ is the prime factorization.

As an example, the sieve of Eratosthenes computes the following primes ≤ 56.

S	T
$\{3, 5, 7, 9, 11, 13, 15, 17, 19, 21, 23, 25, 27, 29,$	
$31, 33, 35, 37, 39, 41, 43, 45, 47, 49, 51, 53, 55\}$	$\varnothing$
$\{3, 5, 7, 9, 11, 13, 15, 17, 19, 21, 23, 25, 27, 29,$	
$31, 33, 35, 37, 39, 41, 43, 45, 47, 49, 51, 53, 55\}$	$\{3\}$
$\{5, 7, 11, 13, 17, 19, 23, 25, 29, 31, 35, 37, 41, 43, 47, 49, 53, 55\}$	$\{5, 3\}$
$\{7, 11, 13, 17, 19, 23, 29, 31, 37, 41, 43, 47, 49, 53\}$	$\{7, 5, 3\}$

Since $11 \cdot 11 > 56$ we have the set of primes ≤ 56:

$$\{2, 3, 5, 7, 11, 13, 17, 19, 23, 29, 31, 37, 41, 43, 47, 53\}.$$

The second algorithm can now be used to factor any positive integer $\leq 56^2 = 3136$. For example suppose $n = 1748$.

n	p_i	q	r	T
1748	2	874	0	(2)
874	2	437	0	(2, 2)
437	2	218	1	(2, 2)
437	3	145	2	(2, 2)
437	5	87	2	(2, 2)
437	7	62	3	(2, 2)
437	11	39	8	(2, 2)
437	13	33	8	(2, 2)
437	17	25	12	(2, 2)
437	19	23	0	(19, 2, 2)
23	19	1	4	(19, 2, 2)
23	23	1	0	(23, 19, 2, 2)

Thus $1748 = 23 \cdot 19 \cdot 2^2$ and $\phi(1748) = (23 - 1)(19 - 1)(2^2 - 2) = 792$.

Neither of the algorithms presented is the most efficient, but they are adequate for our purposes in the sense that they yield a constructive method for computing $\phi(n)$.

We now can prove the following very useful theorem due to Euler.

Theorem 8.5 Let a and n be integers with $\gcd\{a, n\} = 1$. Then $a^{\phi(n)} \equiv 1 \bmod n$.

Proof Let $1 = r_1 < r_2 < \cdots < r_{\phi(n)} < n$ be the $\phi(n)$ distinct integers $< n$ that are relatively prime to n. Since $\gcd\{a, n\} = 1 = \gcd\{r_i, n\}$, Exercise 8-9 implies that $\gcd\{ar_i, n\} = 1$. This shows that $ar_i \equiv r_t \bmod n$ for some t, since $ar_i = qn + r$, with $0 \le r < n$, by the division algorithm and if this r is not relatively prime to n, then $\gcd\{r, n\}$ divides ar_i and n, a contradiction. Furthermore, $ar_i \equiv ar_k \bmod n$ implies $r_i \equiv r_k \bmod n$ by Theorem 8.4. However, $r_i - r_k$ is not divisible by n unless $i = k$. Thus the ar_i are congruent to $\phi(n)$ distinct r_j's. Hence we have

$$(ar_1)(ar_2) \cdots (ar_{\phi(n)}) \equiv r_1 r_2 \cdots r_{\phi(n)} \bmod n$$

$$a^{\phi(n)} r_1 r_2 \cdots r_{\phi(n)} \equiv r_1 r_2 \cdots r_{\phi(n)} \bmod n$$

so that again by Theorem 8.4 $a^{\phi(n)} \equiv 1 \bmod n$.

A direct result of Euler's theorem is the much older theorem due to Fermat which is concerned with the case when n is a prime.

Corollary 8.1 Let p be a prime and a be a nonzero integer not divisible by p. Then $a^{p-1} \equiv 1 \bmod p$.

Proof   Since $\phi(p) = p - 1$, Euler's theorem yields the result.

We are now ready to state and prove the Chinese remainder theorem.

Theorem 8.6   *The Chinese Remainder Theorem*   Let $n_1, n_2, \ldots, n_k$ be positive integers such that $\gcd\{n_i, n_j\} = 1$ for $i \neq j$. If $n = n_1 n_2 \cdots n_k$ and a, $b_1, b_2, \ldots, b_k$ are integers, then there exists a unique integer b such that $a \leq b < a + n$ and $b \equiv b_i$ mod n_i for $i = 1, \ldots, k$.

Proof   Let $c_i = (n/n_i)^{\phi(n_i)}$ for $i = 1, \ldots, k$. Since $n/n_i \equiv 0$ mod n_j, for $j \neq i$, we have $c_i \equiv 0$ mod n_j for $j \neq i$. Furthermore, by Euler's theorem and the fact that $\gcd\{n_i, n/n_i\} = 1$, we have $c_i \equiv 1$ mod n_i. Thus, if

$$(b_1 c_1 + b_2 c_2 + \cdots + b_k c_k) - a = q \cdot n + r \qquad (0 \leq r < n),$$

then $a \leq b = a + r < a + n$ and $b \equiv b_i$ mod n_i for all i.

To show uniqueness, suppose b and c are two solutions. Thus $b \equiv c$ mod n_i, for each i, and $b - c$ is divisible by n_i. Since n_i and n_j are relatively prime for $i \neq j$, it follows that $b - c$ is divisible by $\operatorname{lcm}\{n_1, \ldots, n_k\} = n$. This is impossible for $a \leq b < a + n$ and $a \leq c < a + n$ unless $b = c$.

The proof of the theorem really embodies an algorithm which determines the unique integer b, $a \leq b < a + n$, that satisfies $b \equiv b_i$ mod n_i for each i. Namely, if $n_1, \ldots, n_k$ are relatively prime pairwise,

1   Set $i = 1$.
2   Compute $\phi(n_i)$.
3   Compute $c_i = (n_1 \cdots n_k/n_i)^{\phi(n_i)}$ mod $n_1 n_2 \cdots n_k$.
4   If $i < k$, replace i by $i + 1$ and repeat (2).
5   Compute $x = b_1 c_1 + \cdots + b_k c_k - a$ mod $n_1 n_2 \cdots n_k$.
6   $b = x + a$, so stop.

While the computation of $\phi(n_i)$ is in general difficult, if the n_i are chosen prime, then $\phi(n_i) = n_i - 1$. Thus the major computational effort now involves computing the $c_i = (n/n_i)^{\phi(n_i)}$, where $n = n_1 n_2 \cdots n_k$. This calculation can be simplified by observing the following. Let $x = (n/n_i)^{\phi(n_i)-1}$. By the division algorithm, $x = r + q n_i$, $0 \leq r < n_i$. Thus

$$c_i = (n/n_i)^{\phi(n_i)} = (n/n_i)x = (n/n_i)(r + q n_i) = (n/n_i)r + qn.$$

Since c_i need only be computed modulo n, only $(n/n_i)r$ need be computed. However, r is just x computed modulo n_i, a much simplified task.

For example, let n_1 be 19 and n_2 be 23, and let us compute $0 \le b < 437$ with $b \equiv 5 \bmod 19$ and $b \equiv 14 \bmod 23$. Since 19 and 23 are prime, $\phi(19) = 18$ and $\phi(23) = 22$. The c_i's are computed as follows.

$$c_1 = 23^{18}$$

$$23^{17} \equiv (\{[(4)^2]^2\}^2)^2 \cdot 4 \equiv \{[(16)^2]^2\}^2 \cdot 4 \equiv [(9)^2]^2 \cdot 4$$

$$\equiv (5)^2 \cdot 4 \equiv 6 \cdot 4 \equiv 5 \bmod 19.$$

Thus

$$c_1 \equiv 23 \cdot 5 = 115 \bmod 437$$

$$c_2 = 19^{22}$$

$$19^{21} \equiv (\{[(-4)^2]^2\}^2)^2 \cdot [(-4)^2]^2(-4) \equiv \{[(16)^2]^2\}^2 \cdot 16^2(-4)$$

$$\equiv [(3)^2]^2 \cdot 3(-4) \equiv 9^2 \cdot 11 \equiv 12 \cdot 11 \equiv 17 \bmod 23.$$

Thus $c_2 \equiv 19 \cdot 17 = 323 \bmod 437$.

Once c_1 and c_2 are determined, then b can be found. We have

$$b = 0 + 5 \cdot (23 \cdot 5) + 14 \cdot (19 \cdot 17)$$

$$\equiv 23(19 + 6) + 14 \cdot 19 \cdot (23 - 6)$$

$$\equiv 23 \cdot 6 + (19)(-84)$$

$$\equiv 23 \cdot 6 + 19(-4 \cdot 23 + 8)$$

$$\equiv 23 \cdot 6 + 19(8) = 138 + 152 = 290.$$

The calculation of the constants c_i can be quite lengthy, and an alternative method is to solve $(n/n_i) \cdot x \equiv 1 \bmod n_i$. This can be determined by the algorithm following Theorem 8.1, which calculates integers (essentially by the Euclidean algorithm) s and t such that $1 = \gcd\{n/n_i, n_i\} = s \cdot (n/n_i) + t \cdot n_i$. Once s is determined, we have $x \equiv s \bmod n_i$ and $c_i \equiv (n/n_i) \cdot x \bmod n$. The disadvantage of this method is that the calculation of s involves large integers, while the computation of $(n/n_i)^{\phi(n_i)} \bmod n$ can essentially be accomplished modulo n_i. A variation of the above method, which avoids the computation of such a large s but still relies on the Euclidean algorithm, is given in the exercises.

The power of the Chinese remainder theorem is that it allows exact computation in the range from 0 to n (or $-n/2$ to $n/2$), while actually dealing with addition and multiplication modulo of the much smaller integers n_i.

The reason behind this is the simple fact that, if $x \equiv x_i \bmod n_i$ and $y \equiv y_i \bmod n_i$, where $n_1, n_2, \ldots, n_k$ are relatively prime pairwise, then

$$x + y \equiv x_i + y_i \bmod n_i$$

and

$$x \cdot y \equiv x_i \cdot y_i \bmod n_i .$$

Thus the computation of k products $x_i \cdot y_i$ can be done modulo n_i instead of determining the exact multiplication $x \cdot y$. A further possible advantage occurs if the computer being used is highly parallel and can carry out k multiplications $x_i \cdot y_i$ simultaneously. Thus, instead of one long serial multiplication, k much shorter parallel multiplications can be performed.

Exercises

8-12 Prove Theorem 8.3.

8-13 Calculate $\phi(n)$ for the following n.
    a 1000
    b 2547
    c 901.

8-14 Use the sieve of Eratosthenes to calculate all prime integers ≤ 200.

8-15 Factor the following integers into products of primes:
    a 30,116
    b 10,241
    c 983.

8-16 Calculate $(243)^{82} \bmod 1000$.

8-17 Determine an integer x such that $x \equiv 5 \bmod 32$, $x \equiv 7 \bmod 31$.

8-18 Prove that $2^e \equiv 2^{e \bmod f} \bmod (2^f - 1)$.

8-19 Prove that $\gcd\{2^e - 1, 2^f - 1\} = 2^{\gcd\{e, f\}} - 1$.

8-20 Let p be a prime. Prove that $\phi(p^n) = p^{n-1}(p - 1)$ for any positive integer n.

8-21 Let m, n, and r be positive integers with $\gcd\{m, n\} = 1$. Prove that $jm + r \not\equiv km + r \bmod n$ for $0 \leq j < n$, $0 \leq k < n$, unless $j = k$. Hence show that there exist $\phi(n)$ integers in $\{jm + r : 0 \leq j < n\}$ that are relatively prime to n.

8-22 Let m and n be relatively prime positive integers. Prove that $\phi(mn) = \phi(m)\phi(n)$. (*Hint*: Write the integers from 1 to mn in an $m \times n$ array with the i, j entry $(j - 1)m + i$. Prove that $(j - 1)m + i$ is relatively prime to mn only when i is relatively prime to m. Furthermore, show that, if i is relatively prime to m, then there exist $\phi(n)$ integers k in the ith row such that $\gcd\{k, mn\} = 1$.)

8-23 If $n = p_1^{\alpha_1} \cdots p_k^{\alpha_k}$, p_i distinct primes, prove that

$$\phi(n) = (p_1^{\alpha_1} - p_1^{\alpha_1 - 1}) \cdots (p_k^{\alpha_k} - p_k^{\alpha_k - 1}).$$

8-24 Suppose $n_1, n_2, \ldots, n_k$ are pairwise relatively prime integers and let c_{ij} be k^2 integers with $c_{ij} n_i \equiv 1 \bmod n_j$ for $i = 1, \ldots, k$ and $j = 1, \ldots, k$. Prove that, if

$$v_1 \equiv b_1 \bmod n_1$$

$$v_2 \equiv (b_2 - v_1) c_{12} \bmod n_2$$

$$v_3 \equiv [(b_3 - v_1) c_{13} - v_2] c_{23} \bmod n_3$$

$$\vdots \qquad\qquad \vdots$$

$$v_k \equiv \{\cdots [(b_k - v_1) c_{1k} - v_2] c_{2k} - \cdots - v_{k-1}\} c_{k-1, k} \bmod n_k,$$

then

$$b \equiv v_k n_{k-1} \cdots n_1 + \cdots + v_3 n_2 n_1 + v_2 n_1 + v_1 \bmod n_1 \cdots n_k$$

satisfies

$$b \equiv b_j \bmod n_j \qquad \text{(for all } j\text{)}.$$

8.5 THE INTEGERS MODULO n

In Section 8.4 the notion of congruence modulo n is introduced, and some computational aspects of congruence are examined. This section studies some structural aspects associated with congruence.

Let n be a fixed positive integer. Congruence modulo n is then a relation on the set of integers with a related to b if $a \equiv b \bmod n$. It is not difficult to check that congruent modulo n is an equivalence relation on the set of integers. This is easy to see geometrically, since $a \equiv b \bmod n$ exactly when a and b are a multiple of n units apart on the real line. Thus $a \equiv a \bmod n$, since a is exactly $0 \cdot n$ units from a. If $a \equiv b \bmod n$, then of course $b \equiv a \bmod n$, since the distance from a to b is simply minus the distance from b to a. Finally, if a is a multiple of n from b and b is a multiple of n from c, then certainly a is a multiple of n from c. Thus $\equiv \bmod n$ is an equivalence relation on the set of all integers. This equivalence relation partitions the set of integers into equivalence classes. If $\mathscr{C}$ is an equivalence class under this equivalence relation and a is contained in $\mathscr{C}$, then every integer in $\mathscr{C}$ is a multiple of n from a. Thus $\mathscr{C} = \{c \in Z : c \equiv a \bmod n\}$. We denote $\{c \in Z : c \equiv a \bmod n\}$ by $[a]$. Thus for any integer q, $[a] = [a + qn]$. For any equivalence class $[a]$, there is exactly one integer r such that $0 \le r < n$ and $[r] = [a]$. There cannot be more, since the distance between two such integers r_1 and r_2 would be strictly less than n, contradicting $r_1 \equiv r_2 \bmod n$;

+	[0]	[1]	[2]	[3]	[4]
[0]	[0]	[1]	[2]	[3]	[4]
[1]	[1]	[2]	[3]	[4]	[0]
[2]	[2]	[3]	[4]	[0]	[1]
[3]	[3]	[4]	[0]	[1]	[2]
[4]	[4]	[0]	[1]	[2]	[3]

∘	[0]	[1]	[2]	[3]	[4]
[0]	[0]	[0]	[0]	[0]	[0]
[1]	[0]	[1]	[2]	[3]	[4]
[2]	[0]	[2]	[4]	[1]	[3]
[3]	[0]	[3]	[1]	[4]	[2]
[4]	[0]	[4]	[3]	[2]	[1]

Figure 8.1   Addition and multiplication for $Z/(5)$.

and there must be one, since the division algorithm guarantees that $a = nq + r$, where $0 \leq r < n$. Thus $a - r$ is a multiple of n, $a \equiv r \bmod n$ and $[a] = [r]$. We denote the set of equivalence classes of $\equiv \bmod n$ by $Z/(n)$.

An addition and multiplication can be defined on the set of equivalence classes of integers modulo n. This addition and multiplication is induced by the addition and multiplication of the integers. Define $[a] + [b] = [a + b]$, where a and b are integers. Of course, if this is to be truly a binary operation, it must be well defined. Thus, if $[a] = [a']$ and $[b] = [b']$, then $[a] + [b]$ should be the same as $[a'] + [b']$. This follows from Theorem 8.3, since $a \equiv a' \bmod n$ and $b \equiv b' \bmod n$ implies $a + b \equiv a' + b' \bmod n$. Thus $[a + b] = [a' + b']$, and addition of equivalence classes of integers modulo n is well defined.

Multiplication of equivalence classes of integers modulo n is defined similarly. If a and b are two integers, $[a][b] = [ab]$. This also is easily checked to be well defined. Thus the set $Z/(n) = \{[0], [1], \ldots, [n - 1]\}$ has a well-defined addition and multiplication. If an equivalence class is denoted by $[a]$, the integer a is said to be a representative of the class. Thus we have chosen as representatives of the classes of $Z/(n)$, the integers $0, 1, \ldots, n - 1$. If we multiply $[a][b]$ and the result is $[ab]$, then we can convert the representative ab of $[ab]$ to a representative $0 \leq r < n$ simply by dividing ab by n to obtain the remainder r. Thus $[ab] = [r]$. Figure 8.1 gives the addition and multiplication tables for $Z/(5)$.

Since addition of the integers modulo n is so clearly related to the addition in the integers, we may expect that many of the properties that hold true for the integers also hold true for the integers modulo n. Indeed, it is the case that properties (i) through (v) in the definition of an integral domain are satisfied by the set of integers modulo n under the above-described addition and multiplication. The closure property has already been shown and, as an additional example, we give a proof that multiplication in $Z/(n)$ distributes over addition. This is easily seen, since

$$[a]([b] + [c]) = [a][b + c] = [a(b + c)]$$

$$= [ab + ac] = [ab] + [ac]$$

$$= [a][b] + [a][c].$$

$\circ$	[0]	[1]	[2]	[3]
[0]	[0]	[0]	[0]	[0]
[1]	[0]	[1]	[2]	[3]
[2]	[0]	[2]	[0]	[2]
[3]	[0]	[3]	[2]	[1]

Figure 8.2 Multiplication for $Z/(4)$.

The remaining properties follow in a similar manner. The cancellation property is, however, a different matter. If we examine the multiplication table for $Z/(5)$, and we look for products $[a][b] = [a][c]$; since any row of the multiplication table corresponding to $[a] \neq [0]$ has each entry different, then $[a][b] = [a][c]$ if and only if $[b] = [c]$. Thus the cancellation property holds for $Z/(5)$. However, if we examine the multiplication table for the integers modulo 4 given in Figure 8.2, then $[2][0] = [2][2]$ but $[0]$ does not equal $[2]$. Thus the set of integers modulo 4 does not have the cancellation property.

The two preceding examples of the integers modulo 5 and integers modulo 4 show that the cancellation property in $Z/(n)$ depends on the integer n. In fact, we have the following theorem.

Theorem 8.7 $Z/(n)$ is an integral domain if and only if n is a prime integer.

Proof The proof of the theorem will be complete if we show that $Z/(n)$ satisfies the cancellation property if and only if n is a prime integer. If n is not prime, then $n = ab$, where a and b are positive integers strictly less than n. Thus $[b] \neq [0]$, but $[a][b] = [n] = [0] = [a][0]$, and cancellation does not hold. If n is prime, however, and $[a][b] = [a][c]$ with $[a] \neq [0]$, then $ab \equiv ac \bmod n$; and since $\gcd\{a, n\} = 1$, Theorem 8.4 implies $b \equiv c \bmod n$, so that $[b] = [c]$.

The information in Theorem 8.7 can actually be strengthened. If $\gcd\{a, n\} = 1$, then not only can $[a]$ be cancelled but there actually exists an $[s]$ with $[s][a] = [1]$ in $Z/(n)$. This is a result of Theorem 8.1, which yields $1 = sa + tn$, so that $[1] = [s][a] + [t][n] = [s][a] + [t][0] = [s][a]$. Thus, if n is a prime, then for any $[a] \neq 0$ there exists $[b]$ such that $[a][b] = [1]$. An element x of an integral domain is the *inverse* of the element y if $x \cdot y = 1$. An integral domain for which each nonzero element has an inverse is called a *field*. Thus the integers modulo a prime p is an example of a field, and this field has only a finite number of elements. The structure of finite fields is investigated thoroughly in Chapter 10, and this investigation leads to some applications in the area of error-correcting codes.

The structure of $Z/(n)$ can be further investigated by using the Chinese remainder theorem. If $n = n_1 \cdots n_k$, where $\gcd\{n_i, n_j\} = 1$, for $i \neq j$, and r is an integer, $0 \leq r < n$, then the *modular representation* of r with base $n_1 n_2 \cdots n_k$ is $(r_1, r_2, \ldots, r_k)$, where $0 \leq r_i < n_i$ and $r \equiv r_i \bmod n_i$. The Chinese remainder theorem guarantees that, if the representative of r mod n_i is chosen to be non-negative and less that n_i, then r has a unique representation and every such representation corresponds to a unique r with $0 \leq r < n$. Thus there is a one-to-one correspondence $[r]_n \to ([r_1]_{n_1}, [r_2]_{n_2}, \ldots, [r_k]_{n_k})$ from $Z/(n)$ onto $Z/(n_1) \times \cdots \times Z/(n_k)$. Furthermore, if $r \equiv r_i \bmod n_i$ and $s \equiv s_i \bmod n_i$, then $r + s \equiv r_i + s_i \bmod n_i$ and $r \cdot s \equiv r_i \cdot s_i \bmod n_i$. Thus $[r]_n + [s]_n \to ([r_1]_{n_1} + [s_1]_{n_1}, \ldots, [r_k]_{n_k} + [s_k]_{n_k})$ and

$$[r]_n \cdot [s]_n \to ([r_1]_{n_1} \cdot [s_1]_{n_1}, \ldots, [r_k]_{n_k} \cdot [s_k]_{n_k}).$$

This correspondence embodies two important general concepts in algebra. One is the notion of isomorphism, and the other is the notion of direct sum. To put these concepts into proper perspective, we present the following definition.

Definition   A ring is a nonempty set R with two binary operations $+$ (called addition) and $\cdot$ (called multiplication) such that for all a, b, and c in R the following hold:

i R with the binary operation $+$ forms an Abelian group. The identity for $+$ is denoted by 0, and the inverse of a is denoted by $-a$.

ii R with the binary operation $\cdot$ forms a monoid. The identity for $\cdot$ is denoted by 1.

iii $a \cdot (b + c) = a \cdot b + a \cdot c$ and $(b + c) \cdot a = b \cdot a + c \cdot a$ (distributivity).

A ring R is called a *commutative ring* if $a \cdot b = b \cdot a$ for all a and b in R. $Z/(n)$ is a commutative ring for any positive integer n. All integral domains and fields are commutative rings, and we see in Section 8.7 that certain sets of matrices form rings. Rings and their homomorphisms are investigated in Section 8.8.

Definition   Let R_1 and R_2 be rings. R_1 is said to be isomorphic to R_2 (written $R_1 \cong R_2$) if there is a one-to-one function ϕ from R_1 onto R_2 such that $\phi(r + s) = \phi(r) + \phi(s)$ and $\phi(rs) = \phi(r)\phi(s)$.

The mapping $[r]_n \to ([r_1]_{n_1}, \ldots, [r_k]_{n_k})$ is one-to-one and onto. It also preserves the addition and multiplication if we define $([r_1]_{n_1}, \ldots, [r_k]_{n_k}) + ([s_1]_{n_1}, \ldots, [s_k]_{n_k})$ to be $([r_1]_{n_1} + [s_1]_{n_1}, \ldots, [r_k]_{n_k} + [s_k]_{n_k})$ and

$$([r_1]_{n_1}, \ldots, [r_k]_{n_k}) \cdot ([s_1]_{n_1}, \ldots, [s_k]_{n_k})$$

to be $([r_1]_{n_1} \cdot [s_1]_{n_1}, \ldots, [r_k]_{n_k} \cdot [s_k]_{n_k})$. This idea of componentwise addition and multiplication is formalized by the following definition.

Definition Let $R_1, \ldots, R_k$ be rings. The direct sum of $R_1, \ldots, R_k$ is defined to be $\{(r_1, \ldots, r_k) : r_i \in R_i, i = 1, \ldots, k\}$ with addition and multiplication defined to be componentwise. That is, $(r_1, \ldots, r_k) + (s_1, \ldots, s_k)$ is defined to be $(r_1 + s_1, \ldots, r_k + s_k)$, and $(r_1, \ldots, r_k) \cdot (s_1, \ldots, s_k)$ is defined to be $(r_1 \cdot s_1, \ldots, r_k \cdot s_k)$.

The direct sum of $R_1, \ldots, R_k$ is denoted by $R_1 \oplus \cdots \oplus R_k$, and we have the following result.

Theorem 8.8 If $n = n_1 n_2 \cdots n_k$, where $\gcd\{n_i, n_j\} = 1$, for $i \neq j$, then $Z/(n) \cong Z/(n_1) \oplus \cdots \oplus Z/(n_k)$.

Proof The map $\psi([r]_n) = ([r]_{n_1}, \ldots, [r]_{n_k})$ is one-to-one and onto by the Chinese remainder theorem, and we have previously checked that ψ preserves addition and multiplication.

The isomorphism $Z/(6) \cong Z/(2) \oplus Z/(3)$ is the mapping

$$0 \rightarrow (0, 0)$$
$$1 \rightarrow (1, 1)$$
$$2 \rightarrow (0, 2)$$
$$3 \rightarrow (1, 0)$$
$$4 \rightarrow (0, 1)$$
$$5 \rightarrow (1, 2),$$

where we have deleted the square brackets about each integer for convenience. Since addition is componentwise, we have, for example, $\psi(2 + 5) = \psi(7) = \psi(1) = (1, 1)$ and $\psi(2) + \psi(5) = (0, 2) + (1, 2) = (0 + 1, 2 + 2) = (1, 4) = (1, 1)$.

Exercises

8-25 Solve the following equations:
    a $[12][x] = [15]$ in $Z/(29)$
    b $[4][x] = [8]$ in $Z/(20)$.

8-26 Determine the inverse for each element in $Z/(26)$ that has an inverse.

8-27   Let $\gcd\{a, n\} = d$. Prove that $[a][x] = [b]$ in $Z/(n)$ has a solution if and only if d divides b. Also, if $d \mid b$, prove that there are d different solutions and determine these solutions.

8-28   Write out the explicit isomorphism $Z/(60) \cong Z/(4) \oplus Z/(3) \oplus Z/(5)$.

8-29   If ψ is an isomorphism from the ring R_1 to the integral domain R_2, prove that R_1 is an integral domain.

8-30   If ψ is an isomorphism from the ring R_1 onto the field R_2, prove that R_1 is a field.

8-31   Let G_1 and G_2 be groups. Show that $G_1 \times G_2 = \{(g_1, g_2) : g_1 \in G_1, g_2 \in G_2\}$ is a group under the operation $(g_1, g_2) \cdot (h_1, h_2) = (g_1 h_1, g_2 h_2)$, where g_1 and h_1 are in G_1 and g_2 and h_2 are in G_2.

8-32   Let R be a ring. Define $U(R) = \{r \in R : r^{-1} \text{ exists}\}$. Prove that $U(R)$ is a group under $\cdot$.

8-33   If $R \cong R_1 \oplus R_2$ is a ring, prove that $U(R) \cong U(R_1) \times U(R_2)$.

8-34   Let $\mathbb{R}$ be the field of real numbers. If one of a or b is not zero, $a, b \in \mathbb{R}$, determine $(a + b\sqrt{-1})^{-1}$ in $\mathbb{C}$.

8.6   EUCLIDEAN DOMAINS

Section 8.3 examines the Euclidean algorithm for the set of integers. The ideas and techniques implicit in this examination apply to a much larger class of rings. For example, in the set of polynomials with rational coefficients, there is an algorithm that divides one polynomial by a second polynomial and obtains a quotient and a remainder. The remainder has smaller degree than the divisor. In a way completely similar to the Euclidean algorithm for the integers, a Euclidean algorithm for polynomials with rational coefficients can be deduced and yields a gcd. In both the division and Euclidean algorithms, it is not essential that the coefficients of the polynomial be rational numbers, but only that nonzero coefficients have multiplicative inverses. Thus the algorithms apply to polynomials with coefficients from rings more general than the rational numbers.

Although polynomials, the addition of polynomials, and the multiplication of polynomials are quite familiar, the definitions are now repeated. Let R be a commutative ring. The ring of polynomials in the single indeterminate x, with coefficients from R, is defined to be the set $R[x]$ of elements of the form $a(x) = (a_0, a_1, \ldots, a_k, \ldots)$, where a_i is in R for all i, and for some integer t, $a_j = 0$ for all $j \geq t$. The degree of the polynomial $a(x)$ is defined to be the integer n such that $a_n \neq 0$, but $a_j = 0$ for all $j > n$. Thus the degree of the polynomial is defined for all polynomials, except the polynomial where every component is 0. We denote the degree of the polynomial $a(x)$ by deg $a(x)$. It is conventional to write the polynomial $a(x)$ as

$$\sum_{i=0}^{\deg a(x)} a_i x^i.$$

Addition of polynomials is defined by

$$(a_0, a_1, \ldots, a_k, \ldots) + (b_0, b_1, \ldots, b_k, \ldots)$$
$$= (a_0 + b_0, a_1 + b_1, \ldots, a_k + b_k, \ldots).$$

This is again a polynomial, since $a_j + b_j = 0$ for all $j \geq \max\{\deg a(x),$ deg $b(x)\}$. Multiplication of polynomials is defined by

$$(a_0, a_1, \ldots, a_k, \ldots)(b_0, b_1, \ldots, b_k, \ldots)$$
$$= (a_0 b_0, a_0 b_1 + a_1 b_0, \ldots, \sum_{i=0}^{k} a_i b_{k-i}, \ldots),$$

which again is a polynomial, since for all $k \geq$ deg $a(x) +$ deg $b(x) + 1$, we have

$$\sum_{i=0}^{k} a_i b_{k-i} = 0.$$

Since the coefficients of the polynomial are elements of the ring R, it is clear that $R[x]$ is an Abelian group under addition. To check that multiplication in $R[x]$ is associative, commutative, and distributes over addition takes slightly longer but is nevertheless straightforward. The set $\{(r, 0, 0, \ldots) : r \in R\}$ forms a ring that is isomorphic to R under the mapping $r \to (r, 0, 0, \ldots)$. With this identification the elements of R can be thought of as polynomials. Thus $p(x) = (1, 0, \ldots)$, where 1 is the identity for $\cdot$ in R, is the identity for $\cdot$ in $R[x]$, so that $R[x]$ is a commutative ring.

Under the definition of multiplication in $R[x]$, if R is an integral domain, deg $a(x) \circ b(x) =$ deg $a(x) +$ deg $b(x)$. Thus the only possibility for $a(x) \circ b(x) = 0$ is for both $a(x)$ and $b(x)$ to have degrees equal to 0. However, this implies $a_0 b_0 = 0$, so that one of a_0 or b_0 must be 0. Hence one of $a(x)$ or $b(x)$ must also be 0. The result is, if R is an integral domain, then $R[x]$ is also an integral domain.

If F is a field, then $F[x]$ has a division algorithm such that, if $a(x)$ and $b(x)$ are in $F[x]$ and $b(x)$ does not equal 0, then there exist $q(x)$ and $r(x)$ in $F[x]$, with $r(x) = 0$ or deg $b(x) >$ deg $r(x)$, and $a(x) = q(x)b(x) + r(x)$. This can be seen by the following argument. Since $a(x) = 0 \cdot b(x) + a(x)$, $\{$deg $r(x)$: there exists $q(x) \in R[x]$ such that $a(x) = q(x)b(x) + r(x)\} = \mathscr{S}$ is a nonempty set of non-negative integers if $a(x) \neq 0$. Assume $a(x) \neq 0$, since

$0 = 0 \cdot b(x) + 0$. By the well ordering of the non-negative integers, there exists k minimal in $\mathscr{S}$. Hence there exists $r'(x)$ and $q'(x)$ with $a(x) = q'(x)b(x) + r'(x)$ and $\deg r'(x) = k$. If $k \geq n = \deg b(x)$, $r'(x) = \sum_{i=0}^{k} r_i x^i$, and $b(x) = \sum_{i=0}^{n} b_i x^i$, then $r'(x) - r_k b_n^{-1} x^{k-n} b(x) = r_1(x)$ either equals 0 or has $\deg r_1(x) < \deg r'(x)$. The first case yields $a(x) = (q'(x) + r_k b_n^{-1} x^{k-n}) b(x)$, while the second yields $a(x) = (q(x) + r_k b_n^{-1} x^{k-n}) b(x) + r_1(x)$, where $\deg r_1(x) < \deg r'(x)$, contradicting the minimality of $\deg r'(x)$. Hence $\deg r'(x) < n$, and the division algorithm holds.

The commutative integral domain $F[x]$, where F is a field, is an example of what is called a Euclidean domain. These are integral domains that essentially have a division algorithm.

Definition   A Euclidean domain R is an integral domain with a function v from the nonzero elements R^* in R to the set of non-negative integers such that, for c and d in R^*, $v(c \circ d) \geq v(c)$ and, for a in R and b in R^*, there exist q and r in R such that $a = qb + r$, where $r = 0$ or $v(r) < v(b)$.

The ring of integers is an example of a Euclidean domain where $v(m)$ is the absolute value of the integer m and, from the previous paragraphs in this section, the polynomial ring in one variable with coefficients from a field is a Euclidean domain with $v(f(x)) = \deg(f(x))$. The integer $v(a)$ for an element in a Euclidean domain is called the *degree* of a.

The rings in the definition above are called Euclidean domains, since the Euclidean algorithm holds in these domains. To make this explicit, an element x is said to divide an element y if there exists y_1 with $y = y_1 \circ x$. The element x is called a *divisor* or a *factor* of y. The condition $v(a \circ b) \geq v(a)$, for a nonzero element in a Euclidean domain, essentially states that the degree of an element cannot decrease when it is multiplied by another element. Thus the degree of the divisor is always less than or equal to the degree of the element. A common divisor of two nonzero elements a and b in R is defined to be an element c that is a divisor of both a and b. A gcd of two nonzero elements is a common divisor that is a multiple of every other common divisor.

The following theorem guarantees the existence of a gcd.

Theorem 8.9   Let a and b be nonzero elements in a Euclidean domain R. Then the gcd of a and b exists and furthermore can be written as $as + bt$ for s and t in R.

Proof   Let $M = \{as_1 + bt_1 : s_1 \text{ and } t_1 \text{ are elements in } R\}$. $M \neq \varnothing$ and $M \neq \{0\}$. Pick an element d in M such that $v(d) \leq v(x)$ for all $x \neq 0$ in M. This is possible, since $\{v(x) : x \in M, x \neq 0\}$ is a nonempty set of non-negative integers and thus is well ordered. The element d equals $as + bt$ for some s

and t and furthermore is a gcd. The element d is a common divisor, since if d does not divide a, then there exist q and r with $a = qd + r$ and $v(r) < v(d)$. Hence $qd = q \circ as + q \circ bt = a - r$, so that $r = a(1 - qs) + b(-qt)$ is in M. This contradicts the fact that d has a minimal degree in M, so that d divides a. Similarly, d divides b. If p is a divisor of both a and b, then p divides $as + bt = d$, which shows that d is a gcd of a and b.

Theorem 8.9 guarantees the existence but not the uniqueness of a gcd. In fact, gcd's are only unique up to a multiple by an invertible element. This follows easily, for if d and d_1 are gcd's of the nonzero elements a and b in a Euclidean domain R, then $d = m_1 d_1$ and $d_1 = md$, so that $d = m_1 md$ and by cancelation $1 = m_1 m$. Thus m and m_1 are invertible. If u is invertible, then ud divides any element divisible by d, and $v(d) = v(duu^{-1}) \geq v(du) \geq v(d)$, so that $v(ud) = v(d)$. Thus gcd's are determined exactly up to multiples by invertible elements.

Theorem 8.9 does not indicate a method of computing the gcd, but the Euclidean algorithm given in Section 8.3 for the integers works for Euclidean domains. The only assumption here is that there is an effective way to calculate q and r in the expression $a = qb + r$. The Euclidean algorithm given in Section 8.3 applies for Euclidean domains and computes s, t, and the gcd, while storing only six elements of R. Define $X_1 = (1, 0, a)$ and $X_2 = (0, 1, b)$. If X_{2k-1} and X_{2k} have been computed, define $X_{2k+1} = X_{2k}$ and $X_{2k+2} = X_{2k-1} - q_k \circ X_{2k}$, where $x = q_k y + r_k$, $r_k = 0$, or $v(r_k) < v(y)$ with x the third component of X_{2k-1} and y the third component of X_{2k}. If i is the smallest integer with $r_i = 0$, then

$$X_{2i} = (s, t, \gcd\{a, b\})$$

where

$$as + bt = \gcd\{a, b\}.$$

This last statement follows, since the third component in X_{2i} is simply the integer r_{i-1} defined by the procedure given in Section 8.3. Furthermore, in each vector X_{2j}, it follows easily by induction that

$$ax_{1, 2j} + bx_{2, 2j} = x_{3, 2j}$$

where $x_{1, 2j}$, $x_{2, 2j}$, and $x_{3, 2j}$ are the first, second, and third components respectively of X_{2j}.

As an example, let us compute the gcd of the polynomials $a(x) = x^8 + 2x^7 + 0x^6 + 2x^5 + 2x^4 + 2x^3 + 0x^2 + 2x + 1$ and $b(x) = x^6 + 0x^5 + x^4 + x^3 + x^2 + x + 2$ in $F[x]$, where $F = Z/(3)$. The polynomials can be conveniently represented as $a(x) = 1 \quad 2 \quad 0 \quad 2 \quad 2 \quad 2 \quad 0 \quad 2 \quad 1$ and $b(x) = 1 \quad 0$

1 1 1 1 2, where the $(i + 1)$th digit from the right is the coefficient of x^i. The first division yields

$$1\ 2\ 0\ 2\ 2\ 2\ 0\ 2\ 1 = (1\ \ 2\ \ 2) \circ (1\ \ 0\ \ 1\ \ 1\ \ 1\ \ 1\ \ 2)$$
$$+ (2\ \ 0\ \ 0\ \ 0\ \ 2\ \ 0),$$

so that $X_3 = (0,\ 1,\ 1\ 0\ 1\ 1\ 1\ 1\ 2)$ and $X_4 = (1,\ 2\ 1\ 1,\ 2\ 0\ 0\ 0\ 2\ 0)$. The second division yields $1\ 0\ 1\ 1\ 1\ 1\ 2 = (2\ \ 0) \circ (2\ \ 0\ \ 0\ \ 0\ \ 2\ \ 0) + (1\ \ 1\ \ 0\ \ 1\ \ 2)$ so that $X_5 = (1, 2\ \ 1\ \ 1,\ 2\ 0\ 0\ 0\ 2\ 0)$ and $X_6 = (1\ \ 0,\ 2\ 1\ 1\ 1,\ 1\ 1\ 0\ 1\ 2)$. The third division yields $2\ 0\ 0\ 0\ 2\ 0 = (2\ \ 1) \circ (1\ \ 1\ \ 0\ \ 1\ \ 2) + 2\ 1\ 0\ 1$, so that $X_7 = (1\ \ 0,\ 2\ 1\ 1\ 1,\ 1\ 1\ 0\ 1\ 2)$ and $X_8 = (1\ \ 2\ \ 1, 2\ 2\ 2\ 1\ 0, 2\ 1\ 0\ 1)$. The fourth division yields $1\ 1\ 0\ 1\ 2 = (2\ \ 1) \circ (2\ 1\ 0\ \ 1) + 2\ \ 2\ \ 1$, so that $X_9 = (1\ \ 2\ \ 1, 2\ 2\ 2\ 1\ 0, 2\ 1\ 0\ 1)$ and $X_{10} = (1\ \ 1\ 0\ 2, 2\ 0\ 2\ 0\ 0\ 1, 2\ \ 2\ \ 1)$. The fifth division yields $2\ \ 1\ \ 0\ \ 1 = (1\ \ 1) \circ (2\ \ 2\ \ 1) + 0$, so that the gcd $\{a(x),\ b(x)\} = 2x^2 + 2x + 1$ and, furthermore, $(x^8 + 2x^7 + 2x^5 + 2x^4 + 2x^3 + 2x + 1) \cdot (x^3 + x^2 + 2) + (x^6 + x^4 + x^3 + x^2 + x + 2)(2x^5 + 2x^3 + 1) = 2x^2 + 2x + 1$.

The Euclidean algorithm in a Euclidean domain is a powerful tool which enables us not only to compute the gcd of two elements but also to show the existence of a factorization of an element into a product of primes. A nonzero noninvertible element p in a Euclidean domain R is said to be prime if every divisor of p is either invertible or $u \circ p$, where u in invertible. If an element $a = p_1 \cdots p_r$, where p_i are primes, then the product $p_1 \circ \cdots \circ p_r$ is said to be a factorization of a into primes. In a Euclidean domain, every nonzero noninvertible element can be factored into a product of primes. The following sequence of propositions proves this fact and shows that the factorization is essentially unique.

Proposition 8.3 Let R be a Euclidean domain with a and b in R^*. Then $v(a \circ b) = v(a)$ if and only if b is invertible.

Proof Suppose that $v(a \circ b) = v(a)$. Since R is a Euclidean domain, there exist q and r in R^* such that $a = q \circ (a \circ b) + r$ with $r = 0$ or $v(r) < v(a \circ b)$. If $r = 0$, then $a = a(q \circ b)$ and, since R is cancelative for a in R^*, we have $1 = q \circ b$ and b is invertible. In the second instance $r = a - qab = a(1 - qb)$ and $v(r) = v[a(1 - qb)] \geq v(a)$, since R is a Euclidean domain. Thus $v(a \circ b) > v(r) \geq v(a)$, which contradicts the hypothesis, showing only the first case, namely, $r = 0$, can occur, so that b is invertible. Suppose now that b is invertible. Thus $v(a) = v(abb^{-1}) \geq v(ab) \geq v(a)$ and $v(ab) = v(a)$.

Proposition 8.4 Let R be a Euclidean domain. If p is a prime in R and p divides ab, then p divides a or p divides b.

Proof If p divides a, then the proof is finished. Hence suppose p does not divide a. Thus $u = \gcd \cdot \{a, p\}$ is invertible and by Theorem 8.9 equals $as + pt$ for some s and t in R. Thus $b = u^{-1}ub = u^{-1}(as + pt)b = u^{-1}s(ab) + u^{-1}tbp$. Since p divides p and ab, we have p divides b.

It now follows easily by induction that, if p is a prime in a Euclidean domain and p divides $a_1 \circ a_2 \circ \cdots \circ a_k$, then p divides one of the a_i.

Proposition 8.5 Let R be a Euclidean domain. If a is a nonzero, noninvertible element in R, then there exist a positive integer r and primes $p_1, \ldots, p_r$ such that $a = p_1 \circ p_2 \circ \cdots \circ p_r$.

Proof The proposition is proved by induction on $v(a)$. For all a such that $v(a) = v(a \circ 1) = v(1)$, a is invertible by Proposition 8.3. Hence the induction hypothesis is trivially satisfied for elements of degree $v(1)$. If a is prime, then we are finished. Otherwise, suppose $a = b \circ c$, where b and c are nonzero, noninvertible elements of R. Since b and c are noninvertible, $v(a) > v(b)$ and $v(a) > v(c)$. Hence by induction there exist integers n and m and primes p_1, $p_2, \ldots, p_n$ and $p'_1, p'_2, \ldots, p'_m$, such that $b = p_1 \circ p_2 \circ \cdots \circ p_n$ and $c = p'_1 \circ p'_2 \circ \cdots \circ p'_m$. Hence $a = b \circ c = p_1 \circ p_2 \circ \cdots \circ p_n \circ p'_1 \circ p'_2 \circ \cdots \circ p'_m$, and a has been factored as a product of primes.

The above proposition shows that a nonzero, noninvertible element in a Euclidean domain can be factored into a product of primes. However, the proposition does not indicate that factorization is unique. Indeed, since an integral domain is commutative, the factors can be permuted about arbitrarily, and furthermore factors can differ by arbitrary units. For example, if $a = p_1 \circ p_2$, where p_1 and p_2 are primes, then a also equals $p_2 \circ p_1$ and $(u \circ p_1) \circ (u^{-1} \circ p_2)$ for any invertible element u in R. However, in an Euclidean domain these are essentially the only possibilities for factorization into a product of primes, as the following theorem shows.

Theorem 8.10 Let R be a Euclidean domain. If a is a nonzero, noninvertible element in R such that $a = p_1 \circ p_2 \circ \cdots \circ p_n$ and $a = q_1 \circ q_2 \circ \cdots \circ q_m$, then $m = n$ and there exist a permutation π in S_n and invertible elements $u_1, u_2, \ldots, u_n$ such that $u_i \circ p_i = q_{\pi(i)}$ for $i = 1, \ldots, n$.

Proof The theorem is proved by induction on $\min\{n, m\}$. If a is a prime itself, then the conclusion of the theorem follows. Hence suppose n and m are greater than 1. Since p_1 divides a, the prime p_1 divides one of the q_i, say $q_{\pi(1)}$, and since $q_{\pi(1)}$ is prime, there is an invertible element u_1 such that $u_1 p_1 = q_{\pi(1)}$. Thus by cancellation $p_2 \circ p_3 \circ \cdots \circ p_n = u_1 q'_1 \cdots q'_{m-1}$, where the q'_i are those q_i that are not $q_{\pi(1)}$. By induction, it follows that there is a mapping of $\{2, 3, \ldots, n\}$ onto the set $\{i : i = 1, 2, \ldots, n, \text{ but } i \neq \pi(1)\}$ and units $u_2, \ldots, u_n$ such that $u_i p_i = q_{\pi(i)}$, $i = 2, 3, \ldots, n$, thus proving the theorem.

Exercises

8-35 Determine the gcd of the following pairs of polynomials:
    a 100011 and 110001 in $[Z/(2)][x]$.
    b $x^3 + (2.5)x^2 + (1.6)x + 1.2$ and $x^3 + (4.5)x^2 + (2.6)x + 2.4$ in $Q[x]$, where Q indicates the rationals.

8-36 Determine $t(x)$ and $s(x)$ such that $a(x)s(x) + b(x)t(x) = \gcd\{a(x), b(x)\}$ for $a(x)$ and $b(x)$, the polynomials in Exercise 8-35a.

8-37 Extend the definition of gcd to $\gcd\{a_1, a_2, \ldots, a_n\}$, where $a_1, a_2, \ldots, a_n$ are nonzero elements in a Euclidean domain.

8-38 Calculate $\gcd\{x^3 + 4x^2 + 3x + 5, x^3 + 3x^2 + 3x + 2, x^3 + 2x^2 + 5x + 3\}$ in $[Z/(7)][x]$.

8-39 Prove that the ring $J = \{m + n\sqrt{-1} : m \text{ and } n \text{ are integers}\}$ is a Euclidean domain. (*Hint:* Define $v(m + n\sqrt{-1}) = m^2 + n^2$. For nonzero a and b in J, compute a/b as a complex number and approximate it by an element q in J, so that $a/b - q = s$ is small.)

8-40 Show that the integral domain $\{m + n\sqrt{-5} : m \text{ and } n \text{ are integers}\}$ is not a Euclidean domain. (*Hint:* Find an element that does not have a unique factorization.)

8.7 MODULES

Many of the properties of vectors over the field of rational numbers hold for more general structures. We use some of these facts in the chapter on coding theory.

Definition Let R be a ring. An Abelian group M (with the operation called addition) is said to be a left R-module if there is a function from $R \times M$ into M [denoted by $(r, x) \to rx$ for r in R and x in M and called either multiplication or the action of R] such that for all r and s in R, x and y in M,

  i $r(x + y) = rx + ry$,
  ii $(r + s)x = rx + sx$,
 iii $r(sx) = (rs)x$,
 iv $1 \cdot x = x$, where 1 is the multiplicative identity of R.

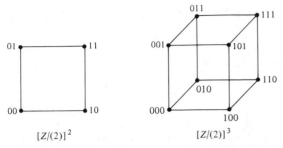

Figure 8.3 Geometrical representation of $(Z/(2))^2$ and $(Z/(2))^3$.

We commonly abbreviate left R-module as R-module. If R is a field, an R-module is called a *vector space*, or a *vector space over* R. An important example of an R-module and the one of most concern to us is

$$R^k = \{(r_1, r_2, \ldots, r_k) : r_i \in R, i = 1, \ldots, k\},$$

where addition is componentwise $(r_1, r_2, \ldots, r_k) + (s_1, s_2, \ldots, s_k) = (r_1 + s_1, r_2 + s_2, \ldots, r_k + s_k)$, r_i and s_i in R for $i = 1, \ldots, k$, and the action of R is $r(r_1, r_2, \ldots, r_k) = (rr_1, rr_2, \ldots, rr_k)$ for r and r_i in R. Since R is an Abelian group under $+$, R^k is an Abelian group, with the additive identity $(0, 0, \ldots, 0)$, 0 the additive identity of R, and the inverse of $(r_1, r_2, \ldots, r_k)$ being $(-r_1, -r_2, \ldots, -r_k)$, r_i in R. Properties (i) through (iv) are easily found to hold for this example. The most important R-modules we encounter are for R a field or the integers modulo n. In the latter case a k-tuple commonly represents, for $n = 26$, a string of k letters in the English alphabet, and $n = 2$, a string of k binary digits. The vector spaces $[Z/(2)]^2$ and $[Z/(2)]^3$ have the geometric representations shown in Figure 8.3. There are analogous geometric representations of $[Z/(n)]^2$ and $[Z/(n)]^3$. When convenient we denote a class $[c]$ in $Z/(n)$ by c.

Along with the concept of R-module, we are concerned with certain mappings of an R-module M into an R-module N.

Definition Let R be a ring and let M and N be R-modules. The function T from M to N is called *linear* if, for x and y in M, r in R, $T(x + y) = T(x) + T(y)$ and $T(rx) = rT(x)$.

If $M = R^k$, R a ring, and (a_{ij}) is a $k \times n$ matrix with entries from R, then the mapping

$$T(r_1, r_2, \ldots, r_k) = (r_1, r_2, \ldots, r_k)(a_{ij}) = \left(\sum_{i=1}^{k} r_i a_{i1}, \sum_{i=1}^{k} r_i a_{i2}, \ldots, \sum_{i=1}^{k} r_i a_{in} \right)$$

takes R^k into R^n. This mapping is linear, since

$$T((r_1, r_2, \ldots, r_k) + (s_1, s_2, \ldots, s_k))$$

$$= T(r_1 + s_1, r_2 + s_2, \ldots, r_k + s_k)$$

$$= \left(\sum_{i=1}^{k} (r_i + s_i)a_{i1}, \sum_{i=1}^{k} (r_i + s_i)a_{i2}, \ldots, \sum_{i=1}^{k} (r_i + s_i)a_{in} \right)$$

$$= \left(\sum_{i=1}^{k} r_i a_{i1} + \sum_{i=1}^{k} s_i a_{i1}, \sum_{i=1}^{k} r_i a_{i2} + \sum_{i=1}^{k} s_i a_{i2}, \ldots, \sum_{i=1}^{k} r_i a_{in} + \sum_{i=1}^{n} s_i a_{in} \right)$$

$$= \left(\sum_{i=1}^{k} r_i a_{i1}, \sum_{i=1}^{k} r_i a_{i2}, \ldots, \sum_{i=1}^{k} r_i a_{in} \right) + \left(\sum_{i=1}^{k} s_i a_{i1}, \sum_{i=1}^{k} s_i a_{i2}, \ldots, \sum_{i=1}^{k} s_i a_{in} \right)$$

$$= T(r_1, r_2, \ldots, r_k) + T(s_1, s_2, \ldots, s_k)$$

and

$$T(r(r_1, r_2, \ldots, r_k)) = T(rr_1, rr_2, \ldots, rr_k)$$

$$= \left(\sum_{i=1}^{k} rr_i a_{i1}, \sum_{i=1}^{k} rr_i a_{i2}, \ldots, \sum_{i=1}^{k} rr_i a_{in} \right)$$

$$= \left(r\sum_{i=1}^{k} r_i a_{i1}, r\sum_{i=1}^{k} r_i a_{i2}, \ldots, r\sum_{i=1}^{k} r_i a_{in} \right)$$

$$= r\left(\sum_{i=1}^{k} r_i a_{i1}, \sum_{i=1}^{k} r_i a_{i2}, \ldots, \sum_{i=1}^{k} r_i a_{in} \right)$$

$$= rT(r_1, r_2, \ldots, r_k).$$

The mapping from $[Z/(2)]^2$ into $[Z/(2)]^3$ given by

$$\begin{bmatrix} 0 & 1 & 0 \\ 1 & 0 & 1 \end{bmatrix}$$

takes 00 to 000, 10 to 010, 01 to 101, and 11 to 111. This is represented in Figure 8.4, where the square representing $[Z/(2)]^2$ is mapped to the rectangle, bisecting the cube representing $[Z/(2)]^3$ diagonally.

Let T and S be linear mappings from the R-module M to the R-module N. Define $T + S$ to be the function that maps x in M to $T(x) + S(x)$ in N. For x and y in M,

$$(T + S)(x + y) = T(x + y) + S(x + y)$$

$$= T(x) + T(y) + S(x) + S(y) = T(x) + S(x) + T(y) + S(y)$$

$$= (T + S)(x) + (T + S)(y)$$

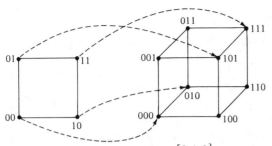

Figure 8.4 The mapping induced by $\begin{bmatrix} 0 & 1 & 0 \\ 1 & 0 & 1 \end{bmatrix}$.

and, for r in R,

$$(T + S)(rx) = T(rx) + S(rx)$$
$$= rT(x) + rS(x) = r(T(x) + S(x))$$
$$= r((T + S)(x)).$$

Thus $T + S$ is again a linear function.

If $M = R^k$ and $N = R^n$, and $T = (a_{ij})$ and $S = (b_{ij})$ are $k \times n$ matrices with a_{ij} and b_{ij} in R, $i = 1, \ldots, k$ and $j = 1, \ldots, n$, then for $(r_1, r_2, \ldots, r_k)$ in R^k,

$$(r_1, r_2, \ldots, r_k)((a_{ij}) + (b_{ij}))$$
$$= (r_1, r_2, \ldots, r_k)(a_{ij}) + (r_1, r_2, \ldots, r_k)(b_{ij})$$
$$= \left(\sum_{i=1}^{k} r_i a_{i1}, \sum_{i=1}^{k} r_i a_{i2}, \ldots, \sum_{i=1}^{k} r_i a_{in} \right) + \left(\sum_{i=1}^{k} r_i b_{i1}, \sum_{i=1}^{k} r_i b_{i2}, \ldots, \sum_{i=1}^{k} r_i b_{in} \right)$$
$$= \left(\sum_{i=1}^{k} r_i a_{i1} + \sum_{i=1}^{k} r_i b_{i1}, \sum_{i=1}^{k} r_i a_{i2} + \sum_{i=1}^{k} r_i b_{i2}, \ldots, \sum_{i=1}^{k} r_i a_{in} + \sum_{i=1}^{k} r_i b_{in} \right)$$
$$= \left(\sum_{i=1}^{k} r_i(a_{i1} + b_{i1}), \sum_{i=1}^{k} r_i(a_{i2} + b_{i2}), \ldots, \sum_{i=1}^{k} r_i(a_{in} + b_{in}) \right)$$
$$= (r_1, r_2, \ldots, r_k)(a_{ij} + b_{ij})$$

Thus the addition of matrices as linear maps corresponds to the addition of matrices componentwise, so that $(a_{ij}) + (b_{ij}) = (a_{ij} + b_{ij})$. As a mapping of $[Z/(2)]^2$ into $[Z/(2)]^3$,

$$\begin{bmatrix} 0 & 1 & 0 \\ 1 & 0 & 1 \end{bmatrix} + \begin{bmatrix} 1 & 1 & 1 \\ 0 & 1 & 1 \end{bmatrix} = \begin{bmatrix} 0+1 & 1+1 & 0+1 \\ 1+0 & 0+1 & 1+1 \end{bmatrix} = \begin{bmatrix} 1 & 0 & 1 \\ 1 & 1 & 0 \end{bmatrix}.$$

Since the R-module N is an Abelian group, we can easily check that the set of linear mappings from the R-module M to the R-module N forms an Abelian group, the additive identity being the mapping $0(x) = 0$ for all x in N, where 0 is the additive identity of N, the additive inverse of the linear mapping T being defined by $(-T)(x) = -[T(x)]$. If T and S are linear mappings from the R-module M into M, then T and S can be composed to obtain $T \circ S$. The mapping $I(x) = x$, x in M, satisfies $I \circ T = T \circ I = T$, so that the set of linear mappings from M into M forms a monoid under composition of mappings. Finally, for linear mappings T, S, and U, from M into M,

$$(T \circ (S + U))(x) = T((S + U)(x))$$

$$= T(S(x) + U(x)) = T(S(x)) + T(U(x))$$

$$= (T \circ S)(x) + (T \circ U)(x) = (T \circ S + T \circ U)(x),$$

and, similarly, $(T + S) \circ U = T \circ U + S \circ U$, so that the set of linear mappings from M into M actually forms a ring.

If $T = (a_{ij})$ and $S = (b_{ij})$ are two $k \times k$ matrices with entries from R, then $T \circ S$ is again a mapping from R^k into R^k. We note here that for the matrices T and S we are following standard convention and writing the matrix on the right of the vector. Thus composition $T \circ S$ of matrix mappings is $((x)T)S$ which is opposite the convention of Chapter 1 where functions were composed as $T(S(x))$. Thus $T \circ S$ maps $(r_1, r_2, \ldots, r_k)$ to

$$((r_1, r_2, \ldots, r_k)(a_{ij}))(b_{ij})$$

$$= \left(\sum_{i=1}^{k} r_i a_{i1}, \sum_{i=1}^{k} r_i a_{i2}, \ldots, \sum_{i=1}^{k} r_i a_{ik} \right)(b_{ij})$$

$$= \left(\sum_{t=1}^{k} \left(\sum_{i=1}^{k} r_i a_{it} \right) b_{t1}, \sum_{t=1}^{k} \left(\sum_{i=1}^{k} r_i a_{it} \right) b_{t2}, \ldots, \sum_{t=1}^{k} \left(\sum_{i=1}^{k} r_i a_{it} \right) b_{tk} \right)$$

$$= \left(\sum_{i=1}^{k} r_i \left(\sum_{t=1}^{k} a_{it} b_{t1} \right), \sum_{i=1}^{k} r_i \left(\sum_{t=1}^{k} a_{it} b_{t2} \right), \ldots, \sum_{i=1}^{k} r_i \left(\sum_{t=1}^{k} a_{it} b_{tk} \right) \right)$$

$$= (r_1, r_2, \ldots, r_k)\left(\sum_{t=1}^{k} a_{it} b_{tj} \right),$$

which implies that $(a_{ij}) \circ (b_{ij})$ is the matrix $(\sum_{t=1}^{k} a_{it} b_{tj})$. As we have seen, for any ring R, this product is an associative binary operation on the set of $n \times n$ matrices over R, which distributes over matrix addition. We denote the ring of $n \times n$ matrices with entries from the ring R by $(R)_n$. As an example of matrix multiplication, where $R = Z/(26)$ and a class $[c]$ is denoted by c,

$$\begin{bmatrix} 1 & 2 & 0 \\ 15 & 21 & 4 \\ 0 & 2 & 13 \end{bmatrix} \circ \begin{bmatrix} 9 & 14 & 5 \\ 7 & 1 & 17 \\ 2 & 6 & 0 \end{bmatrix}$$

$$= \begin{bmatrix} 1 \cdot 9 + 2 \cdot 7 + 0 \cdot 2 & 1 \cdot 14 + 2 \cdot 1 + 0 \cdot 6 & 1 \cdot 5 + 2 \cdot 17 + 0 \cdot 0 \\ 15 \cdot 9 + 21 \cdot 7 + 4 \cdot 2 & 15 \cdot 14 + 21 \cdot 1 + 4 \cdot 6 & 15 \cdot 5 + 21 \cdot 17 + 4 \cdot 0 \\ 0 \cdot 9 + 2 \cdot 7 + 13 \cdot 2 & 0 \cdot 14 + 2 \cdot 1 + 13 \cdot 6 & 0 \cdot 5 + 2 \cdot 17 + 13 \cdot 0 \end{bmatrix}$$

$$= \begin{bmatrix} 23 & 16 & 13 \\ 4 & 21 & 16 \\ 14 & 2 & 8 \end{bmatrix}.$$

A system of linear equations

$$x_1 a_{11} + x_2 a_{21} + \cdots + x_k a_{k1} = b_1$$
$$x_1 a_{12} + x_2 a_{22} + \cdots + x_k a_{k2} = b_2$$
$$\vdots \qquad\qquad \vdots$$
$$x_1 a_{1n} + x_2 a_{2n} + \cdots + x_k a_{kn} = b_n,$$

with coefficients from the real numbers, can be put in matrix form, namely, $(x_1, x_2, \ldots, x_k)(a_{ij}) = (b_i)$. The set of solutions for a system of linear equations with coefficients from the real numbers can be determined by the usual Gaussian elimination process (or in the language of matrices, row reduction to row echelon form). The elimination process is valid for any system of equations whose coefficients are contained in some field. Often, the coefficients of a linear equation are not even contained in a field, but yet solutions may exist and the elimination process may still work. For example, the equation $5x = 4$, where the coefficients 5 and 4 are integers modulo 6, has a solution in the integers modulo 6, namely, $x = 2$. In determining this solution, simply note that 5^{-1} exists in $Z/(6)$ and equals 5. Thus

$$x = 1 \cdot x = (5^{-1} \cdot 5) \cdot x = 5^{-1} \cdot (5 \cdot x) = 5 \cdot 4 = 2.$$

In a more general setting a matrix $T = (a_{ij})$, a_{ij} in the ring R, $i = 1, \ldots, n$ and $j = 1, \ldots, n$, may have a multiplicative inverse even though R is not a field. If R is the field of real numbers, then an $n \times n$ matrix over R has an inverse if and only if the determinant d of the matrix is nonzero (hence has an inverse) and, in this case, the inverse is just $d^{-1} \cdot S$, where S is the adjoint matrix of T. For any $n \times n$ matrix (a_{ij}), where a_{ij} are in a commutative ring R, $i = 1, \ldots, n$ and $j = 1, \ldots, n$, the element [called the determinant of (a_{ij})] $\sum_{\sigma \in S_n} (-1)^\sigma a_{1\sigma(1)} a_{2\sigma(2)} \cdots a_{n\sigma(n)}$ can be calculated, where $(-1)^\sigma$ is 1 if σ is an even permutation and $(-1)^\sigma = -1$ if σ is odd, and has many of the desirable properties of the determinant for $n \times n$ matrices with entries from the real numbers. It can be shown that (a_{ij}) has a multiplicative inverse if and only if the determinant of (a_{ij}) has an inverse in R. The inverse of an invertible matrix A can be calculated either by taking the inverse of the determinant of A multiplied by the adjoint of A or by performing elementary row operations on the matrix $(A|I)$ until the matrix $(I|P)$ is obtained, which gives $A^{-1} = P$.

As an example, the determinant of

$$(a_{ij}) = \begin{bmatrix} 1 & 0 & 2 \\ 2 & 3 & 2 \\ 0 & 1 & 0 \end{bmatrix},$$

with entries from $Z/(9)$, is

$$a_{11}a_{22}a_{33} - a_{11}a_{23}a_{32} + a_{13}a_{21}a_{32} - a_{12}a_{21}a_{33} + a_{12}a_{23}a_{31}$$

$$- a_{13}a_{22}a_{31}$$

$$= 1 \cdot 3 \cdot 0 - 1 \cdot 2 \cdot 1 + 2 \cdot 2 \cdot 1 - 0 \cdot 2 \cdot 0 + 0 \cdot 2 \cdot 0 - 2 \cdot 3 \cdot 0 = 2.$$

Since 2 has an inverse, namely, 5, in $Z/(9)$, (a_{ij}) has an inverse, which can be computed by row operations:

$$\begin{bmatrix} 1 & 0 & 2 & | & 1 & 0 & 0 \\ 2 & 3 & 2 & | & 0 & 1 & 0 \\ 0 & 1 & 0 & | & 0 & 0 & 1 \end{bmatrix} \rightarrow \begin{bmatrix} 1 & 0 & 2 & | & 1 & 0 & 0 \\ 0 & 3 & -2 & | & -2 & 1 & 0 \\ 0 & 1 & 0 & | & 0 & 0 & 1 \end{bmatrix}$$

$$\rightarrow \begin{bmatrix} 1 & 0 & 2 & | & 1 & 0 & 0 \\ 0 & 0 & -2 & | & -2 & 1 & -3 \\ 0 & 1 & 0 & | & 0 & 0 & 1 \end{bmatrix} \rightarrow \begin{bmatrix} 1 & 0 & 2 & | & 1 & 0 & 0 \\ 0 & 0 & 1 & | & 1 & -5 & 6 \\ 0 & 1 & 0 & | & 0 & 0 & 1 \end{bmatrix}$$

$$\rightarrow \begin{bmatrix} 1 & 0 & 0 & | & -1 & 1 & -3 \\ 0 & 0 & 1 & | & 1 & -5 & 6 \\ 0 & 1 & 0 & | & 0 & 0 & 1 \end{bmatrix} \rightarrow \begin{bmatrix} 1 & 0 & 0 & | & -1 & 1 & -3 \\ 0 & 1 & 0 & | & 0 & 0 & 1 \\ 0 & 0 & 1 & | & 1 & -5 & 6 \end{bmatrix}$$

$$= \begin{bmatrix} 1 & 0 & 0 & | & 8 & 1 & 6 \\ 0 & 1 & 0 & | & 0 & 0 & 1 \\ 0 & 0 & 1 & | & 1 & 4 & 6 \end{bmatrix},$$

so that

$$\begin{bmatrix} 1 & 0 & 2 \\ 2 & 3 & 2 \\ 0 & 1 & 0 \end{bmatrix}^{-1} = \begin{bmatrix} 8 & 1 & 6 \\ 0 & 0 & 1 \\ 1 & 4 & 6 \end{bmatrix}.$$

The inverse can also be computed as

$$(a_{ij})^{-1} = d^{-1}[\text{adjoint } (a_{ij})]$$

$$= 5 \begin{bmatrix} 3 \cdot 0 - 1 \cdot 2 & -(0 \cdot 0 - 2 \cdot 1) & 0 \cdot 2 - 3 \cdot 2 \\ -(2 \cdot 0 - 0 \cdot 2) & (1 \cdot 0 - 0 \cdot 2) & -(1 \cdot 2 - 2 \cdot 2) \\ 2 \cdot 1 - 3 \cdot 0 & -(1 \cdot 1 - 0 \cdot 0) & 1 \cdot 3 - 2 \cdot 0 \end{bmatrix} = \begin{bmatrix} 8 & 1 & 6 \\ 0 & 0 & 1 \\ 1 & 4 & 6 \end{bmatrix}.$$

We now restrict ourselves to vector spaces. The concepts of subspace, spanning set, linearly independent set, and basis, valid for a vector space over the reals, apply to the much wider class of vector spaces over an arbitrary field. These concepts are used in the discussion of finite fields in Chapter 10.

Definition A nonempty subset U of a vector space V over a field F is a subspace of V, if U is a subgroup under $+$, and $r\mathbf{u}$ is in U for each r in F and $\mathbf{u}$ in U.

A vector space is of course a subspace of itself. If F is a field, the set of vectors in F^k, which have 0 as the first component, is a subspace of F^k. If fact, if $J \subset \{1, 2, \ldots, k\}$, the set of vectors in F^k, which have a 0 in the jth component for each j in J, is a subspace of F^k. Let $F = Z/(3)$. The set $U = \{(0, 0, 0), (1, 2, 1), (1, 0, 2), (2, 1, 2), (2, 0, 1), (2, 2, 0), (1, 1, 0), (0, 2, 2), (0, 1, 1)\}$ is a subspace of F^3. To see this, we must check that the set is closed under addition and closed under multiplication by elements in F. Even for our simple example, this procedure involves $9 \cdot 8/2 = 36$ vector additions and 9 multiplications, assuming that we do not bother multiplying by 0 or 1. However, if we take the multiples of $(1, 2, 1)$, observe that $(1, 0, 2)$ is not among them, take the multiples of $(1, 0, 2)$, add the three multiples of $(1, 2, 1)$ to the three multiples of $(1, 0, 2)$ in all possible ways, and finally observe that the resulting set V equals U, we have made 2 multiplications and 9 additions only. Furthermore, V must be a subspace, as we shall soon see, hence U is a subspace.

Definition Let S be a set of vectors in the subspace U of the vector space V over F. S is said to span the subspace U if, for each $\mathbf{u}$ in U, there exists a positive integer k, where $\mathbf{u}_1, \mathbf{u}_2, \ldots, \mathbf{u}_k$ is in S and $c_1, c_2, \ldots, c_k$ is in F, with $\mathbf{u} = c_1\mathbf{u}_1 + c_2\mathbf{u}_2 + \cdots + c_k\mathbf{u}_k$.

If S is a nonempty set of vectors in the vector space V over F, then

$$\langle S \rangle = \left\{ \sum_{i=1}^{k} c_i\mathbf{u}_i : k \text{ is a positive integer}, c_i \in F, \mathbf{u}_i \in S, i = 1, 2, \ldots, k \right\}$$

is a nonempty subset of V. Furthermore, $\langle S \rangle$ is a subspace of V, since

$$\sum_{i=1}^{k} c_i\mathbf{u}_i - \sum_{i=1}^{n} c_i'\mathbf{u}_i' = \sum_{i=1}^{k} c_i\mathbf{u}_i + \sum_{i=1}^{n} (-c_i')\mathbf{u}_i'$$

is in $\langle S \rangle$ for c_i, c_i' in F and $\mathbf{u}_i$, $\mathbf{u}_i'$ in S, and for r in F, $r(\sum_{i=1}^{k} c_i\mathbf{u}_i) = \sum_{i=1}^{k} (rc_i)\mathbf{u}_i$ is in $\langle S \rangle$. Thus $\langle S \rangle$ is the subspace of V spanned by S. In the previous example involving the subspace of $[Z/(3)]^3$, we showed that $\langle(1, 2, 1), (1, 0, 2)\rangle = U$, hence concluded that U must be a subspace.

Definition   A set S of vectors in a vector space V over F is said to be linearly independent if $\sum_{i=1}^{k} c_i \mathbf{u}_i = 0$, for c_i in F and $\mathbf{u}_i$ in S, $i = 1, 2, \ldots, k$, implies that $c_i = 0$, $i = 1, 2, \ldots, k$.

The set of vectors $\{(1, 2, 1), (1, 0, 2)\}$ in $[Z/(3)]^3$ is actually linearly independent. To see this observe that $c_1(1, 2, 1) + c_2(1, 0, 2) = (0, 0, 0)$ implies that $(c_1 + c_2, 2c_1, c_1 + 2c_2) = (0, 0, 0)$. Hence $c_1 + c_2 = 0$, $2c_1 = 0$, and $c_1 + 2c_2 = 0$, so that $c_1 = 2(2c_1) = 0$ and $c_2 = -c_1 = 0$. Thus $\{(1, 2, 1), (1, 0, 2)\}$ is linearly independent. A nonempty set S of vectors is said to be *linearly dependent* if S is not linearly independent. That is, if there exist c_1, $c_2, \ldots, c_k$ in the field F and $\mathbf{u}_1, \mathbf{u}_2, \ldots, \mathbf{u}_k$ in the set S such that $\sum_{i=1}^{k} c_i \mathbf{u}_i = 0$ but not all the c_i are 0, $i = 1, 2, \ldots, k$. The set of vectors $\{(1, 2, 1), (1, 0, 2), (2, 2, 0), (1, 0, 0)\}$ in $[Z/(3)]^3$ is linearly dependent, since $1 \cdot (1, 2, 1) + 1 \cdot (1, 0, 2) + 2 \cdot (2, 2, 0) + 0 \cdot (1, 0, 0) = (0, 0, 0)$.

Definition   The set S of vectors in the vector space V over F is a basis for V if S spans V and S is also linearly independent.

The set $\{(1, 0, 0), (0, 1, 0), (0, 0, 1)\}$ is easily seen to be a basis of $[Z/(3)]^3$, as is $\{(1, 2, 1), (1, 0, 2), (1, 0, 0)\}$. Both these basis sets contain the same number of elements. This fact is true in general.

Theorem 8.11   Let $S = \{\mathbf{u}_1, \mathbf{u}_2, \ldots, \mathbf{u}_n\}$ and $T = \{\mathbf{v}_1, \mathbf{v}_2, \ldots, \mathbf{v}_m\}$ be basis sets for the vector space V over F. Then $m = n$.

Proof   Suppose $m \geq n$. We prove the theorem by showing that there exists $\mathbf{v}_{i_{k+1}}, \mathbf{v}_{i_{k+2}}, \ldots, \mathbf{v}_{i_m}$ distinct in T such that $\{\mathbf{u}_1, \mathbf{u}_2, \ldots, \mathbf{u}_k, \mathbf{v}_{i_{k+1}}, \mathbf{v}_{i_{k+2}}, \ldots, \mathbf{v}_{i_m}\}$ is a basis for V, $0 \leq k \leq n$. If this statement is true, then for $k = n$, $T_n = \{\mathbf{u}_1, \mathbf{u}_2, \ldots, \mathbf{u}_n, \mathbf{v}'_{i_{n+1}}, \mathbf{v}'_{i_{n+2}}, \ldots, \mathbf{v}'_{i_m}\}$ is a basis for V, where $\mathbf{v}'_{i_{n+1}}, \mathbf{v}'_{i_{n+2}}, \ldots, \mathbf{v}'_{i_m}$ are distinct vectors in T. However, $\{\mathbf{u}_1, \ldots, \mathbf{u}_n\}$ spans V, so there exists a_i in F, $i = 1, \ldots, n$, such that $\mathbf{v}'_{i_{n+1}} = \sum_{i=1}^{n} a_i \mathbf{u}_i$. This gives the equation $\sum_{i=1}^{n} a_i \mathbf{u}_i - \mathbf{v}'_{i_{n+1}} = 0$, which contradicts the fact that T_n is linearly independent. Hence there is no $\mathbf{v}'_{i_{n+1}}$ in T. This shows that $n = m$. We now proceed by induction on k to show that there exist $\mathbf{v}_{i_{k+1}}, \ldots, \mathbf{v}_{i_m}$ distinct in T such that $\{\mathbf{u}_1, \ldots, \mathbf{u}_k, \mathbf{v}_{i_{k+1}}, \ldots, \mathbf{v}_{i_m}\}$ is a basis for V, $0 \leq k \leq n$. If $k = 0$, the statement holds. Suppose $T_k = \{\mathbf{u}_1, \ldots, \mathbf{u}_k, \mathbf{v}_{i_{k+1}}, \ldots, \mathbf{v}_{i_m}\}$ is a basis for V, $\mathbf{v}_{i_j}$ distinct in T. Since $\mathbf{u}_{k+1} \in V$ and T_k spans V, there exists b_i, $i = 1, \ldots, m$, such that

$$\mathbf{u}_{k+1} = \sum_{i=1}^{k} b_i \mathbf{u}_i + \sum_{j=k+1}^{m} b_j \mathbf{v}_{i_j}.$$

If $b_j = 0$ for $j = k + 1, \ldots, m$, then $0 = -\mathbf{u}_{k+1} + \sum_{i=1}^{k} b_i \mathbf{u}_i$, which contradicts the linear independence of S. Suppose $b_t \neq 0$, for some t, $k + 1 \leq t \leq m$, so that

$$v_{i_t} = b_t^{-1}\left(\sum_{i=1}^{k} (-b_i)u_i + u_{k+1} + \sum_{\substack{j=k+1 \\ j \neq t}}^{m} (-b_j)v_{i_j}\right).$$

The set $T_{k+1} = \{u_1, u_2, \ldots, u_{k+1}, v_{i_j} : j = k+1, \ldots, m,\ \text{but}\ j \neq t\}$ is a basis for V. To see this, observe that, if T_k spans V, then any element in V has the form

$$\sum_{i=1}^{k} d_i u_i + \sum_{j=k+1}^{m} d_j v_{i_j} = \sum_{i=1}^{k} d_i u_i + d_t b_t^{-1}\left[\sum_{i=1}^{k} (-b_i)u_i + u_{k+1} + \sum_{\substack{j=k+1 \\ j \neq t}}^{m} (-b_j)v_{i_j}\right]$$

$$+ \sum_{\substack{j=k+1 \\ j \neq t}}^{m} d_j v_{i_j}$$

$$= \sum_{i=1}^{k} (d_i - b_t^{-1} d_t b_i)u_i + d_t b_t^{-1} u_{k+1} + \sum_{\substack{j=k+1 \\ j \neq t}}^{m} (-b_t^{-1} d_t b_j + d_j)v_{i_j}, d_j$$

in F, $i = 1, \ldots, m$, so that T_{k+1} spans V. If

$$\sum_{i=1}^{m} c_i u_i + c u_{k+1} + \sum_{\substack{j=k+1 \\ j \neq t}}^{m} c_j v_{i_j} = 0,$$

then

$$0 = \sum_{i=1}^{k} c_i u_i + c\left(\sum_{i=1}^{k} b_i u_i + \sum_{j=k+1}^{m} b_j v_{i_j}\right) + \sum_{\substack{j=k+1 \\ j \neq t}}^{m} c_j v_{i_j}$$

$$= \sum_{i=1}^{k} (c_i + c b_i)u_i + c b_t v_{i_t} + \sum_{\substack{j=k+1 \\ j \neq t}}^{m} (c b_j + c_j)v_{i_j},$$

and the linear independence of T_k then implies $c b_t = 0$. Since $b_t \neq 0$, c must be 0, and we have the dependency

$$\sum_{i=1}^{k} c_i u_i + \sum_{\substack{j=k+1 \\ j \neq t}}^{m} c_j v_{i_j} = 0$$

in T_k. This implies that the c_i are 0, and we have shown that T_{k+1} is linearly independent. Thus T_{k+1} is a basis for V and the theorem now follows.

It is not difficult to check that $\{E_i = (0, \ldots, 0, 1, 0, \ldots, 0)$, where 1 occurs in the ith component: $i = 1, \ldots, n\}$ is a basis for F^n, F a field. Thus the dimension of F^n is n.

Exercises

8-41 Solve completely the following systems of equations:
  a $3x + y = 9$
  $x + 2y = 6$ modulo 10
  b $3x + y = 9$
  $x + 2y = 6$ modulo 9
  c $2x + 3y = 11$
  $6x + 6y = 0$ modulo 12.

8-42 Calculate the determinants of the following matrices:

  a $\begin{bmatrix} 1 & 1 & 2 \\ 3 & 0 & 1 \\ 1 & 2 & 4 \end{bmatrix}$ modulo 5

  b $\begin{bmatrix} 2 & 3 \\ 0 & 1 \end{bmatrix}$ modulo 6

  c $\begin{bmatrix} 4 & 7 \\ 6 & 8 \end{bmatrix}$ modulo 9.

8-43 Determine A^{-1} for the matrices in Exercise 8-42.

8-44 Find all the invertible matrices in $[Z/(2)]_2$.

8-45 If R_1 and R_2 are rings and $R \cong R_1 \oplus R_2$, prove that $(R)_n \cong (R_1)_n \oplus (R_2)_n$. Explicitly, give the element of $[Z/(2)]_2 \oplus [Z/(3)]_2$ that corresponds to

$$\begin{bmatrix} 5 & 3 \\ 2 & 1 \end{bmatrix}$$

  in $[Z/(6)]_2$.

8-46 Let R be a ring and M be an R-module. Prove that $0 \cdot x = 0$ for any x in R. (Note that the first 0 is the additive identity for R and the second 0 is the identity of M.)

8-47 Prove that, if R is a ring and M and N are R-modules, the set of linear mappings from M into N forms an Abelian group under $+$.

---

*8.8 RINGS AND HOMOMORPHISMS

The integers modulo n is a ring consisting of a set of equivalence classes of integers. The mapping ϕ, which takes each integer to its equivalence class, satisfies $\phi(k) + \phi(m) = \phi(k + m)$ and $\phi(k)\phi(m) = \phi(km)$, since $[k] + [m]$ is defined to be $[k + m]$ and $[k][m]$ is $[km]$ for integers k and m.

Definition A function ϕ from a ring R_1 onto a ring R_2 is a *homomorphism* if $\phi(r + s) = \phi(r) + \phi(s)$ and $\phi(r)\phi(s) = \phi(rs)$ for all r and s in R_1.

The mapping $\phi(k) = [k]$ is an example of a homomorphism from the ring of integers onto the integers modulo n.

The integers modulo n is a set of equivalence classes with addition and multiplication dependent both on addition and multiplication of the integers and on the particular partition chosen—different n yield different partitions.

Definition Let R be a ring. A ring congruence on R is a partition of R such that, for classes X and Y of the partition, $\{x + y : x \in X \text{ and } y \in Y\}$ and $\{xy : x \in X \text{ and } y \in Y\}$ are each contained in a unique set of the partition.

Congruence modulo n is a ring congruence on the set of integers, since $\{x' + y' : x' \in [x] \text{ and } y' \in [y]\} \subseteq [x + y]$ and $\{x'y' : x' \in [x] \text{ and } y' \in [y]\} \subseteq [xy]$. Just as the set of classes of integers under congruence modulo n forms a ring, any ring congruence induces a ring structure on the classes of the partition. The proof is quite analogous to the proof that a semigroup congruence on a group induces a group structure on the classes of the partition, and we make use of this fact. If $\mathscr{P}$ is a ring congruence for the R, let $R/\mathscr{P}$ be the set of classes of the partition with the binary operation $[x] + [y]$ defined to be $[x + y]$, the unique class containing $\{x' + y' : x' \in [x], y' \in [y]\}$, and the binary operation $[x][y]$ defined to be $[xy]$ the unique class containing $\{x'y' : x' \in [x], y' \in [y]\}$.

Theorem 8.12 If $\mathscr{P}$ is a ring congruence for the ring R, then $R/\mathscr{P}$ is a ring. Furthermore, the mapping $\phi(r) = [r]$ is a ring homomorphism from R onto $R/\mathscr{P}$.

Proof By Theorem 7.19, $R/\mathscr{P}$ is a semigroup under $+$ and ϕ is a homomorphism from R under $+$ to $R/\mathscr{P}$ under $+$. Exercise 7-33 then shows that $R/\mathscr{P}$ is a group under $+$. $R/\mathscr{P}$ is Abelian, since $[x] + [y] = [x + y] = [y + x] = [y] + [x]$, x and y in R, so we have shown that $R/\mathscr{P}$ is an Abelian group under $+$. Since $\mathscr{P}$ is also a semigroup congruence under $\cdot$, Theorem 7.19 again implies that $R/\mathscr{P}$ is a semigroup under $\cdot$ and that ϕ is a semigroup homomorphism from R under $\cdot$ onto $R/\mathscr{P}$ under $\cdot$. Thus we have already shown that ϕ is a ring homomorphism. Exercise 7-32 shows that $R/\mathscr{P}$ is a monoid under $\cdot$. The proof is finished once we show that $R/\mathscr{P}$ satisfies the distributivity condition. However, for x, y, and z in R,

$$[x]([y] + [z]) = [x][y + z] = [x(y + z)] = [xy + xz] = [xy] + [xz]$$
$$= [x][y] + [x][z]$$

and, similarly,

$$([x] + [y])[z] = [x][z] + [y][z].$$

A ring homomorphism not only arises from a ring congruence, as shown in Theorem 8.12, but also determines a ring congruence.

Theorem 8.13   Let ϕ be a homomorphism from the ring R_1 onto the ring R_2. The set of classes consisting of elements of R_1 mapped to the same image by ϕ is a ring congruence $\mathscr{P}$, and $R_1/\mathscr{P}$ is isomorphic to R_2.

Proof   The proof can be shown by using the analogous Theorem 7.20 for semigroup congruences and is left as an exercise.

Theorems 8.12 and 8.13 show that all homomorphisms of rings arise (up to isomorphism of rings) from the mapping of ring elements to their classes, determined by a ring congruence. The ring congruence of congruent modulo n on the integers has some properties that hold true in more general cases. The classes in $Z/(n)$ have the form $[a] = \{a + qn : q$ is any integer$\}$. Thus $[a] = \{a + b : b \in [0]\}$. The class containing 0 plays a special role, and all other classes are determined by this class.

Definition   Let ϕ be a homomorphism from the ring R_1 onto the ring R_2. The kernel of ϕ is defined to be $\{r \in R_1 : \phi(r) = 0\}$.

Since a homomorphism ϕ of the ring R is also a homomorphism of the group R under $+$, Theorem 7.21 shows that the partition $\mathscr{P}$ determined by ϕ is actually the set of cosets of the kernel of ϕ, hence $\mathscr{P} = \{r + I : r \in R$ and I is the kernel of $\phi\}$. Since R under $+$ is an Abelian group, any subgroup of R under $+$ is a normal subgroup, so that $R/\mathscr{P}$, where $\mathscr{P}$ is the set of cosets of I, is a group under $+$. In general, $R/\mathscr{P}$ is not a ring, but an additional condition on the kernel of ϕ will ensure that it is a ring. If ϕ is a homomorphism of the ring R, x is in the kernel of ϕ, and r is in R, then $\phi(rx) = \phi(r)\phi(x) = \phi(r) \cdot 0 = 0$, so that rx is in the kernel of ϕ. Similarly, r in R and x in I implies xr is in I.

Definition   Let I be a subgroup, under $+$, of the ring R. I is an ideal of R if rx and xr are in I for any r in R and x in I.

The condition that I be an ideal of the ring R is considerably stronger that the condition that I be a subgroup of R under $+$. As an example, $S = \{n/2 : n$ is an integer$\}$ is a normal subgroup in the field (hence the ring) of rational numbers $\mathscr{Q}$, but S is certainly not an ideal of $\mathscr{Q}$.

Theorem 8.14   Let I be an ideal of the ring R. The set $\mathscr{P}$ of cosets of I in R is a ring congruence for R.

Proof Since I is a normal subgroup of R under $+$, $\mathscr{P}$ is a semigroup congruence for R under $+$ by Theorem 7.22. It remains only to show for classes P and Q in $\mathscr{P}$ that $\{pq : p \in P \text{ and } q \in Q\}$ is contained in a unique class of $\mathscr{P}$. However, $P = r + I$ for some r in R, and $Q = s + I$ for some s in R. Thus an element in P must have the form $r + x$ for x in I, and an element in Q must have the form $s + y$ for y in I. Hence $(r + x) \cdot (s + y) = rs + xs + ry + xy$. Since I is an ideal containing x and y, the elements xs, ry, and xy are in I. In addition, I is a subgroup under $+$, so that $z = xs + ry + xy$ is in I. Thus $(r + x)(s + y) = rs + z$, where z is in I. We have shown that $\{pq : p \in P \text{ and } q \in Q\} \subseteq rs + I$, so the proof is complete.

If I is an ideal of the ring R, the ring $R/\mathscr{P}$, where $\mathscr{P}$ is the set of cosets of I in R, is denoted by R/I. Theorem 8.13 now implies that, if I is an ideal of the ring R, the mapping $\phi(r) = [r] = r + I$ is a ring homomorphism from R onto R/I.

Exercises

8-48 Prove Theorem 8.13.

8-49 Determine all ideals of a field F.

8-50 Let ψ be a homomorphism from a ring R_1 onto a ring R_2 and let I be the kernel of ψ. Suppose $s \in R_2$ and $\psi(r) = s$. Prove that $\phi(s) = r + I$ is an isomorphism from R_2 onto R_1/I.

8-51 Let ϕ be an isomorphism of rings. Prove that ϕ^{-1} is an isomorphism.

Coding Theory

9.1 INTRODUCTION

Communication of information from a source to a destination is a complex process which can be schematically illustrated as in Figure 9.1. In the transmission of information we assume that we are concerned with the transmission of some unit called a message. This message is first encoded in a form suitable for transmission, and then processed by a transmitter and sent across a channel. A receiver then picks up the information coming across the channel. This information is then decoded by a decoder which transforms the information into a received message.

Often in practice it is difficult to distinguish the encoder from the transmitter and the receiver from the decoder. However, in some situations it is essential to distinguish the several functions. The process described in the diagram occurs in numerous examples. A radio broadcast takes a message in the English language and transmits it across space to a receiver which then converts the radio waves into sound waves. Another example of communication of information is visual input into the retina, which consists of patterns of photons hitting the retina. These patterns are encoded into electric impulses in some of the cells affected by the incoming photons. These impulses

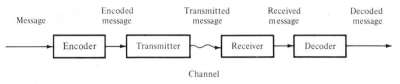

Figure 9.1   Schematic outline of information transmission.

are transmitted across a network of neurons and received in a visual area of the brain, where the visual pattern is recognized.

Two aspects of the transmission of information are our principal concern. A very ancient concern is ensuring the secrecy of a transmitted message. During the transmission of a message across a channel there may be numerous opportunities for its interception. This may consist of the interception and detention of a courier carrying the message, or more often in modern times the interception of a radio transmission by a radio receiver. In either of these cases, if the message can be comprehended by the interceptors, then the secrecy is lost. Thus an encoding process is often used, which makes the message unintelligible to an unintended receiver. After this encoded message is received it must be decoded in order for the recipient to understand the transmitted information. The study of encoding and decoding to ensure secrecy is called cryptography, and Sections 9.2–9.4 deal with some of its aspects. The second and, in present times, very important aspect of information transmission is concerned with reception and decoding in the presence of unreliable transmission. This unreliability of transmission may be due to noise in the channel or to very weak signals. For an unreliable channel, the correction and detection of errors in the transmission assumes paramount significance. This aspect is dealt with in Sections 9.5–9.7 of this chapter and in Sections 10.6 and 10.7.

9.2   CRYPTOGRAPHY

This section is concerned with the process of encoding, decoding, and deciphering a message. Deciphering is the process of discovering the decoding procedure when only the transmitted message is available (by interception).

Definition   An encoding ϕ of a set $\mathscr{A}$ (called the base set) into the set X is a one-to-one function ϕ from $\mathscr{A}$ into X.

The encoding ϕ must be one-to-one, since decoding is desired, and if $\phi(a_1) = \phi(a_2) = r$, then it will be ambiguous as to whether r should be

Figure 9.2   A Caesar cypher encoding.

decoded as a_1 or a_2. The encoding ϕ is extended to the set of all sequences $a_1 a_2 \cdots a_n$, where a_i is contained in $\mathscr{A}$, by

$$a_1 a_2 \cdots a_n \to \phi(a_1)\phi(a_2) \cdots \phi(a_n).$$

The decoding of ϕ is defined to be the function ϕ^{-1} from $\phi(\mathscr{A})$ to $\mathscr{A}$. This likewise is extended to a decoding of sequences $x_1 x_2 \cdots x_n$, where x_i is in $\phi(\mathscr{A}) \subset X$ by $x_1 x_2 \cdots x_n \to \phi^{-1}(x_1)\phi^{-1}(x_2) \cdots \phi^{-1}(x_n)$.

We generally take $\mathscr{A}$ to be one of the sets {the letters of the English alphabet}, {n-tuples of letters of the English alphabet with n a small positive integer}, $Z/(k)$ with $k = 26, 29,$ or 2, and $[Z/(k)]^n$ with $k = 26, 29,$ or 2 and n a small positive integer. If $\mathscr{A}$ is a set of letters of a standard alphabet or $Z/(k)$, then the encoding is called *monoalphabetic*.

Approximately 2000 years ago, Julius Caesar used monoalphabetic encoding to conceal the information contained in some of his written communications. This encoding is called a Caesar cypher and ϕ(letter) is the letter three letters after a given letter; except that the procedure is continued cyclically to determine the image of the last three letters of the alphabet. Such an encoding of the English alphabet is shown in Figure 9.2. This Caesar encoding has a very simple mathematical explanation. If we associate with each letter of the alphabet one of the integers from 0 to 25 taken modulo 26, for example, the correspondence given in Figure 9.3 then this Caesar encoding can be given by $\phi([x]) = [x] + [3]$, where addition takes place in $Z/(26)$.

Thus encoding the message

It is not our level of prosperity that makes for happiness

can proceed as

9   20   9   19   14   15   20   15   21   18   12   5   22   5   12   15

6   16   18   15   19   16   5   18   9   20   25   20   8   1   20   13   1

11   5   19   6   15   18   8   1   16   16   9   14   5   19   19

then

12   23   12   22   17   18   23   18   24   21   15   8   25   8   15

18   9   19   21   18   22   19   8   21   12   23   2   23   11   4   23

16   4   14   8   22   9   18   21   11   4   19   19   12   17   8   22   22,

A	B	C	D	E	F	G	H	I	J	K	L	M
[1]	[2]	[3]	[4]	[5]	[6]	[7]	[8]	[9]	[10]	[11]	[12]	[13]

N	O	P	Q	R	S	T	U	V	W	X	Y	Z
[14]	[15]	[16]	[17]	[18]	[19]	[20]	[21]	[22]	[23]	[24]	[25]	[0]

Figure 9.3 The correspondence between the alphabet and $Z/(26)$.

and then

LW LV QRW RXU OHYHO RI SURVSHULWB WKDW
PDNHV IRU KDSSLQHVV.

The procedure illustrated above in general is not explicitly written out, since the correspondence between the letters of the alphabet and the encoded letters is all that is needed. A mathematical formulation, however, indicates an easy generalization of the above example, which is more difficult to decode. If a and b are integers with the gcd$\{a, 26\} = 1$, then define a *modular encoding* $\phi([x]) = [a][x] + [b]$. The *Caesar cypher* is defined to be a modular encoding with $a = 1$. The gcd$\{a, 26\}$ must equal 1, since otherwise the modular encoding would not be one-to-one. In fact, $\phi(0) = [b]$ and $\phi(26/\gcd\{a, 26\}) = [b]$. Thus if the letter corresponding to $[b]$ were received, it would be ambiguous as to whether this should be decoded as the letter corresponding to $[0]$ or $[26/\gcd\{a, 26\}]$. However, if the gcd$\{a, 26\} = 1$, then $[a]^{-1}$ exists and there is a decoding $\phi^{-1}(y) = [a]^{-1}y - [a]^{-1}[b]$. The element $[a]^{-1}$ can be determined by the Euclidean algorithm.

The encoding ϕ and the decoding ϕ^{-1} give all the information needed to encode a message and decode an encoded message. However, if $[a]^{-1}$ and $[b]$ are unknown to a person intercepting the encoded message, then the message cannot be readily deciphered. There are, however, several procedures for determining $[a]$ and $[b]$, so that the decoding can be calculated. If it is suspected that the code is a Caesar cypher, then simply take an intercepted encoded word and construct a table as in Figure 9.4. In this example the intercepted encoded message contains the word XTWTELCJ. The first row of the table consists of the intercepted encoded word, and underneath each letter of the encoded word is a column which continues the alphabet from that letter on. The rows of the table are scanned to see if any word is recognized. In the example the word MILITARY occurs as a row in the table. Hence we suppose that XTWTELCJ is decoded as "military," and that this encoding is an example of a Caesar cypher in which the displacement is 11 letters. Hence the decoding is $\phi^{-1}([y]) = [y] + [15]$, and the remainder of the message can be decoded.

If a is not 1, then this procedure will not be effective. However, if there is

	X	T	W	T	E	L	C	J	Encoded word
	Y	U	X	U	F	M	D	K	
	Z	V	Y	V	G	N	E	L	
	A	W	Z	W	H	O	F	M	
	B	X	A	X	I	P	G	N	
	C	Y	B	Y	J	Q	H	O	
	D	Z	C	Z	K	R	I	P	
15	E	A	D	A	L	S	J	Q	
	F	B	E	B	M	T	K	R	
	G	C	F	C	N	U	L	S	
	H	D	G	D	O	V	M	T	
	I	E	H	E	P	W	N	U	
	J	F	I	F	Q	X	O	V	
	K	G	J	G	R	Y	P	W	
	L	H	K	H	S	Z	Q	X	
	M	I	L	I	T	A	R	Y	Decoded word
	N	J	M	J	U	B	S	Z	
	O	K	N	K	V	C	T	A	
	P	L	O	L	W	D	U	B	
	Q	M	P	M	X	E	V	C	
	R	N	Q	N	Y	F	W	D	
	S	O	R	O	Z	G	X	E	
	T	P	S	P	A	H	Y	F	
	U	Q	T	Q	B	I	Z	G	
	V	R	U	R	C	J	A	H	
	W	S	V	S	D	K	B	I	

Figure 9.4 Decipher table for Caesar cyphers.

some means to determine $\phi^{-1}([y])$ for several different values of y, then the system of equations

$$y_1 z_1 + z_2 = \phi^{-1}(y_1)$$
$$y_2 z_1 + z_2 = \phi^{-1}(y_2)$$

can possibly be solved for z_1 and z_2 in $Z/(26)$, where $z_1 = [a]^{-1}$ and $z_2 = -[a]^{-1}[b]$. Since this system of equations has coefficients in $Z/(26)$, there may not always be a unique solution, even when the determinant of the matrix

$$\begin{bmatrix} y_1 & 1 \\ y_2 & 1 \end{bmatrix}$$

is not 0. From the previous chapter, this matrix has an inverse if and only if the determinant is invertible in $Z/(26)$, hence if and only if gcd{determinant, 26} = 1. However, solutions may exist even when the determinant is not invertible, since subtracting the second equation from the first yields $(y_1 - y_2)z_1 = \phi^{-1}(y_1) - \phi^{-1}(y_2)$. This has a solution if and only if gcd{$(y_1 - y_2)$, 26} divides $\phi^{-1}(y_1) - \phi^{-1}(y_2)$, and in this case there are gcd{$(y_1 - y_2)$, 26} possibilities for z_1, one of which will yield the correct decoding equation.

If $\phi^{-1}([y])$ is known for several values of y, then the decoding function can be calculated. However, the problem remains of determining $\phi^{-1}([y])$ for some values of $[y]$. An extremely valuable tool in this search is a standard frequency count of the occurrence of the letters of the English alphabet. This count is made visually striking by putting the letters of the alphabet in a row and, beneath each letter, a horizontal stroke for each occurrence of that letter in the message.

In normal English text, the letters of the alphabet do not occur with identical frequency. The letter E occurs more often than any other letter, and the letter Z occurs very infrequently. By taking a sample of encoded text and counting the occurrences of the letters in that text, a tentative correspondence between encoded letters and the letters for which they stand can be made. Thus one may assume that the most frequently occurring letter of the encoding text stands for the letter E. The next most frequently occurring letter may stand for the letter T. This gives two equations in two unknowns, which can be solved (at least up to a multiple), and a portion of the text can be decoded to see if the calculated values for a and b give a sensible decoding. If not, other matchings of frequent letters or infrequent letters can be attempted until by trial and error the decoding is accomplished. The standard frequency count of letters occurring in newspaper text is given in Figure 9.5. Thus the frequency count of an encoded message can be compared with this frequency count to obtain a tentative first correspondence. For example, suppose Figure 9.6 is an intercepted encoded message. Notice that the message is written in blocks of five letters so that a surreptitious decoder does not have the advantage of knowing individual word lengths. In other words the text has been run together, leaving out the blank spaces, and then written in blocks of five letters.

The frequency count for the encoded message in Figure 9.6 is given in Figure 9.7.

If we assume we have a monoalphabetic encoding, then since W is by

A	7.3	H	3.5	O	7.4	U	2.7
B	0.9	I	7.4	P	2.7	V	1.3
C	3.0	J	0.2	Q	0.3	W	1.6
D	4.4	K	0.3	R	7.7	X	0.5
E	13.0	L	3.5	S	6.3	Y	1.9
F	2.8	M	2.5	T	9.3	Z	0.1
G	1.6	N	7.8				

Figure 9.5 Percentage occurrence of letters of the alphabet in a sample text.

KMIUT	RKJKM	MWMMU	WXPQK	XNWUK
TWYIP	FJWMD	WQPPA	CWXWJ	KPIXC
WRWQP	JIQDA	YWJZJ	AUKRP	WJXKP
WWXWJ	CEMAS	JQWM		

Figure 9.6 An intercepted coded message.

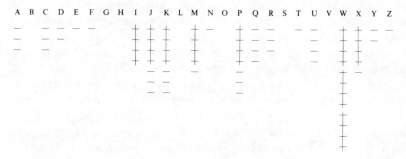

Figure 9.7 Frequency count for the code in Figure 9.6.

far the most frequently occurring letter, we may assume $\phi^{-1}(W) = E$. Since the letters T, N, R, O, I, and A occur with about the same high frequency in English text, it may be difficult to decide ϕ^{-1} for the code letters J, K, and P, each of which occurs eight times in the code. One possible way is by trial and error, assuming that $\phi^{-1}(J) = T$, solving the set of equations, and then attempting to decode the message to see if we actually have the proper solution. If not, we then try $\phi^{-1}(K) = T$ and repeat the procedure. If this does not give a solution, we then try $\phi^{-1}(P) = T$ and again go through the procedure to see if we obtain a possible decoding. There are short cuts, however, since in the English language not only do certain single letters occur more frequently than other single letters, but also certain pairs of

TH	2161	AN	1216	TI	865
HE	2053	EN	1029	OR	861
IN	1550	AT	1019	ST	823
ER	1436	ES	917	AR	764
RE	1280	ED	890	ND	761
ON	1232	TE	872	TO	756

Figure 9.8 Most frequent digraphs (out of 80,000 characters of text).

Figure 9.9 Digraph frequency for W_ in the code in Figure 9.6.

letters occur more frequently than other pairs of letters. Adjacent pairs of letters in the English language are called *digraphs*, and Figure 9.8 gives a table of the most frequently appearing digraphs.

A count of the digraphs in the code in Figure 9.6 that begin with the letter W gives the frequency distribution shown in Figure 9.9. Since WJ occurs very frequently in the code, and ET does not occur very frequently in English text, we can assume that $\phi^{-1}(J)$ is not T but is probably R, N, or S. The digraph frequency for digraphs ending in W in the code is given in Figure 9.10. If we assume that $\phi(T)$ is either K or P, then since TE occurs rather frequently as a digraph in English text, and PW occurs twice in the code whereas KW does not occur at all, we may assume that PW can be decoded as TE. Thus we try $\phi^{-1}(P) = T$:

$$\phi^{-1}(P) = T, \qquad \phi^{-1}([16]) = 20, \qquad [16]Z_1 + Z_2 = [20]$$

$$\phi^{-1}(W) = E, \qquad \phi^{-1}([23]) = 5, \qquad [23]Z_1 + Z_2 = [5],$$

which yields

$$[7]Z_1 = [-15] = [11] \qquad \text{and} \qquad Z_1 = [15][11] = [9],$$

so that $Z_2 = [6]$.

Hence we have a tentative decoding function $\phi^{-1}(*) = *Z_1 + Z_2$. Substituting J for $*$ yields $\phi^{-1}([10]) = [10][9] + [6] = [96] = [18]$. Thus $\phi^{-1}(J) = R$, which agrees with the analysis of the digraphs. We can now decode the message as shown in Figure 9.11.

The previous example illustrates the use of frequency considerations in decoding. Not only can use be made of the frequency of occurrence of digraphs, but also the frequency of occurrence of triples of adjacent letters

```
          W
C        |
D        ||
J        |
M        |
N        |
P        ||
Q        |
R        |
T        |
U        |
W        |
X        ||
Y        |
```

Figure 9.10 Digraph frequency for _W in the code in Figure 9.6.

ASIMI	LARAS	SESSM	ENTCA	NBEMA
DEWIT	HRESP	ECTTO	GENER	ATING
ELECT	RICPO	WERFR	OMALT	ERNAT
EENER	GYSOU	RCES

A similar assessment can be made with respect to generating
electric power from alternate energy sources.

Figure 9.11 Decoded version of Figure 9.6.

(called *trigraphs*). Figure 9.12 gives the frequency of trigraphs taken from the
same material as the digraph sample.

A modular code has the advantage that it is relatively simple to encode
and decode. It has the disadvantage that a knowledge of how two letters are
decoded is sufficient to determine how all letters are decoded. Thus to
decode a message requires only that the modular integers Z_1 and Z_2 be
known. It is much more difficult to devise a decoding method for arbitrary
encoding functions ϕ. In this case the receiver of the encoded message must
in general have the decoding function ϕ^{-1} available—in tabular form written on paper, in the form of a specially constructed decoding machine, or in
memorized form. Since written form or a specially constructed machine
constitutes physical evidence, often it is desired to have the decoding function in memorized form. Because of the difficulty and unreliability of the
human memory, it is desirable to have decoding information in as concise a
form as possible. This is one advantage of modular decoding. Another type

THE	1717	FOR	284	ERE	212
AND	483	THA	255	CON	206
TIO	384	TER	232	TED	187
ATI	287	RES	219	COM	185

Figure 9.12 Frequency count of trigraphs (in 80,000-character text).

```
   A  B  C  D  E  F  G  H  I  J  K  L  M  N  O  P  Q  R  S  T  U  V  W  X  Y  Z
φ↓
   "Q  U  E  B  C  L  I  R  A  T  O  N"  D  F  G  H  J  K  M  P  S  V  W  X  Y  Z
```

Figure 9.13 A key-word encoding.

of monoalphabetic encoding requiring minimal information on the part of the decoder is *key-word encoding*. This encoding is determined by a key word by the following method. List the alphabet on a line. Write the key word below the alphabet with the first letter of the key word corresponding to A, the second to B, and so on, with repeated letters omitted. After the key word, continue writing the alphabet but omit the letters occurring in the key word. This gives the encoding correspondence, hence the decoding correspondence. For example, suppose the key word is " Quebec liberation." The encoding will then be as shown in Figure 9.13. To decode such an encoding, one must discover the key word, or treat the encoding as an arbitrary monoalphabetic encoding.

The reader may enjoy inventing different monoalphabetic encodings which are not of the types discussed previously and yet require a minimal amount of memorization to decode the messages.

Exercises

9-1 Determine the decoding function for a Caesar cypher having CAXSJWB as an encoded word.

9-2 Decode the following encoded message:

IPYKM	IUUWX	MWREF	WKVEK	YOYKJ	TKXTS
XUKXK	CWKNR	WNSPM	SQQWW	TWTIX	UKOIXC
PFWJK	PFWJS	XWBDW	QPWTJ	WQAJT	AZPYA
KXTKF	KRZUI	RWMDW	JFASJ.		

(*Hint:* This is a modular encoding.)

9-3   Use the encoding function $\phi([x]) = [15][x] + [6]$ to encode the following: "But the Snark is at hand, let me tell you again! 'Tis your glorious duty to seek it."

9-4   Decode the following and determine the type of code. (*Hint*: Try a keyword beginning with W.)

HGLUL	HDHGU	DMVNB	BUKPM	AHGUM	VUKUR
NMLHT	UKURW	GRNPV	WMUMP	WADNM	OURAU
YHGRW	RHQWP	POWPW	PQCOW	RUWPU	GONFP
OUWFU	KNLWG	MUXIU	LPURM	VNSPE	QMPNL
UPOUY	OWRGH	PSNBQ	KURHG	POUSK	UMOMI
NKNPH	SGWPN	HGWDN	MFPOW	PVWMK	WFIWG
PNGPO	WRHEN	GNHG.			

9-5   Invent a monoalphabetic encoding that is easily remembered but different from both modular encodings and key-word encodings.

9-6   Determine the number of distinct modular encodings.

9-7   Determine the number of arbitrary monoalphabetic encodings of the English alphabet.

9-8   By using the encoding $\varepsilon(n) = n + 5$ encode the following: "Reading week is coming."

9.3   MATRIX ENCODINGS

Monoalphabetic encoding is only one possibility among numerous methods of encoding. This section deals with a type of block encoding called *matrix encoding*. The alphabet is again represented by the integers modulo 26. The base set of this encoding is the vector space of m-tuples with elements in the integers modulo 26. Thus $\mathscr{A}$ can be thought of as blocks of m letters. Let M be an invertible $m \times m$ matrix with entries in $Z/(26)$. The encoding thus takes a block of m letters, realizes this as a vector in $[Z/(26)]^m$, multiplies this vector by M, and then produces the corresponding block of letters.

For example, if we encode blocks of two letters by multiplication by the matrix

$$M = \begin{bmatrix} 1 & 1 \\ 13 & 2 \end{bmatrix},$$

then "to" becomes

$$[20, 15] \begin{bmatrix} 1 & 1 \\ 13 & 12 \end{bmatrix} = [7, 18] \quad \text{or} \quad GR.$$

The word "do" becomes

$$[4, 15]\begin{bmatrix} 1 & 1 \\ 13 & 12 \end{bmatrix} = [17, 2] \quad \text{or} \quad \text{QB}.$$

This encoding is clearly not monoalphabetic, since in the first case the letter O was replaced by the letter R, and in the second case the letter O was replaced by the letter B. If the matrix M^{-1} is calculated, then the encoding is simply multiplication by M^{-1}, since $(vM)M^{-1} = v$ for each vector v. In the example,

$$M^{-1} = \begin{bmatrix} 1 & 1 \\ 13 & 12 \end{bmatrix}^{-1} = \begin{bmatrix} 14 & 1 \\ 13 & 25 \end{bmatrix},$$

and multiplication by M^{-1} transforms GR back to "to" and OB back to "do."

If the encoding and decoding matrices are unknown, but samples of encoded messages are available, then the following procedure is often successful in cracking the code. First, guess whether the code is monoalphabetic or not. This can be judged by considering the frequency distribution of the code letters. A monoalphabetic code has great variation in the frequencies of individual letters, which should match the frequencies given in Figure 9.5. A matrix encoding has a more even frequency distribution of the letters. Once it has been decided that the code is not monoalphabetic, and that it is possibly a matrix encoding, the next important step is to determine the block size (i.e., the dimension of the vector space). If a complete message has been intercepted, then the total number of characters can be counted. This corresponds to an integer multiple of a certain number of blocks, so that the block size is a divisor of the total number of characters. If several complete encoded messages have been intercepted, then the block size will be a divisor of the number of characters in each message, hence will be a common divisor of the number of characters in each message. This restricts the block size to only a few (hopefully one) possibilities. For example, suppose the following two messages are intercepted:

LMRSX	CCHDV	SHBUS	NBTGU	RDKDV
WLUQE	MQKYK	YHWSA	KYURG	SPRYV
WQPTT	UYM.			

OXJRM	FURYK	AGDVS	HBUPH	OBKYH
WSAKY	SBUVS	FKVQT	MEOTV	M.

A frequency count of the characters in these two messages gives the following:

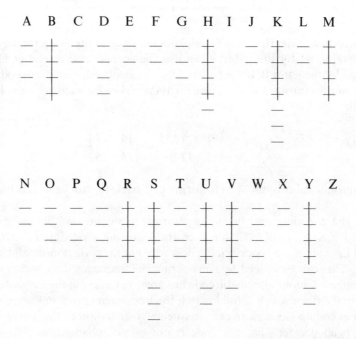

This frequency count is much more evenly distributed than the standard frequency count. Hence we may assume that the code is not monoalphabetic and that it is possibly a matrix encoding. The first message contains 58 characters, hence the block length is 2, 29 or 58. The second message contains 46 characters, so that the block length is 2, 23 or 46. Hence, if the code is a matrix encoding, then the block size is 2.

The method can be easily confounded, because the person who sends the message may add a few dummy letters at the end of the message. However, if a sequence of letters is repeated in the text, one may assume that the number of letters from the start of the first occurrence of the sequence to the start of the repetition is a multiple of the block size, and the same procedure as above can be used.

To continue the analysis of deciphering a matrix encoding, a large sample of encoded text is needed. In the above example, with block length 2, the frequencies of the digraphs corresponding to vectors can be counted and a correspondence between frequent digraphs in the encoded text and frequent digraphs in the English language can be attempted. For example, if

$\phi^{-1}(\mathbf{v})$ and $\phi^{-1}(\mathbf{w})$ are known for vectors $\mathbf{v}$ and $\mathbf{w}$ in $[Z/(26)]^2$, then the system of four equations and four unknowns given by $\mathbf{v}M^{-1} = \phi^{-1}(\mathbf{v})$ and $\mathbf{w}M^{-1} = \phi^{-1}(\mathbf{w})$ can possibly be solved. Since there are so many digraphs, an encoded message of considerable size must be available to make a useful count. The previously given messages have far too few characters to give a useful digraph count. However, the code breaker may have other information available, which may be helpful in cracking the code. For example, the code breaker may know the general nature of the messages (which, for example, may deal with relevant political events), hence may expect the occurrence of certain phrases or certain words. Thus, if strings of characters are repeated, this may indicate a possible decoding. In the example, the code breaker may suspect that the messages deal with events in Indochina, hence may suspect that the word "Indochina" occurs in the text. This word begins with IN and six characters later repeats the IN. Thus the occurrence of a digraph and its repetition six characters later may indicate the word "Indochina." In the first message the sequence KYHWSAKY occurs, and furthermore this sequence occurs in the second message. Hence assume $\phi^{-1}(\text{KY}) = \text{IN}$ and $\phi^{-1}(\text{HW}) = \text{DO}$. Thus we have

$$[[11], [25]] \begin{bmatrix} x_1 & x_2 \\ x_3 & x_4 \end{bmatrix} = [[9], [14]]$$

$$[[8], [23]] \begin{bmatrix} x_1 & x_2 \\ x_3 & x_4 \end{bmatrix} = [[4], [15]],$$

where

$$\begin{bmatrix} x_1 & x_2 \\ x_3 & x_4 \end{bmatrix}$$

is the inverse of the encoding matrix. This yields the equations in $Z/(26)$:

$$11x_1 + 25x_3 = 9, \qquad 11x_2 + 25x_4 = 14$$

$$8x_1 + 23x_3 = 4, \qquad 8x_2 + 23x_4 = 15,$$

which have the unique solutions $x_1 = 3$, $x_2 = 25$, $x_3 = 24$, and $x_4 = 1$. To see if the code is actually a matrix encoding and the matrix

$$\begin{bmatrix} 3 & 25 \\ 24 & 1 \end{bmatrix}$$

is actually the decoding matrix, we attempt to decode the message. The first eight letters in the first message yield

$$\phi^{-1}(LM) = \phi^{-1}[12, 13] = [12, 13]\begin{bmatrix} 3 & 25 \\ 24 & 1 \end{bmatrix} = [10, 1] = JA$$

$$\phi^{-1}(RS) = \phi^{-1}[18, 19] = [18, 19]\begin{bmatrix} 3 & 25 \\ 24 & 1 \end{bmatrix} = [16, 1] = PA$$

$$\phi^{-1}(XC) = \phi^{-1}[24, 3] = [24, 3]\begin{bmatrix} 3 & 25 \\ 24 & 1 \end{bmatrix} = [14, 5] = NE$$

$$\phi^{-1}(CH) = \phi^{-1}[3, 8] = [3, 8]\begin{bmatrix} 3 & 25 \\ 24 & 1 \end{bmatrix} = [19, 5] = SE,$$

so that $\phi^{-1}(LMRSXCCH) = $ "Japanese."

Decoding the remainder of the encoded text gives the following messages:

Japanese troops currently stationed in Indochina will be withdrawn.

Withdrawal of troops from Indochina is a smokescreen.

Deciphering an encoded message encoded by matrix multiplication of vectors of large block size is extremely difficult. However, for block size 2 or 3 the problem is tractable. One may suspect that matrix encodings of large block size are extremely attractive, since cracking the code is so difficult. There is, however, one serious drawback. If a single error occurs in a block during the handling of an encoded message, then that error will affect the decoding of every character in that block. For example, if blocks of length 5 are encoded by matrix multiplication by the matrix

$$M = \begin{bmatrix} 1 & 1 & 1 & 1 & 1 \\ 0 & 1 & 0 & 0 & 0 \\ 0 & 0 & 1 & 0 & 0 \\ 0 & 0 & 0 & 1 & 0 \\ 0 & 0 & 0 & 0 & 1 \end{bmatrix},$$

then the word "Prize" will be encoded as

$$\phi(PRIZE) = [16, 18, 9, 0, 5]\begin{bmatrix} 1 & 1 & 1 & 1 & 1 \\ 0 & 1 & 0 & 0 & 0 \\ 0 & 0 & 1 & 0 & 0 \\ 0 & 0 & 0 & 1 & 0 \\ 0 & 0 & 0 & 0 & 1 \end{bmatrix} = [16, 8, 25, 16, 21]$$

$$= PHYPU.$$

The inverse of the matrix M is the decoding matrix

$$M^{-1} = \begin{bmatrix} 1 & 25 & 25 & 25 & 25 \\ 0 & 1 & 0 & 0 & 0 \\ 0 & 0 & 1 & 0 & 0 \\ 0 & 0 & 0 & 1 & 0 \\ 0 & 0 & 0 & 0 & 1 \end{bmatrix}.$$

If in the handling of the encoded message PHYPU is changed to QHYPU, then the decoding of QHYPU will be

$$(17, 8, 25, 16, 21)M^{-1} = (17, 17, 8, 25, 4) = \text{QQHYD}.$$

Thus what should have been decoded as "prize" will be decoded as "qqhyd," and thus the error that occurred in the first component of the block was propagated throughout the whole block. For block size 2 or 3, this is not a serious problem, since much of the message can still be constructed from the context. However, for large block sizes a single error results in a decoding that is unreadable in that block.

Exercises

9-9 Determine the number of distinct 2×2 matrix encodings of $Z/(26)$. (*Hint:* Use Exercise 8-33.)

9-10 It is suspected that the following intercepted message deals with Norad radar defense. Make a frequency count of the single letters and decode the message.

VCDHM	ZPQUJ	YXYWZ	YWZQN	IIAOU
XXFKY	LWMXT	SHOBU	AZAKO	GWSYN
ABCUK	UTPRI	JXMNY	GKLEN	IOVRW
JGOLM	DFSKM	UQRWX	FIAHG	JUNXY
ANSYE	KOYRE	ALFEF	WEBOC	QCE.

9-11 Given that the following 2×2 matrix encoding is likely to contain the phrase "some homomorphisms," decode the message.

KJGB	LGUF	UFHH	NOCD
KWSZ	KJUF	HHNO	CD.

9-12 Suppose a matrix encoding is given by the matrix

$$\begin{bmatrix} 3 & 7 \\ 2 & 5 \end{bmatrix}$$

with entries in $Z/(26)$. Determine the decoding matrix and decode ORRVWA.

*9.4   SCRAMBLED CODES

Permutations are the basis for a type of cryptographic code called a scrambled code. If π is a permutation on $\{1, 2, \ldots, n\}$, then we define the encoding function π to be the map from $(a_1, \ldots, a_n)$ to $(a_{\pi(1)}, \ldots, a_{\pi(n)})$. This is actually a very special type of matrix encoding, since the mapping is linear (this is easily checked). However, the fact that it is a matrix encoding is of little help in analyzing the code.

For example, suppose $\pi = (1\ \ 3\ \ 2\ \ 5\ \ 4)$ and we wish to use the encoding induced by this permutation to encode the message, "The trial begins tomorrow." The message is divided into blocks of five, and to encode a block the $\pi(1)$ letter is placed in the first position, the $\pi(2)$ letter in the second position, the $\pi(3)$ letter in the third position, the $\pi(4)$ letter in the fourth position, and the $\pi(5)$ letter in the fifth position. The blocked message is

THETR IALBE GINST OMORR OWZZZ

which is encoded as

ERHTT LEAIB NTIGS ORMOR ZZWOZ

To decode a permutation encoding, first make sure that the encoding is indeed a permutation encoding, second, determine the block size, and, third, determine the permutation. The frequency count of the occurrences of letters in a permutation encoding yields a frequency distribution very similar to a standard distribution. Thus one can assume that the letters in the original message are permuted. Block size is determined in the same manner as the block size for a matrix encoding. In other words, if a sequence of letters is repeated, then it can be assumed that the same word or phrase was repeated in the original message, hence the block size is a divisor of the number of letters separating the successive occurrences of the repeated sequence. Once the block size is determined, construct a table whose ith row is the ith block. Permute the columns of the table to obtain a reasonable fit of pairs and continue until the message can be read from the table.

The following example illustrates the process. Suppose the following encoded message is intercepted.

SAIRL	GEINR	EELOA	MHDSE
YNAAA	SSYSA	IRLFE	IREOC
WLSIP	LLUBC	LATMK	OTAIL
ASPSZ.			

A frequency count performed on this message is shown in Figure 9.14 and compared to the standard frequency count.

Since the frequency of occurrence of letters in the message so closely matches the standard count, we assume that the code is a permutation code. The block size must now be determined. The sequence SAIRL is repeated with an interval of 28 letters from the start of the first occurrence to the start of the second occurrence. Thus the block size of the encoding is a divisor of 28, hence must be 2, 4, 7, or 28. Since the only permutations of two elements are the identity permutation and a permutation interchanging the two elements, a quick check shows that the block length is not 2. Suppose now that the block length is 4. If we write the message in a table with four columns, where row i is simply block i of the message, then by permutating the columns we will eventually, if the block size is 4, obtain the message. The rectangular array in the above example is

S	A	I	R
L	G	E	I
N	R	E	E
L	O	A	M
H	D	S	E
Y	N	A	A
A	S	S	Y
S	A	I	R
L	F	E	I
R	E	O	C
W	L	S	I
P	L	L	U
B	C	L	A
T	M	K	O
T	A	I	L
A	S	P	S
Z,			

and we can attempt to permute the columns to determine a message. Since column 1 and column 2 do not seem to belong together, we can try column 1 and column 3, but in this case we obtain the unusual combinations HS from row 5 and PK from row 14. If we try column 1 adjacent to column 4, there

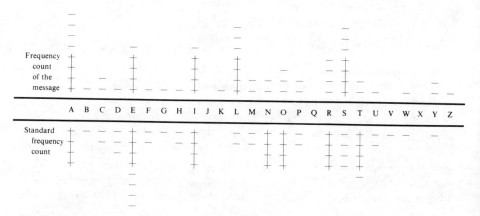

Figure 9.14   Frequency of occurrence of letters in the message and in a standard message.

will be fewer unnatural two-letter combinations, so we may assume column 1 and column 4 are adjacent. This gives

S	R
L	I
N	E
L	M
H	E
Y	A
A	Y
S	R
L	I
R	C
W	I
P	U
B	A
T	O
T	L
A	S.

If column 2 or column 3 is placed before column 1, column 3 will yield slightly better three-letter sequences. Putting column 2 before the already determined portion yields nonsense, but putting it after the determined portion yields

I	S	R	A
E	L	I	G
E	N	E	R
A	L	M	O
S	H	E	D
A	Y	A	N
S	A	Y	S
I	S	R	A
E	L	I	F
O	R	C	E
S	W	I	L
L	P	U	L
L	B	A	C
K	T	O	M
I	T	L	A
P	A	S	S,

which can then be read:

> Israeli general Moshe Dayan says Israeli forces will
> pull back to Mitla Pass.

This method works only if the block length is relatively short compared to the length of the total message. However, there are numerous ways to construct a permutation encoding with the block lengths equal to the message lengths. These encodings are more difficult to decipher, and we investigate only one of this type.

One kind of scrambled code having the block length equal to the message length is a completely filled rectangle code. To encode a message using this method choose a rectangle width k and place the integers from 1 through k in the top row of a table, in arbitrary order. Write the message in blocks of k letters underneath the first row to form a rectangle. The encoded message is now written out by first writing the column labeled 1 horizontally, followed by the column labeled 2, and continuing until the final column k is written horizontally. For example, the message, "The Chilean junta wishes to meet," can be encoded by the following table.

2	1	3
T	H	E
C	H	I
L	E	A
N	J	U
N	T	A
W	I	S
H	E	S
T	O	M
E	E	T.

The message then becomes

HHEJTIEOE

TCLNNWHTE

EIAUASSMT,

which is written

HHEJT   IEOET   CLNNW   HTEEI   AUASS   MT.

To decode a message encoded by a completely filled rectangle, the dimension of the rectangle must be determined. If the rectangle is completely filled, then the length multiplied by the width will be the number of letters in the message. Hence the length and width of the rectangle are factors of the number of letters in the message. Once the dimensions of the rectangle are decided, fill in the rectangle with the encoded message by writing the encoded message vertically. Once this is done, permute the columns until the message can be read.

As an example, suppose the message

SCOPI	TNUDO	TSERR	NYAPN	HUVMF
OCZLT	OAROT	EREEF	NTAEL	PSRIF
ELNUR	OEHGE	MATTE	POIAS

is intercepted. A frequency count indicates that the message is a scrambled code, and we can see if it is a completely filled rectangle encoding. Since there are 70 letters in the message, the rectangle could be 35 by 2, 14 by 4, or 10 by 7. It is easily checked that the encoding is not a 35 by 2 completely filled rectangle encoding, so the size 14 by 5 is next tried. The decoding rectangle is given in Figure 9.15. The columns of the table should now be permuted until a message is formed. If we examine the third row, a permutation gives the suffix OLOGY and, if we try this ordering on the columns, we obtain

S	A	L	E	R		L	A	S	E	R
C	E	T	H	N		T	E	C	H	N
O	L	O	G	Y	or	O	L	O	G	Y
P	P	A	E	A		A	P	P	E	A
I	S	R	M	P		R	S	I	M	P
T	R	O	A	N		O	R	T	A	N
N	I	T	T	H		T	I	N	T	H
U	F	E	T	U		E	F	U	T	U
D	E	R	E	V		R	E	D	E	V
O	L	E	P	M		E	L	O	P	M
T	N	E	O	F		E	N	T	O	F
S	U	F	I	O		F	U	S	I	O
E	R	N	A	C		N	R	E	A	C
R	O	T	S	Z		T	O	R	S	Z.

The message now reads:

> Laser technology appears important in the future development of fusion reactorsz.

In the above example of a completely filled rectangle encoding, the dummy letter Z was placed in the encoding to fill the rectangle. The encoding procedure can be used even when the rectangle is not completely filled. The deciphering, however, is much more difficult, since the lengths of the columns are not in general known and the dimensions of the rectangle cannot be easily determined. However, if the message is suspected to contain a word or a phrase, then is additional information is often enough to help provide a decipherment.

S	R	L	A	E
C	N	T	E	H
O	Y	O	L	G
P	A	A	P	E
I	P	R	S	M
T	N	O	R	A
N	H	T	I	T
U	U	E	F	T
D	V	R	E	E
O	M	E	L	P
T	F	E	N	O
S	O	F	U	I
E	C	N	R	A
R	Z	T	O	S

Figure 9.15 Filled rectangle for given code.

As an example suppose the following message is intercepted and is suspected to contain the phrase "heavy water."

HWALA   AAETY   LEDLT   CVPRE   GNAHT

TCDPD   AARAT   UILEE   SAOOG   YEANO

TSNB.

Suppose the width of the rectangle is less than 10. If the width is exactly 9, then the R in "heavy water" will occur in the column directly beneath the initial letter H. Thus the encoded version will contain an HR. Since the message does not contain an HR, the width of the rectangle is not 9. If the width of the rectangle is 8, then during the encoding the letter R is placed beneath the letter E and the letter E beneath the letter H so the encoded version will contain HE and ER. Since neither occurs in the encoded message, the width of the rectangle is not 8. If the width of the rectangle is 7, then during the encoding the letter R will be placed beneath the letter A, the letter E beneath the letter E, and the letter T beneath the letter H, so that the encoded version will contain HT, EE, and AR. These combinations do occur, so we may assume the width of the rectangle is 7 and that there are seven complete rows and a final unfinished row which contains four letters.

Thus the procedure is to block the suspected word into appropriate widths and examine the resulting columns to see if these combinations of letters occur. This yields the width of the rectangle and, in our example, located somewhere in the message are letter sequences corresponding to the columns in one of the following,

HEAVYWATE	HEAVYWAT	HEAVYWA	HEAVYW	HEAVY	HEAV	HEA	HE
R	ER	TER	ATER	WATER	YWAT	VYW	AV
				ER	ER	ATE	YW
					R	R	AT
							ER

corresponding to rectangle widths 9, 8, 7, 6, 5, 4, 3, and 2, respectively.

Now we form the rectangle by extending the columns corresponding to HT, EE, and AR:

P	R	T
R	A	C
E	T	D
G	U	P
N	I	D
A	L	A
H	**E**	**A**
T	**E**	**R**
T	S	A
C	A	T
D	O	U
P	O	I
D	G	L
A	Y	E.

Since V occurs exactly once in the message, adjoin the column containing V to the pattern to obtain

```
P  R  T  L
R  A  C  E
E  T  D  D
G  U  P  L
N  I  D  T
A  L  A  C
H  E  A  V
T  E  R  P
T  S  A  R
C  A  T  E
D  O  U  G
P  O  I  N
D  G  L  A
A  Y  E  H.
```

The first five rows of this pattern do not seem to be recognizable patterns of four letters, nor does the last row, so these need not be considered. Since there are two Y's in the message, columns containing Y can be added to the pattern to create the word "heavy."

A	L	A	C	T	G
H	E	A	V	Y	Y
T	E	R	P	L	E
T	S	A	R	E	A
C	A	T	E	D	N
D	O	U	G	L	O
P	O	I	N	T	T
O	G	L	A	C	S
				↑	↑

Either one of these

Also, there is one W in the encoded message, so we add a column with a W in it. If this column is placed after the column containing Y, the first row of the pattern will be ALACTH or ALACGH. The first choice seems more reasonable, so we obtain the pattern

$$
\begin{array}{cccccc}
A & L & A & C & T & H \\
H & E & A & V & Y & W \\
T & E & R & P & L & A \\
T & S & A & R & E & L \\
C & A & T & E & D & A \\
D & O & U & G & L & A \\
P & O & I & N & T & A \\
D & G & L & A & C & E.
\end{array}
$$

The remaining unused A now indicates the last column:

$$
\begin{array}{ccccccc}
A & L & A & C & T & H & E \\
H & E & A & V & Y & W & A \\
T & E & R & P & L & A & N \\
T & S & A & R & E & L & O \\
C & A & T & E & D & A & T \\
D & O & U & G & L & A & S \\
P & O & I & N & T & A & N \\
D & G & L & A & C & E & B.
\end{array}
$$

The first four letters of the message do not make sense, so we assume that the message begins with the word THE. Thus the final incompletely filled rectangle is

$$
\begin{array}{ccccccc}
2 & 1 & 7 & 4 & 6 & 5 & 3 \\
T & H & E & H & E & A & V \\
Y & W & A & T & E & R & P \\
L & A & N & T & S & A & R \\
E & L & O & C & A & T & E \\
D & A & T & D & O & U & G \\
L & A & S & P & O & I & N \\
T & A & N & D & G & L & A \\
C & E & B & A & Y,
\end{array}
$$

which yields the message:

The heavy-water plants are located at Douglas Point and Glace Bay.

In general, the deciphering of an incompletely filled rectangular encoding is difficult, but an analysis of the digraphs that can possibly occur often helps in starting the decipherment. For example, if the letter Q occurs in the encoded message, then in the decoding rectangle it will most likely be followed by U, which may indicate a possible start in the decipherment.

Exercises

9-13 Show that the composition of two scrambled encodings is again a scrambled encoding and determine the block size.

9-14 Let $\varepsilon(a_1, a_2, a_3, a_4, a_5) = (a_{\pi(1)}, a_{\pi(2)}, a_{\pi(3)}, a_{\pi(4)}, a_{\pi(5)})$, where $\pi = (1\ 2) \cdot (3\ 4\ 5)$. Determine the decoding map ε^{-1}. Encode "Xerox."

9.5   THE HAMMING METRIC

In the last three sections dealing with cryptography, the encoding function ϕ mapped the base set $\mathscr{A}$ in a one-to-one fashion onto the base set $\mathscr{A}$. However, for the error detection and error correction aspects of coding theory, the function ϕ must map the base set properly into the image set X. If $\phi(\mathscr{A}) = X$, and an error in transmission occurs, then the received word is still an element in $\phi(\mathscr{A})$, hence will be decoded improperly. However, if $\phi(\mathscr{A})$ is a proper subset of X, then quite possibly $\phi(a)$ could be transmitted and received as x, an element not in $\phi(\mathscr{A})$. Thus someone receiving the transmission would know there was an error in the transmission.

Usually data, whether occurring as deep-space communication or communication between earthbound computers, is coded in binary. Thus the messages are sequences of 0's and 1's. These sequences code naturally into blocks, so the base set is $\mathscr{A} = [Z/(2)]^m$. Since the image set must be properly larger than the base set, we take the image set to be $[Z/(2)]^n$, where $n > m$. A one-to-one map ϕ from $[Z/(2)]^m$ into $[Z/(2)]^n$ is called an (m, n) encoding. An (m, n) encoding can detect errors in transmission if it takes many errors to change one encoded block into another encoded block. Thus two encoded words should be far apart in terms of numbers of errors required to transform one encoded word into another. This notion is made precise by the following definitions.

The weight of a vector $\mathbf{x}$ in $[Z/(2)]^n$ is defined to be the number of nonzero components of the vector and is denoted by $w(\mathbf{x})$. If $\mathbf{x}$ and $\mathbf{y}$ are two vectors in $[Z/(2)]^n$, then the *Hamming distance* between $\mathbf{x}$ and $\mathbf{y}$ is defined to be the number of nonzero components in $\mathbf{x} - \mathbf{y}$ and is denoted by $d(\mathbf{x}, \mathbf{y})$. Since addition in $Z/(2)$ is the same as subtraction, and $1 + 1 = 0$, the distance from $\mathbf{x}$ to $\mathbf{y}$ is simply the number of components where the entry in $\mathbf{x}$ is different from the corresponding entry in $\mathbf{y}$. It is easy to check that the Hamming distance is actually a metric, since $d(\mathbf{x}, \mathbf{y}) \geq 0$ for all vectors $\mathbf{x}$ and $\mathbf{y}$, $d(\mathbf{x}, \mathbf{y}) = 0$ if and only if $\mathbf{x} = \mathbf{y}$, and $d(\mathbf{x}, \mathbf{y}) + d(\mathbf{y}, \mathbf{z}) \geq d(\mathbf{x}, \mathbf{z})$ for all vectors $\mathbf{x}$, $\mathbf{y}$, and $\mathbf{z}$ in $[Z/(2)]^n$.

This notion of distance determines the error-detecting capability of an encoding. An (m, n) encoding ϕ is said to detect k or fewer errors if there is a procedure that indicates that a received block is incorrect whenever there are j errors, $1 \leq j \leq k$, in that received block.

Theorem 9.1   An (m, n) encoding ϕ detects k or fewer errors if and only if the minimal distance between encoded words is at least $k + 1$.

Proof   Suppose ϕ detects all sets of k or fewer errors and suppose $\mathbf{x}$ is an encoded word of distance j, $1 \leq j \leq k$, from another encoded word $\mathbf{y}$. If the encoded word $\mathbf{x}$ is transmitted and errors occur in exactly the components of $\mathbf{x}$ that differ from the corresponding components of $\mathbf{y}$, then the received message will appear to be a normal transmission of $\mathbf{y}$. Thus no error is noticed and yet j errors occurred in the transmission. This is a contradiction, hence the minimum distance between encoded words must be at least $k + 1$.

To complete the proof of the theorem, assume that the minimum distance between encoded words is at least $k + 1$. Thus, if j errors, $1 \leq j \leq k$, occur during the transmission of an encoded word $\mathbf{x}$, the received word will not be an encoded word, hence there must have been errors in the transmission. Since the list of encoded words is finite, the received word can be compared with each encoded word in the list to determine whether or not it represents an encoded vector. If not, then errors have been made.

The procedure for detecting errors implicit in Theorem 9.1 is very inefficient, since each received word must essentially be compared with all possible encoded words. More efficient methods are investigated later.

An (m, n) encoding ϕ is said to correct k or fewer errors if there is a procedure that will correct a received word to yield the original encoded word, whenever j errors, $1 \leq j \leq k$, occur in transmission of the block. The Hamming metric also describes the error-correcting possibilities of an encoding.

Theorem 9.2   An (m, n) encoding ϕ corrects k or fewer errors if and only if the minimum distance between encoded words is at least $2k + 1$.

Proof Suppose that ϕ corrects k or fewer errors and that $\mathbf{x}$ is an encoded word of distance $1 \le h \le 2k$ from an encoded word $\mathbf{y}$. Thus $\mathbf{x} - \mathbf{y} = \mathbf{z}$, where the number of nonzero components in $\mathbf{z}$ is h. Write $\mathbf{z} = \mathbf{a} + \mathbf{b}$, where $\mathbf{a}$ has at most k nonzero entries and $\mathbf{b}$ has at most k nonzero entries. If the transmission of the encoded word $\mathbf{x}$ results in $\mathbf{x} + \mathbf{a}$ being received, then at most k errors occurred in the transmission. Likewise, if the transmission of the encoded word $\mathbf{y}$ results in $\mathbf{y} + \mathbf{b}$ being received, then at most k errors were made during transmission. However, $\mathbf{x} + \mathbf{a} = \mathbf{y} + \mathbf{b}$, so the correct decoding is not possible. This contradicts the ability of ϕ to correct k or fewer errors, hence the minimum distance between encoded words is at least $2k + 1$.

Suppose now that the minimum distance between encoded words is at least $2k + 1$. If the transmission of an encoded word $\mathbf{x}$ results in an encoded word $\mathbf{x} + \mathbf{e}$, where $d(\mathbf{x}, \mathbf{x} + \mathbf{e}) \le k$, then the encoded word $\mathbf{x}$ can be recovered, since $\mathbf{x}$ is the closest encoded word to $\mathbf{x} + \mathbf{e}$. If another encoded word $\mathbf{y}$ is at least as close to $\mathbf{x} + \mathbf{e}$ as $\mathbf{x}$, then by the triangular law of the metric, $2k = k + k \ge d(\mathbf{x}, \mathbf{x} + \mathbf{e}) + d(\mathbf{x} + \mathbf{e}, \mathbf{y}) \ge d(\mathbf{x}, \mathbf{y})$, which contradicts the fact that the minimum distance between encoded words is at least $2k + 1$. Thus to correct k or fewer errors, calculate the distance between the received word and each encoded word. The received word is then decoded as the closest encoded word.

A common and simple example of a single-error-detecting code is the parity-check code. The block $(a_1, \ldots, a_m)$ is encoded as $(a_1, \ldots, a_m, \sum a_i)$. This is an $(m, m + 1)$ encoding and has a minimum distance of 2 between encoded words. This code has the additional advantage that a received word does not have to be compared with all possible encoded words in order to detect an error. To see if an error occurred during transmission simply sum the components of the received vector modulo 2. If no errors occurred during transmission, then the sum of the components is $\sum a_i + \sum a_i = 0$, and if a single error occurred during transmission, then the sum of the components is 1. It is extremely important in the implementation of codes that a simple and relatively fast method exists for the correction or detection of errors. Sections 10.6 and 10.7 are devoted to describing certain encodings for which there exist efficient, fast, easily implemented detection and correction algorithms.

A common type of block encoding is illustrated in Section 9.3. Thus a vector in $[Z/(2)]^m$ can be encoded as that vector multiplied by a fixed $m \times n$ matrix. The encoding is one-to-one if and only if the rank of the matrix equals m, which automatically implies that $m \le n$. Error detection capabilities are possible only if the vector space is mapped properly into the image space, hence in this case m is strictly less than n. These types of encodings are studied in detail in Section 9.6 and in Chapter 10.

9.6   BINARY GROUP CODES

This section describes certain types of (m, n) block codes which map $[Z/(2)]^m$ into $[Z/(2)]^n$ by multiplication by an $m \times n$ matrix of rank m. The error correction capabilities of such a code, along with a perfect single-error-correcting code called the Hamming code, are described.

One of the simplest types of block encoding is encoding induced by multiplication by an $m \times n$ matrix of rank m. The set of encoded words is simply the image of the vector space $[Z/(2)]^m$ under the linear transformation induced by matrix multiplication. Since the image of the vector space is again a vector subspace, the set of encoded words forms a group under the usual addition of vectors. Alternatively, if M is the encoding matrix, and $\mathbf{x}$ and $\mathbf{y}$ are message vectors, so that $\mathbf{x} \circ M$ and $\mathbf{y} \circ M$ are encoded vectors, then $\mathbf{x} \circ M + [-(\mathbf{y} \circ M)] = [\mathbf{x} + (-\mathbf{y})] \circ M$, which again is an encoded vector, since $\mathbf{x} + (-\mathbf{y})$ is a message vector. Thus by Proposition 7.4 the set of encoded words is a subgroup of the group $[Z/(2)]^n$. Such a code is called a *binary group code*.

The calculation of the minimum distance between encoded words in binary group codes is somewhat simpler than for an arbitrary code. The distance from a code word $\mathbf{u}$ to a code word $\mathbf{v}$ is the weight of $\mathbf{u} - \mathbf{v}$ and, in a binary group code, the vector $\mathbf{u} - \mathbf{v}$ is again an encoded word, so that the minimum distance between encoded words equals the minimum weight of a nonzero encoded word. This simplifies the calculation of the $2^m(2^m - 1)/2$ distances between encoded words to the calculation of the 2^m weights of encoded words.

We now describe an algorithm which gives an error correction procedure for an (m, n) matrix encoding. If $\mathbf{z}$ is a vector in $[Z/(2)]^n$, then a correction procedure is said to correct the error pattern $\mathbf{z}$ if whenever a vector $\mathbf{z} + \mathbf{v}$ is received, where $\mathbf{v}$ is an encoded vector, then the decoding procedure changes this received word to $\mathbf{v}$. The set of vectors of the form $\mathbf{z} + \mathbf{v}$, where $\mathbf{v}$ ranges over the encoded vectors, is a coset of the subgroup of encoded vectors in $[Z/(2)]^n$ with coset representative $\mathbf{z}$. Furthermore, any element in this coset is of the form $\mathbf{z} + \mathbf{u}$ for a unique encoded word $\mathbf{u}$ and the correction of $\mathbf{z} + \mathbf{u}$ yields $\mathbf{u}$. Hence for a binary group code, we can institute the following error correction procedure. Let H be the subgroup of encoded vectors. Construct a table with the first row of the table being the elements of H beginning with the 0 vector. Let $\mathbf{z}_2, \ldots, \mathbf{z}_n$ be vectors such that $0 + H, \mathbf{z}_2 + H, \ldots, \mathbf{z}_t + H$ are the t distinct cosets of H. The remainder of the table is now filled in by putting $\mathbf{z}_i + \mathbf{v}$ in the ith row and the column corresponding to the encoded vector $\mathbf{v}$. This table contains all 2^n elements of

$00000 + H = \{00000, 00111, 01001, 01110, 10011, 10100, 11010, 11101\}$

$00001 + H = \{00001, 00110, 01000, 01111, 10010, 10101, 11011, 11100\}$

$00010 + H = \{00010, 00101, 01011, 01100, 10001, 10110, 11000, 11111\}$

$10000 + H = \{10000, 10111, 11001, 11110, 00011, 00100, 01010, 01101\}$

Figure 9.16   Cosets of H in V.

$[Z/(2)]^n$, so that any possible received vector is listed in the table. To correct a received vector simply determine its position in the table and correct that vector to the encoded word at the top of the column. Such a table is called a coset table, and the elements $z_2, \ldots, z_t$ are called the coset leaders. This correction procedure corrects exactly the error patterns that occur as coset leaders, since any received word $z_i + v$, where v is an encoded word, is corrected to v.

As an example, suppose $U = [Z/(2)]^3$ is mapped into $V = [Z/(2)]^5$ by matrix multiplication with the matrix

$$M = \begin{bmatrix} 1 & 0 & 0 & 1 & 1 \\ 0 & 1 & 0 & 0 & 1 \\ 0 & 0 & 1 & 1 & 1 \end{bmatrix}.$$

The correspondence between the message words and the encoded words induced by matrix multiplication is given by

$$000 \rightarrow 00000$$

$$001 \rightarrow 00111$$

$$010 \rightarrow 01001$$

$$011 \rightarrow 01110$$

$$100 \rightarrow 10011$$

$$101 \rightarrow 10100$$

$$110 \rightarrow 11010$$

$$111 \rightarrow 11101.$$

The minimum weight of the nonzero encoded words is 2, hence the minimum distance between encoded words is 2. Thus we know from Theorem 9.1 that this encoding is single-error-detecting. The cosets of the subgroup H of encoded vectors are shown in Figure 9.16.

00000	00111	01001	01110	10011	10100	11010	11101
00001	00110	01000	01111	10010	10101	11011	11100
00010	00101	01011	01100	10001	10110	11000	11111
00100	00011	01101	01010	10111	10000	11110	11001

Figure 9.17 Error correction table for a group code.

We now must choose three coset leaders for the last three cosets, and then our error correction procedure will correct exactly the error patterns that are the coset leaders. If we assume that error patterns of weight 1 (patterns containing exactly one error) are more common than other patterns, then we should choose these as our coset leaders if possible. In the second coset we have two possible choices, namely, 00001 and 01000. In the third coset we have only one choice, namely, 00010, and in the fourth coset we again have two choices, namely, 10000 and 00100. Hence one possibility for our coset leaders is $z_2 = 00001$, $z_3 = 00010$, and $z_4 = 00100$. The error correction table is then shown in Figure 9.17. Thus if we receive the transmitted vector 01100, this vector occurs in the fourth column, hence is corrected to be 01110. This particular coset table corrects exactly the error patterns 00001, 00010, and 00100. The error correction procedure is not single-error-correcting (as we knew it could not be since the minimum distance is not ≥ 3), since the single-error pattern 10000 will not be corrected to 00000 but instead to 10100.

The above example illustrates a method of choosing the coset leaders in the error correction table for a binary group code. Simply choose an element of minimal weight in a particular coset (there may be several such elements of minimal weight). This element is the coset leader for that coset. The rationale behind this choice is that it is more likely that an error pattern of smaller weight will occur than an error pattern of larger weight. Thus to make the most efficient use of the error correction capabilities, the error patterns that will actually be corrected should be the error patterns that are most likely to occur.

The binary group code given in the example does not correct all single-error patterns. In general, if a binary group code corrects exactly the single-error patterns, then the code is called a perfect single-error-correcting code. If a binary group code corrects exactly those error patterns of weight $\leq j$, then the code is called a perfect j-error-correcting code. In a perfect single-error-correcting code, the order of the subgroup of encoded words is 2^m, the order of the group of all n-tuples of 0's and 1's is 2^n, and the number of cosets needed in the coset table is n (one for each position of a possible single error) plus one (the subgroup itself). Hence by Lagrange's theorem $2^n = (1 + n)2^m$, so that $n = 2^k - 1$, where $k = n - m$. Thus $m = n - k = 2^k - 1 - k$, and the only possible perfect single-error-correcting group codes are $(2^k - 1 - k,$ $2^k - 1)$ matrix encodings. The actual existence of perfect single-error-correcting $(2^k - 1 - k, 2^k - 1)$ matrix encodings for each integer $k \geq 2$ is due to R. W. Hamming, who furthermore determined an efficient error-correcting procedure.

The error-correcting procedure for a binary group code using the coset table requires that a transmitted message be compared with possibly 2^n other vectors. This is extremely inefficient. However, in a group code of type $(2^k - 1 - k, 2^k - 1)$, in addition to the message digits there are k additional digits in a transmitted vector. It requires exactly k digits to specify the integers $1, 2, \ldots, 2^k - 1$ in binary notation. Hopefully, enough information is contained in these extra k digits so that any single-error location can be computed. This can be accomplished by the following procedure. Suppose our code has the following desirable properties. First a $(2^k - 1) \times k$ matrix P can be found such that $\mathbf{v} \circ P = 0$ for every encoded vector $\mathbf{v}$ (this indicates that there are no errors in the transmission). Furthermore, if $\mathbf{e}_i$ is a vector with 0 in every component except for the ith component, which contains a 1 (this corresponds to the error pattern with a 1 in the ith spot), then $\mathbf{e}_i \circ P =$ the binary representation of the integer i. Thus if a transmitted vector $\mathbf{v} + \mathbf{e}_i$ is received, then $(\mathbf{v} + \mathbf{e}_i) \circ P = \mathbf{v} \circ P + \mathbf{e}_i \circ P = \mathbf{0} + \mathbf{e}_i \circ P$, which is the representation of i in binary, and we know that an error has occurred in the ith digit of the received vector. Thus we need only change the ith component of the received vector to obtain the correct encoded vector.

Since $\mathbf{e}_i P$ is simply the ith row of P, the ith row of the matrix P is simply the k-digit binary representation of the integer i. For example, for a $(2^3 - 1 - 3, 2^3 - 1) = (4, 7)$ code the matrix P is

$$P = \begin{bmatrix} 0 & 0 & 1 \\ 0 & 1 & 0 \\ 0 & 1 & 1 \\ 1 & 0 & 0 \\ 1 & 0 & 1 \\ 1 & 1 & 0 \\ 1 & 1 & 1 \end{bmatrix}.$$

Suppose now that $\mathbf{v} = (a_1, a_2, \ldots, a_n)$ is a vector of indeterminates. The condition that $\mathbf{v} \circ P = 0$ yields a system of k equations in n unknowns. In fact, this system of equations is already in column echelon form with the first nonzero entry in the jth column occurring in the 2^{k-j}th row. Thus the indeterminates a_{2^i} are equal to a sum of certain a_t with $t > 2^i$ and $t \neq 2^s$ for any integer s. In the (4, 7) code,

$$[a_1, a_2, a_3, a_4, a_5, a_6, a_7] \begin{bmatrix} 0 & 0 & 1 \\ 0 & 1 & 0 \\ 0 & 1 & 1 \\ 1 & 0 & 0 \\ 1 & 0 & 1 \\ 1 & 1 & 0 \\ 1 & 1 & 1 \end{bmatrix} = (0, 0, 0)$$

yields

$$a_4 + a_5 + a_6 + a_7 = 0$$

$$a_2 + a_3 + a_6 + a_7 = 0$$

$$a_1 + a_3 + a_5 + a_7 = 0,$$

hence

$$a_4 = a_5 + a_6 + a_7$$

$$a_2 = a_3 + a_6 + a_7$$

$$a_1 = a_3 + a_5 + a_7.$$

The three equations thus give a_1, a_2, and a_4 as dependent indeterminates, while a_3, a_5, a_6, and a_7 are independent indeterminates. In general we then have the k-dependent indeterminates a_{2^i}, where $i = 0, 1, \ldots, k - 1$, while the remaining $n - k$ indeterminates are freely chosen. This system of equations actually shows an encoding procedure for the code. For example, in the (4, 7) code, the map

$$(b_1, b_2, b_3, b_4) \rightarrow (a_1, a_2, b_1, a_4, b_2, b_3, b_4),$$

with b_i in $Z/(2)$, $a_1 = b_1 + b_2 + b_4$, $a_2 = b_1 + b_3 + b_4$, and $a_4 = b_2 + b_3 + b_4$, is certainly one-to-one and linear and, furthermore, satisfies the set of equations necessary in order to have $(a_1, a_2, b_1, a_3, b_2, b_3, b_4)P = (0, 0, 0)$. In the general case, the components of the vector $(b_1, b_2, \ldots, b_m)$ are substituted in order for the $n - k = m$ free indeterminates, while the dependent indeterminates a_{2^i} are determined by the k equations with the b_j substituted into the corresponding free variables. The construction of the encoding guarantees that we have a $(2^k - 1 - k, 2^k - 1)$ matrix encoding such that vP, where v is a transmitted vector, yields the location expressed in binary of any single error occurring in transmission.

The example of the (4, 7) Hamming code can be examined in more detail. Since the encoding is

$$(b_1, b_2, b_3, b_4)$$

$$\rightarrow (b_1 + b_2 + b_4, b_1 + b_3 + b_4, b_1, b_2 + b_3 + b_4, b_2, b_3, b_4),$$

the encoding matrix is

$$M = \begin{bmatrix} 1 & 1 & 1 & 0 & 0 & 0 & 0 \\ 1 & 0 & 0 & 1 & 1 & 0 & 0 \\ 0 & 1 & 0 & 1 & 0 & 1 & 0 \\ 1 & 1 & 0 & 1 & 0 & 0 & 1 \end{bmatrix}.$$

The vector 1011 is thus encoded as $(1 + 0 + 1, 1 + 1 + 1, 1, 0 + 1 + 1, 0, 1, 1) = 0110011$. If the transmission of this vector results in the vector 0110111 being received, then the product

$$[0110111] \begin{bmatrix} 0 & 0 & 1 \\ 0 & 1 & 0 \\ 0 & 1 & 1 \\ 1 & 0 & 0 \\ 1 & 0 & 1 \\ 1 & 1 & 0 \\ 1 & 1 & 1 \end{bmatrix} = [101]$$

being nonzero indicates the occurrence of an error in transmission. Furthermore, since 101 is 5 in binary, the fifth component of the received word is changed to yield 0110011 as the encoded word. This encoded word is then decoded as 1011 by examining the third, fifth, sixth, and seventh components of the encoded word.

Hamming codes are perfect single-error-correcting codes. If an encoded word is transmitted correctly or has an error in exactly one component, then the correction followed by the decoding will yield the correct message word. However, if more than two components are in error after transmission, the Hamming code will not correct these errors but will change the received word to the nearest encoded word.

Exercises

9-15 Determine a coset table with coset leaders of minimal weight for the (3, 5) block code with encoding matrix

$$\begin{bmatrix} 1 & 1 & 1 & 0 & 0 \\ 0 & 1 & 0 & 1 & 0 \\ 1 & 0 & 0 & 1 & 1 \end{bmatrix}.$$

What error patterns are associated with the received words 11010 and 10111, what are the corrected versions of the received words, and what are the decoded corrected vectors?

9-16 Prove that the minimum distance between encoded vectors for any (4, 10) matrix encoding is ≤ 6.

9-17 A set of encoded vectors S is defined to be equivalent to a set of encoded vectors T if there is a one-to-one distance-preserving map from S onto T. If M is an encoding matrix, prove that the set of vectors $\mathbf{v}M$ is equivalent to the set of vectors $\mathbf{v}M'$, where

    a M' is obtained from M by interchanging two rows of M.

    b M' is obtained from M by interchanging two columns of M.

    c M' is obtained from M by adding a scalar multiple of one row of M to a different row of M.

9-18 If M is an $m \times n$ encoding matrix, prove that there is a matrix

$$M' = \left(I_{m \times m} \, P_{mx(n-m)}\right)$$

such that the set of vectors $\mathbf{v}M$ is equivalent to the set $\mathbf{v} \circ M'$.

9-19 Determine the encoding of $(b_1, b_2, b_3, b_4, b_5, b_6, b_7, b_8, b_9, b_{10}, b_{11})$ for the $(11, 15)$ Hamming code. If 110111001010111 is a transmitted vector, what is the corrected vector and what is the decoded corrected vector?

9-20 Prove that, in a binary group code, either all the code words have even weight or half have even weight and half have odd weight. (*Hint:* The code words of even weight form a subgroup.)

9-21 Determine all perfect double-error-correcting group codes (those that correct exactly the error patterns of weight ≤ 2) of size (m, n) for $n \leq 15$.

9-22 If 1101110 is a received word for the Hamming $(4, 7)$ code, what is the correct code word and the correct message word?

9-23 Design a $(2, 5)$ group code that will correct all single errors. Write out the coset table and determine exactly what error patterns are corrected.

9-24 Why does a $(2, 4)$ code not correct all single errors?

9-25 Suppose a $(3, 4)$ group code encodes 100 as 1001, 010 as 0100, and 001 as 0011. Determine the set of all encoded words, and a coset table for the code. Determine the set of error patterns corrected with this coset table.

9-26 Let G be an (m, n) group code over $Z/(2)$. Prove that the probability of an error going undetected is $\sum_{i=1}^{n} a_i p^{n-i} q^i$, where a_i is the number of encoded words of weight i, p is the probability of correctly transmitting one digit, and $q = 1 - p$.

---

*9.7 EQUIVALENT CODES

Let S and T be subspaces of $[Z/(2)]^n$. S is said to be *equivalent* to T if there is a one-to-one linear map ϕ from S onto T that preserves the Hamming distance between vectors, that is, $d(\mathbf{x}, \mathbf{y}) = d(\phi(\mathbf{x}), \phi(\mathbf{y}))$ for $\mathbf{x}$ and $\mathbf{y}$ in

S. If *S* and *T* are equivalent subspaces, then *S* and *T* are said to be *equivalent codes*. For example, $S = \{00000, 00110, 01001, 11011, 01111, 10010, 11101, 10100\}$ is a subspace of $[Z/(2)]^5$ and in fact is the set of encoded vectors for the (3, 5) encoding determined by

$$M = \begin{bmatrix} 0 & 0 & 1 & 1 & 0 \\ 0 & 1 & 0 & 0 & 1 \\ 1 & 1 & 0 & 1 & 1 \end{bmatrix}.$$

The set of encoded vectors for the (3, 5) encoding determined by

$$M' = \begin{bmatrix} 1 & 0 & 0 & 1 & 0 \\ 0 & 0 & 1 & 0 & 1 \\ 0 & 1 & 1 & 1 & 1 \end{bmatrix}.$$

is the subspace $T = \{00000, 10010, 00101, 01111, 10111, 01010, 11101, 11000\}$. The map

$$\phi : \mathbf{v} \to \mathbf{v} \begin{bmatrix} 0 & 0 & 1 & 0 & 0 \\ 1 & 0 & 0 & 0 & 0 \\ 0 & 1 & 0 & 0 & 0 \\ 0 & 0 & 0 & 1 & 0 \\ 0 & 0 & 0 & 0 & 1 \end{bmatrix}$$

is a linear map from *S* onto *T*, which simply maps the first component to the second, second to the third, and third back to the first component of each vector in *S*. In fact, $d(\mathbf{x}, \mathbf{y}) = d(\phi(\mathbf{x}), \phi(\mathbf{y}))$, so that *S* is equivalent to *T*.

Let $\mathbf{E}_i$ be the vector $(0, \ldots, 0, 1, 0, \ldots, 0)$ in $[Z/(2)]^n$, where 1 occurs in the *i*th component of $\mathbf{E}_i$. If *S* is a subspace of $[Z/(2)]^n$ and if π is a permutation of $\{1, 2, \ldots, n\}$, then the mapping $\phi_\pi : \mathbf{v} = \sum_{i=1}^n c_i \mathbf{E}_i \to \sum_{i=1}^n c_i \mathbf{E}_{\pi(i)}$ is a one-to-one linear transformation of $[Z/(2)]^n$ onto itself. Furthermore, since ϕ_π simply permutes the components of each vector in the same manner, ϕ_π preserves the Hamming distance. Thus *S* and $\phi_\pi(S)$ are equivalent. We now prove that all equivalent codes arise in this manner.

Theorem 9.3 Let *S* and *T* be equivalent codes in $[Z/(2)]^n$. Then there exists a permutation π of $\{1, 2, \ldots, n\}$ such that $\phi_\pi(S) = T$.

The proof of Theorem 9.3 consists of a series of lemmas. Since $[Z/(2)]^n$ is the set of *n*-tuples over $Z/(2)$, with addition being componentwise, we identify $[Z/(2)]^n$ with the ring $R = [Z/(2)] \oplus \cdots \oplus [Z/(2)]$, $Z/(2)$ taken *n* times. Multiplication in *R* is componentwise and $\mathbf{xy}$ has a 1 in the *j*th component exactly when both **x** and **y** have 1's in the *j*th component, where **x** and **y** are in *R*. The distance $d(\mathbf{x}, \mathbf{y})$ between **x** and **y** is the number of components of **x** and **y** that differ. The sum $w(\mathbf{x}) + w(\mathbf{y})$ includes the number of components of **x** and **y** that differ plus twice the number of components, where $\mathbf{x}$ and $\mathbf{y}$ are both 1. However, $w(\mathbf{xy})$ is the number of components where both $\mathbf{x}$ and $\mathbf{y}$ are 1. Thus

$$w(\mathbf{x} + \mathbf{y}) = d(\mathbf{x}, \mathbf{y}) = w(\mathbf{x}) + w(\mathbf{y}) - 2w(\mathbf{xy}). \tag{1}$$

Lemma 9.1 If $\mathbf{xy} = \mathbf{x}$ and $w(\mathbf{x}) = w(\mathbf{y})$, for $\mathbf{x}$ and $\mathbf{y}$ in $[Z/(2)]^n$, then $\mathbf{x} = \mathbf{y}$.

Proof Intuitively, $\mathbf{xy} = \mathbf{x}$ says that $\mathbf{y}$ has a 1 in each component that $\mathbf{x}$ does. However, $w(\mathbf{x}) = w(\mathbf{y})$ says that $\mathbf{x}$ and $\mathbf{y}$ have the same number of nonzero components, so that $\mathbf{x} = \mathbf{y}$. Alternatively, $w(\mathbf{x}) = w(\mathbf{xy}) = [w(\mathbf{x}) + w(\mathbf{y}) - d(\mathbf{x}, \mathbf{y})]/2 = w(\mathbf{x}) - d(\mathbf{x}, \mathbf{y})/2$, so that $d(\mathbf{x}, \mathbf{y}) = 0$ and $\mathbf{x} = \mathbf{y}$.

For the remainder of this section, let S and T be subspaces of $[Z/(2)]^n$ and suppose that ϕ is a one-to-one linear map from S onto T such that $d(\mathbf{x}, \mathbf{y}) = d(\phi(\mathbf{x}), \phi(\mathbf{y}))$, where $\mathbf{x}$ and $\mathbf{y}$ are in S.

Lemma 9.2 For $\mathbf{x}$ and $\mathbf{y}$ in S, $w(\mathbf{xy}) = w(\phi(\mathbf{x})\phi(\mathbf{y}))$.

Proof For any $\mathbf{s}$ in S, $w(\mathbf{s}) = d(\mathbf{s}, \mathbf{0}) = d(\phi(\mathbf{s}), \mathbf{0}) = w(\phi(\mathbf{s}))$. Thus

$$w(\mathbf{xy}) = [w(\mathbf{x}) + w(\mathbf{y}) - d(\mathbf{x}, \mathbf{y})]/2 = [w(\phi(\mathbf{x})) + w(\phi(\mathbf{y})) - d(\phi(\mathbf{x}), \phi(\mathbf{y}))]/2$$
$$= w(\phi(\mathbf{x})\phi(\mathbf{y})).$$

Lemma 9.3 For $\mathbf{x}$, $\mathbf{y}$, and $\mathbf{z}$ in S, $w(\mathbf{xyz}) = w(\phi(\mathbf{x})\phi(\mathbf{y})\phi(\mathbf{z}))$.

Proof For arbitrary $\mathbf{x}$, $\mathbf{y}$, and $\mathbf{z}$ in S,

$$\begin{aligned}
w(\mathbf{x} + \mathbf{y} + \mathbf{z}) &= w(\mathbf{x}) + w(\mathbf{y} + \mathbf{z}) - 2w(\mathbf{x}(\mathbf{y} + \mathbf{z})) \\
&= w(\mathbf{x}) + w(\mathbf{y} + \mathbf{z}) - 2w(\mathbf{xy} + \mathbf{xz}) \\
&= w(\mathbf{x}) + w(\mathbf{y}) + w(\mathbf{z}) - 2w(\mathbf{yz}) - 2w(\mathbf{xy}) \\
&\quad - 2w(\mathbf{xz}) + 4w(\mathbf{xyxz}) \\
&= w(\mathbf{x}) + w(\mathbf{y}) + w(\mathbf{z}) - 2w(\mathbf{yz}) - 2w(\mathbf{xy}) \\
&\quad - 2w(\mathbf{xz}) + 4w(\mathbf{xyz}). \tag{2}
\end{aligned}$$

The last equality follows, since $\mathbf{xx} = \mathbf{x}$. Since ϕ preserves distance, $w(\mathbf{x} + \mathbf{y} + \mathbf{z}) = w(\phi(\mathbf{x} + \mathbf{y} + \mathbf{z}))$. Since ϕ is linear, $\phi(\mathbf{x} + \mathbf{y} + \mathbf{z}) = \phi(\mathbf{x}) + \phi(\mathbf{y}) + \phi(\mathbf{z})$. Thus $w(\mathbf{x} + \mathbf{y} + \mathbf{z}) = w[\phi(\mathbf{x}) + \phi(\mathbf{y}) + \phi(\mathbf{z})]$. However,

$$\begin{aligned}
w(\phi(\mathbf{x}) + \phi(\mathbf{y}) + \phi(\mathbf{z})) &= w(\phi(\mathbf{x})) + w(\phi(\mathbf{y})) + w(\phi(\mathbf{z})) - 2w(\phi(\mathbf{y})\phi(\mathbf{z})) \\
&\quad - 2w(\phi(\mathbf{x})\phi(\mathbf{y})) - 2w(\phi(\mathbf{x})\phi(\mathbf{z})) \\
&\quad + 4w(\phi(\mathbf{x})\phi(\mathbf{y})\phi(\mathbf{z})). \tag{3}
\end{aligned}$$

Using Eqs. (2) and (3), the fact that $w(\mathbf{t}) = w(\phi(\mathbf{t}))$, and the fact that $w(\mathbf{st}) = w(\phi(\mathbf{s})\phi(\mathbf{t}))$, for any $\mathbf{s}$ and $\mathbf{t}$ in S, we obtain $w(\mathbf{xyz}) = w(\phi(\mathbf{x})\phi(\mathbf{y})\phi(\mathbf{z}))$.

Lemma 9.4 Let $\mathbf{x}$ and $\mathbf{y}$ be in S. Then $\mathbf{xy}$ is in S if and only if $\phi(\mathbf{x})\phi(\mathbf{y})$ is in $\phi(S)$. In this case $\phi(\mathbf{xy}) = \phi(\mathbf{x})\phi(\mathbf{y})$.

Proof If $\mathbf{xy}$ is in S, then $w(\phi(\mathbf{xy})) = w(\mathbf{xy}) = w(\phi(\mathbf{x})\phi(\mathbf{y}))$. Since $\mathbf{xx} = \mathbf{x}$, $w(\phi(\mathbf{x})\phi(\mathbf{xy})) = w(\mathbf{xxy}) = w(\mathbf{xy}) = w(\phi(\mathbf{xy}))$. This implies that $\phi(\mathbf{x})\phi(\mathbf{xy}) = \phi(\mathbf{xy})$. Likewise, $\phi(\mathbf{y})\phi(\mathbf{xy}) = \phi(\mathbf{xy})$. Thus $\phi(\mathbf{x})\phi(\mathbf{y})\phi(\mathbf{xy}) = \phi(\mathbf{xy})$. Lemma 9.1 now implies that $\phi(\mathbf{x})\phi(\mathbf{y}) = \phi(\mathbf{xy})$, and so $\phi(\mathbf{x})\phi(\mathbf{y})$ is in $\phi(S)$. To see the converse, suppose $\phi(\mathbf{x})\phi(\mathbf{y}) = \phi(\mathbf{z})$, where $\mathbf{z}$ is in S. Thus $\phi(\mathbf{x})\phi(\mathbf{z}) = \phi(\mathbf{z})$, and $w(\phi(\mathbf{x})\phi(\mathbf{z})) = w(\phi(\mathbf{z}))$, so by Lemma 9.2 $w(\mathbf{xz}) = w(\mathbf{z})$. Similarly, $w(\mathbf{yz}) = w(\mathbf{z})$. Since $\mathbf{z}(\mathbf{xz}) = \mathbf{xz}$ and $w(\mathbf{z}) = w(\mathbf{xz})$, Lemma 9.1 shows that $\mathbf{z} = \mathbf{xz}$. Likewise, $\mathbf{z} = \mathbf{yz}$, so that $(\mathbf{xy})\mathbf{z} = \mathbf{z}$. However, $w(\mathbf{xy}) = w(\phi(\mathbf{x})\phi(\mathbf{y})) = w(\phi(\mathbf{z})) = w(\mathbf{z})$, so again by Lemma 9.1, $\mathbf{xy} = \mathbf{z}$ is in S.

Proof of Theorem 9.3 If S contains elements $\mathbf{x}$ and $\mathbf{y}$, with $\mathbf{xy}$ not in S, then the subspace spanned by S and $\mathbf{xy}$, namely, $S' = \{\mathbf{s} + c\mathbf{xy} : \mathbf{s}$ is in S and c is in $Z/(2)\}$, is properly larger than S. Define $\phi' : S' \to [Z/(2)]^n$ by $\phi'(\mathbf{s} + c\mathbf{xy}) = \phi(\mathbf{s}) + c\phi(\mathbf{x})\phi(\mathbf{y})$. Since $\mathbf{xy}$ is not in S, ϕ' is linear and, by Lemma 9.4, ϕ' is one-to-one. Finally,

$$w(\mathbf{s} + \mathbf{xy}) = w(\mathbf{s}) + w(\mathbf{xy}) - 2w(\mathbf{sxy}) = w(\phi(\mathbf{s})) + w(\phi(\mathbf{x})\phi(\mathbf{y}))$$
$$- 2w(\phi(\mathbf{s})\phi(\mathbf{x})\phi(\mathbf{y}))$$
$$= w(\phi(\mathbf{s}) + \phi(\mathbf{x})\phi(\mathbf{y})) = w(\phi'(\mathbf{s} + \mathbf{xy}))$$

by Lemmas 9.2 and 9.3. Thus ϕ' is a one-to-one distance-preserving linear map from S' into $[Z/(2)]^n$. Continuing this process, we may assume that $\mathbf{xy}$ is in S for all $\mathbf{x}$ and $\mathbf{y}$ in S and that ϕ is a one-to-one distance-preserving map from S into $[Z/(2)]^n$. Define the relation $\mathbf{E}_i \underset{S}{\sim} \mathbf{E}_j$, $\mathbf{E}_i = (0, \ldots, 0, 1, 0, \ldots, 0)$, where 1 occurs in the ith component, if for each $\mathbf{s} = \sum_{k=1}^{n} c_k \mathbf{E}_k$ in S, $c_i \neq 0$ exactly when $c_j \neq 0$. The relation $\underset{S}{\sim}$ is an equivalence relation on $\{\mathbf{E}_k : k = 1, \ldots, n\}$. Let $\mathscr{C}_1, \mathscr{C}_2, \ldots, \mathscr{C}_p$ be the equivalence classes under $\underset{S}{\sim}$ and define $\mathbf{b}_i = \sum_{\mathbf{E}_j \in \mathscr{C}_i} \mathbf{E}_j$. Since $\mathbf{s} = \sum_{k=1}^{n} c_k \mathbf{E}_k$ has either $c_j = 1$ for all $\mathbf{E}_j$ in $\mathscr{C}_i$ or $c_j = 0$ for all $\mathbf{E}_j$ in $\mathscr{C}_i$, $\mathbf{s}$ is a linear combination of $\{\mathbf{b}_i : i = 1, \ldots, p\}$. If $\mathbf{s} = \sum_{k=1}^{n} c_k \mathbf{E}_k$ is a vector in S, and $c_k \neq 0$ for all E_k in $\mathbf{b}_i$, then $\mathbf{b}_i$ is called a *constituent* of $\mathbf{s}$, written $\mathbf{b}_i \subset \mathbf{s}$. It is not difficult to show that $\mathbf{b}_i = \prod_{\mathbf{b}_i \subset \mathbf{s}} \mathbf{s}$, $\mathbf{s}$ in S. Since S is closed under multiplication, $\mathbf{b}_i \in S$ and $\{\mathbf{b}_i\}$ is a basis for S. Finally, $\{\phi(\mathbf{b}_i) : i = 1, \ldots, p\}$ is a basis for T, and $\phi(\mathbf{b}_i) = \phi(\prod_{\mathbf{b}_i \subset \mathbf{s}} \mathbf{s}) = \prod_{\mathbf{b}_i \subset \mathbf{s}} \phi(\mathbf{s})$ by Lemma 9.4. Let $\mathscr{C}_1', \mathscr{C}_2', \ldots, \mathscr{C}_q'$ be the classes under $\underset{T}{\sim}$ and let $\mathbf{b}_i' = \sum_{\mathbf{E}_k \in \mathscr{C}_i'} \mathbf{E}_k$. Since both $\{\phi(\mathbf{b}_i) : i = 1, \ldots, p\}$ and $\{\mathbf{b}_i' : i = 1, \ldots, q\}$ are bases for T, we have $p = q$. Furthermore, since $\phi(\mathbf{b}_i) = \prod_{\mathbf{b}_i \subset \mathbf{s}} \phi(\mathbf{s}) \neq 0$, we have $\phi(\mathbf{b}_i) = \mathbf{b}'_j$ for some j. Since ϕ is weight-preserving, $|\mathscr{C}_i| = |\mathscr{C}'_j|$. Thus choose any permutation of $\{1, 2, \ldots, n\}$ such that $\mathbf{E}_k \in \mathscr{C}_i$ implies $\mathbf{E}_{\pi(k)} \in \mathscr{C}'_j = \phi(\mathscr{C}_i)$. This gives $\phi_\pi(\mathbf{b}_i) = \phi_\pi(\sum_{\mathbf{E}_k \in \mathscr{C}_i} \mathbf{E}_k) = \sum_{\mathbf{E}_k \in \mathscr{C}_i} \mathbf{E}_{\pi(k)} = \sum_{\mathbf{E}_{\pi(k)} \in \mathscr{C}'_j} \mathbf{E}_{\pi(k)} = \mathbf{b}'_j = \phi(\mathbf{b}_i)$. Thus $\phi = \phi_\pi$, and the theorem is proven.

---

*9.8 ADDRESSING SYSTEMS FOR GRAPHS

The elements of $[Z/(2)]^n$ are well adapted to represent pulses in a circuit, and the Hamming metric is a convenient measure of distance in $[Z/(2)]^n$. This section gives an example of such a representation and its relationship to the Hamming distance.

Let $G = (V, E)$ be a finite connected graph with no loops or multiple edges. The length of a chain in the graph is the number of edges in the chain, and the distance $d_G(u, v)$ between two vertices u and v is the length of a shortest chain connecting u and v (or 0 if $u = v$). The function d_G is a metric and measures the closeness of vertices to each other. The addressing problem in graph theory tries to relate the graph distance d_G to the Hamming distance between vectors representing vertices. To be precise, the addressing problem asks if it is possible to label each vertex of G with a distinct vector in $[Z/(2)]^n$—called the address of the vertex—such that the Hamming distance between addresses of the vertices is exactly the graph distance between the vertices. If such a labeling of the vertices exists, the graph is said to have a Hamming addressing system (or to be an addressable graph).

The addressing problem arises naturally with regard to information exchange in a telephone network connecting digital computers. To make a voice call using the normal telephone system, a closed circuit between caller and receiver is made, and the conversation then ensues. The time needed to set up the circuit, including alternative searches made before a suitable circuit is found, is usually quite short compared to the time the circuit is in use. Thus it is reasonable to have the first part of the circuit completed while a search is being made to establish the final connection. However, if the message is short, as in much of the communication between digital computers, compared to the time needed to set up a complete circuit, then it may be more efficient to have the message work its way through the telephone system without first setting up a complete circuit from the sender to the destination.

A model of a telephone system that does this is the loop switching system, in which certain sets of subscribers are on certain one-way loops and these loops are interconnected by switching devices. A message, with destination address leading, is sent by a subscriber and circulates around the

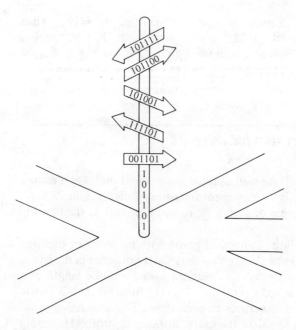

Figure 9.18

originating loop until it comes to a suitable switching point, at which time it may enter a new loop. This process is continued until the message reaches its final destination. In this system, only a small part of the circuit, namely, the loop, is in use at any one time. The principal problem now remaining is to devise a system in which a message goes from the sender to the destination rapidly and does not circulate around the system endlessly.

If each loop is thought of as a vertex of a graph, and each switching point between two loops as an edge, then the loop switching system is represented as a graph. To ensure that the message goes from the sender to the destination, it is sufficient to devise an addressing system for the vertices of the graph such that a message, with destination address leading, can proceed along a chain (route) of smallest length from the sender to the destination. If the addresses are binary n-tuples, and the graph distance between two vertices equals the Hamming distance between the addresses of the vertices, then the route is easily found by determining, at the current vertex, the Hamming distance from the destination to each of the vertices adjacent (i.e., joined by an edge) to the current vertex and choosing the edge joining the current vertex to the adjacent vertex with the smallest Hamming distance to the destination. Thus the new vertex is closer to the destination, and the destination will eventually be reached.

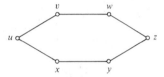

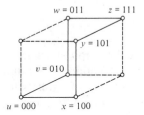

Figure 9.19 Graph and an addressing.

This chapter gives necessary and sufficient conditions on the graph *G* for an addressing system to exist. Furthermore, a generalization of the Hamming metric yields an addressing system that exists for every connected graph, and constructive methods are given which determine such an adressing system for a given graph.

The general problem of addressing the vertices of a graph so that the Hamming distance (or generalization thereof) between vertices equals the graph distance yields an interesting model of addressing a city street system. Every intersection would have a sign labeled with the address of that intersection, and direction pointers indicating the addresses of the adjacent intersections (e.g., Figure 9.18). Thus for a stranger to go from intersection A to intersection B in the city would require only a knowledge of the address of the final destination and the ability to determine, at each intersection, the adjacent intersection that has the smallest Hamming distance to the destination. The person would then move to the intersection closer to his or her destination. Thus a stranger would always be able to find a shortest route from intersection A to intersection B without the necessity of a map and without encountering deadends or having to take unnecessary detours because of rivers, ravines, railroads, or other obstacles which may be in the way.

We are now ready to attack and solve the addressing problem. Consider first the following two examples. The vertices of the graph in Figure 9.19 can be addressed so that the Hamming distance equals the graph distance, as is done in Figure 9.19. There are numerous ways to accomplish such an addressing and many more ways to make an improper addressing. Figure 9.20 gives an example of an improper addressing, since the Hamming distance be-

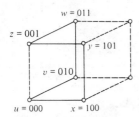

Figure 9.20 Improper addressing for a graph.

tween z and u is 1 but the graph distance is 3. While the graph of Figure 9.19 is addressable, the graph of Figure 9.21 is not, since the address of a differs from the address of b in one component, and the address of a differs from that of c in one different component. Thus the address of c differs from that of a in two components, so that the Hamming distance from b to c is 2 but the graph distance is 1.

In fact, suppose that the graph G is addressable in $[Z/(2)]^n$. The set of vertices of G is then partitioned into two sets, namely, the set A of vertices with addresses containing an even number of 1's and the set B of vertices with addresses containing an odd number of 1's. Since the Hamming distance between the addresses of two distinct vertices of A (or two distinct vertices of B) is at least 2, the graph distance between two distinct vertices of A (respectively, B) is at least 2. Thus no edge connects two vertices of A or two vertices of B. A finite graph $G = (V, E)$ with $V = A \cup B$ and $A \cap B = \varnothing$, where no edge has both end points in A or both end points in B, is called *bipartite*. Thus an addressable graph must be bipartite. Furthermore, since the Hamming distance between two addresses is always finite, an addressable graph is connected. The graph in Figure 9.21 is not bipartite and so cannot be addressed. The graph in Figure 9.19 is addressable, hence bipartite, as Figure 9.22 shows.

By trial and error, it is not difficult to fit addressing systems to all connected bipartite graphs, where $|A| \le 2$ and $|B| \le 2$. However, if $|A| = 2$ and $|B| = 3$, then the graph H in Figure 9.23 occurs. If we try to address the vertices of H, we may assume (by reordering the components simultaneously) that v has address $(a_1, a_2, a_3, \ldots, a_n)$, w has address $(a_1', a_2, a_3, \ldots, a_n)$, x has address $(a_1, a_2', a_3, \ldots, a_n)$, and y has address $(a_1, a_2, a_3', \ldots, a_n)$, where $a_i \ne a_i'$. Thus u must have address $(a_1', a_2', a_3, \ldots, a_n)$, since it is adjacent to both w and x, but u's address must differ from y's in only one component, which is a contradiction. Thus the graph in Figure 9.23 is not addressable.

The graph in Figure 9.23 has the property that u is directly between w and x, which are both closer to v than to y, and yet u is closer to y than to v. Such a thing cannot happen in an addressed graph. Suppose that two ver-

Figure 9.21 Graph which cannot be addressed.

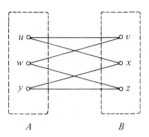

Figure 9.22 Bipartite graph of Figure 9.19.

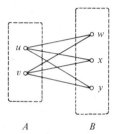

Figure 9.23 Bipartite graph H.

tices a and b in an addressed graph are joined by an edge. The addresses of a and b thus differ in exactly one component, say for convenience the first component, and the remaining corresponding components of the address are identical. Thus the address of any other vertex c differs from the addresses of a and b in exactly the same components except for the first component. Suppose now that c is closer to a, so that the first component of the address of c equals the first component of the address of a. Likewise, suppose that d is closer to a than to b. Thus the first component of the address of d equals the first component of the address of c. Any shortest chain from c to d corresponds to a sequence of vertices whose addresses change one component at a time and change only in components in which the addresses of c and d differ. Thus vertices on any shortest chain from c to d will have the first component of their address equal to the first component of the address of a, hence will be closer to a than to b. This condition is violated by the graph H in Figure 9.23.

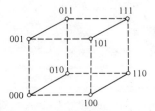

Figure 9.24 Edges with the same direction.

Let us make the above condition precise. Let a and b be vertices of a graph G, which are joined by an edge. Define $D(a < b) = \{v : d(a, v) < d(b, v)\}$, where $d(x, y)$ is the graph distance between vertices x and y. Thus $D(a < b)$ are vertices that are closer to a than to b. The set $D(a < b)$ is said to be closed if, for x and y in $D(a < b)$, each vertex on a shortest chain from x to y is again in $D(a < b)$. That is, if $d(x, z) + d(z, y) = d(x, y)$ and $x, y \in D(a < b)$, then $z \in D(a < b)$. By the previous paragraph, we see that any graph with an addressing system must have $D(a < b)$ closed for every pair of adjacent vertices a and b. Thus an addressable graph must be a connected bipartite graph with $D(a < b)$ closed for all adjacent a and b. This condition is not only necessary but also sufficient.

Theorem 9.4 Let G be a finite graph without loops or multiple edges. The graph G has an addressing system if and only if G is connected and bipartite, and $D(a < b)$ is closed for all adjacent vertices a and b in G.

Proof We have already shown necessity and now show sufficiency. Suppose G is connected and bipartite, and $D(a < b)$ is closed for adjacent vertices a and b. To find an addressing, the notion of direction is very useful, since an address in $[Z/(2)]^n$ can then be determined by specifying the n possible directions. In the cube, for example, the edges joining 000 to 010, 100 to 110, 101 to 111, and 001 to 011 all differ in exactly the second component, hence have the same direction (Figure 9.24). Furthermore, if we pick one of these edges, say 001 to 011, then $D(001 < 011) = \{001, 101, 100, 000\}$ and $D(011 < 001) = \{011, 111, 010, 110\}$. Thus all edges going in the same direction as the edge joining 001 to 011 have one end point in $D(001 < 011)$ and the other in $D(011 < 001)$. In general, let edge e_1 have end points a and b and define $e_1 \sim e_2$ if e_2 has end points u and v with $u \in D(a < b)$ and $v \in D(b < a)$. We show that $\sim$ is an equivalence relation on E. It is clear that $\sim$ is reflexive. If $D(a < b) = D(u < v)$ [and $D(b < a) = D(v < u)$], then $\sim$ will certainly be symmetric and transitive, hence an equivalence relation. In particular, it is sufficient to show that $D(a < b) \subset D(u < v)$, since this implies $e_2 \sim e_1$ which then would imply $D(u < v) \subset D(a < b)$. Suppose $x \in D(a < b)$. Since G is bipartite, any two vertices the same distance from x

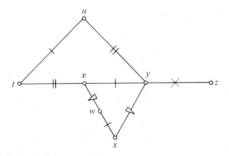

Figure 9.25 Equivalence classes of edges.

must be in the same partition of the bipartite graph, hence cannot be joined by an edge. Since u and v are joined by an edge, either $d(x, u) < d(x, v)$, so that $x \in D(u < v)$, or $d(x, v) < d(x, u)$. In the latter case, $d(x, v) + d(u, v) = d(x, u)$, since $d(u, v) = 1$, so that $D(a < b)$ being closed implies $v \in D(a < b)$, which is a contradiction to v in $D(b < a)$. Hence $x \in D(u < v)$ and $D(a < b) \subset D(u < v)$.

The graph in Figure 9.25 has the edges marked $|, \|, \nabla, \times$ to designate the equivalence classes. We are now in a position to determine an addressing system for the graph. Let n be the number of equivalence classes of edges (for Figure 9.25 $n = 4$) and order these classes $1, 2, 3, \ldots, n$. Pick an arbitrary vertex p in G as the origin and label $p\, 000 \cdots 0$ in $[Z/(2)]^n$. For any vertex x in G take a shortest chain between p and x and label x with the n-tuple having 0 in a component, if no edge of the shortest chain is in the class designated by that component, and which has 1 in a component if that class contains some edge of the shortest chain. This labeling is well defined, since the classes containing edges belonging to a shortest chain from p to x are exactly those classes that contain an edge e with end points a and b such that $x \in D(a < b)$ and $p \in D(b < a)$. If both x and p are in the same set $D(a < b)$, then the shortest chain from p to x does not contain vertices outside $D(a < b)$, since $D(a < b)$ is closed and in particular does not contain e. Furthermore, if $x \in D(a < b)$ and $p \in D(b < a)$, then any chain from p to x must have an edge that joins a vertex of $D(b < a)$ to a vertex of $D(a < b)$.

In the addressing of the graph in Figure 9.25, let $|, \|, \nabla, \times$ be the ordering of the classes and choose, for example, t as the origin. The shortest-distance tree rooted at t is given in Figure 9.26, as is the addressing obtained from it.

It now remains to show that the Hamming distance between the addresses so obtained equals the graph distance between the addressed vertices. Suppose vertices a and b are graph distance m apart, and suppose $e_1, e_2, \ldots, e_m$ is a shortest chain from a to b. If we show that the addresses of a and b agree, except at the components corresponding to the $e_1, \ldots, e_m$

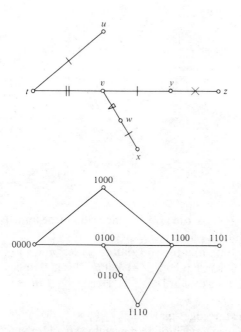

Figure 9.26 Shortest distance tree and resulting addressing.

classes, then the Hamming distance equals the graph distance and the graph is addressed. Suppose that the address of a differs from the address of b in the kth component, say the kth component of the address of a is 1 and that of the address of b is 0. There is then an edge of the kth class with end points q and r such that $p \in D(q < r)$ and $a \in D(r < q)$. Since b has a 0 in the kth component, $b \in D(q < r)$ and any shortest chain from a to b has an edge which joins a vertex of $D(r < q)$ to a vertex of $D(q < r)$, so that the kth class is represented in any shortest chain from a to b. Also, if the kth class is represented in a shortest chain, then there is an edge with end points w, z such that $a \in D(w < z)$ and $b \in D(z < w)$. Since p is in exactly one of $D(w < z)$ or $D(z < w)$, say $D(w < z)$, then a shortest chain from p to a has no kth component, but a shortest chain from p to b must have an edge in the kth class. The addresses of a and b differ in the components corresponding to $e_1, \ldots, e_m$, and the Hamming distance between the addresses of a and b equals the graph distance between a and b, proving the theorem.

The theorem conceals an addressing algorithm, namely, (1) determine the classes of edges, (2) pick an origin, (3) determine a shortest-distance tree rooted at the origin, and (4) label each vertex according to the chain in the shortest-distance tree joining the origin to the vertex.

Figure 9.27

Figure 9.28

Theorem 9.4 gives criteria for the existence of an addressing system and presents a method that produces a labeling. However, the class of addressable graphs is very restricted and is certainly not satisfactory for the original problem. If the addressing is not required to come from $[Z/(2)]^n$ or to have a true distance function associated with it, then there exists a system such that the distance between addresses equals the graph distance between vertices. The graph in Figure 9.27 is not bipartite, hence is not addressable in $[Z/(2)]^n$. However, suppose x is tentatively addressed (0,   ), y is addressed (1,   ), and z is addressed (1,   ). The second component of the address of x must now be such that the distance from it to the second components of y and z is 0, and yet the second component of y and z must be a distance of 1 apart. Thus label y by (1, 0) and z by (1, 1), and introduce a third symbol * with the property that * and 0, and * and 1, are 0 apart. (* can be thought of as "do not care"). Thus label x by (0, *) so that Figure 9.28 yields the desired addressing.

In general, let $S = \{0, 1, *\}$ and define an address to be an element of S^n. If v and w are in S^n, define $d(v, w)$ to be the number of components such that both components of v and w are in $\{0, 1\}$ and not the same. The function d satisfies none of the properties of a metric, except that $d(u, v) = d(v, u)$. An advantage, however, is that this is easily implemented electronically by identifying S^n with a subset of $[Z/(2)]^{2n}$, where 0 is encoded as 00, 1 is encoded as 01, and * is encoded as 10 or 11. Thus, if the $(2k - 1)$-digit of n in $[Z/(2)]^{2n}$ and the $(2k - 1)$-digit of v are both 0, compute the Hamming distance for the $2k$-component, otherwise go on to the $(2k + 1)$-component.

The addressing in S^n of a graph depends on factorization of a quadratic polynomial with coefficients determined by the distance matrix of the graph. Let $G = (V, E)$ be a finite connected graph with vertices 1, 2, ..., k. The distance matrix of G is the matrix (d_{ij}), where d_{ij} is the length of the shortest

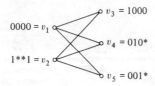

$v_3 = 1000$

$0000 = v_1$

$v_4 = 010*$

$1**1 = v_2$

$v_5 = 001*$

Figure 9.29

path joining vertex i and vertex j. The addressing polynomial of G is the polynomial $\sum_{1 \leq i \leq j \leq k} d_{ij} x_i x_j$, where $x_1, \ldots, x_k$ are indeterminates associated with the vertices $1, \ldots, k$.

Theorem 9.5 Let G be a finite connected graph. G is addressable in S^n, so that the distance between addresses of vertices equals the graph distance between vertices if and only if

$$\sum_{1 \leq i \leq j \leq k} d_{ij} x_i x_j$$

can be written as

$$\sum_{i=1}^{n} (x_{1(i)} + x_{2(i)} + \cdots + x_{j(i)})(x_{1'(i)} + \cdots + x_{j'(i)}),$$

where $1(i), \ldots, j(i), 1'(i), \ldots, j'(i)$ are distinct indices for each fixed i.

Before we proceed with the proof of the theorem, let us consider the graph in Figure 9.29. The graph is addressed, and the graph distance between vertices equals the distance between the addresses of the vertices. The first component of v_2 and v_3 is 1, while the first component of v_1, v_4, and v_5 is 0. Thus all possible pairs with one element from $\{x_2, x_3\}$ and another from the set $\{x_1, x_4, x_5\}$ represent the contributions to the distance between the addresses made by the first component. Thus the product $(x_2 + x_3) \cdot (x_1 + x_4 + x_5) = x_1 x_2 + x_1 x_3 + x_2 x_4 + x_3 x_4 + x_2 x_5 + x_3 x_5$ represents the contributions to distances between addresses made by the first component. Likewise, x_4 has a second component 1, while x_1, x_3, and x_5 have a second component 0, so that $x_4(x_1 + x_3 + x_5) = x_4 x_1 + x_4 x_3 + x_4 x_5$ shows the contributions to distances between addresses made by the second component. Similarly, $x_5(x_1 + x_3 + x_4)$ and $x_2(x_1 + x_3)$ represent the contributions to distances between addresses made by the third and fourth components, respectively. Summing the contributions gives

$$(x_2 + x_3)(x_1 + x_4 + x_5) + x_4(x_1 + x_3 + x_5) + x_5(x_1 + x_3 + x_4)$$

$$+ x_2(x_1 + x_3)$$

$$= 2x_1 x_2 + x_1 x_3 + x_1 x_4 + x_1 x_5 + x_2 x_3 + x_2 x_4 + x_2 x_5 + 2x_3 x_4$$

$$+ 2x_3 x_5 + 2x_4 x_5,$$

which equals $\sum_{1 \le i \le j \le 5} d_{ij} x_i x_j$ for (d_{ij}), the distance matrix of the graph in Figure 9.29.

Proof of Theorem 9.5   Let G have an addressing in S^n. Since the distance between addresses and the graph distance are equal, the distances d_{ij} can be computed from the addresses. Let $1(i), 2(i), \ldots, j(i)$ be all vertices with 1 in the ith component and $1'(i), \ldots, j'(i)$ be all the vertices with 0 in the ith component. Thus $(x_{1(i)} + \cdots + x_{j(i)})(x_{1'(i)} + \cdots + x_{j'(i)})$ has product terms representing each pair of addresses of distance 1 apart in the ith component. Thus

$$\sum_{i=1}^{n} (x_{1(i)} + \cdots + x_{j(i)})(x_{1'(i)} + \cdots + x_{j'(i)}) = \sum_{1 \le i \le j \le k} d_{ij} x_i x_j \qquad (4)$$

gives the total distance d_{ij} between vertex i and vertex j.

Now suppose we have a factorization of the form of Eq. (4). The term $(x_{1(i)} + \cdots + x_{j(i)})(x_{1'(i)} + \cdots + x_{j'(i)})$ gives an addressing of the ith component in S^n by putting 1 in the ith component of the vertices $1(i), \ldots, j(i)$, and 0 in the ith component $1'(i), \ldots, j'(i)$, the remaining vertices having an ith component *. The distance between the addresses is then d_{ij} which corresponds to the graph distance. Thus the theorem is proved.

Theorem 9.5 does not contain an algorithm which gives the addresses. However, once a factorization of the form of Eq. (4) is obtained, the addressing procedure is specified. There are several candidates for factorization of the form (1). The most obvious is

$$\sum d_{ij} x_i x_j = \underbrace{x_1 x_2 + \cdots + x_1 x_2}_{d_{12} \text{ times}} + \cdots + \underbrace{x_{k-1} x_k + \cdots + x_{k-1} x_k}_{d_{k-1\,k} \text{ times}}$$

which requires $\sum_{1 \le i \le j \le k} d_{ij}$ coordinates. A more efficient address in terms of a smaller number of components is obtained from the factorization

$$\sum_{1 \le i \le j \le k} d_{ij} x_i x_j = x_1(x_2 + \cdots + x_k) + x_1(x_{2(2,\,1)} + \cdots + x_{k(2,\,1)}) + \cdots$$

$$+ x_1(x_{2(s,\,1)} + \cdots + x_{k(s,\,1)}) + x_2(x_3 + \cdots + x_k) + \cdots$$

$$+ x_i(x_{i+1(j,\,i)} + \cdots + x_{k(j,\,i)}) + \cdots + x_{k-1} x_k,$$

where $x_{l(j,\,i)}$ represent vertices of index $> i$ and of distance at least j from vertex i. This yields at most $s(k-1)$ components for the address, where s is the maximum distance between vertices. It is as yet unknown whether or not shorter addresses are in general possible, but it is conjectured that $k-1$ components will suffice.

Exercises

9-27   Determine all pairwise nonisomorphic connected bipartite graphs without multiple edges between vertices such that $|A| = 3$ and $|B| = 3$.

9-28   Determine which of the following graphs are bipartite:

   a

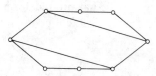

   b The graph with adjacency matrix $\begin{bmatrix} 0 & 1 & 0 & 1 & 1 \\ 1 & 0 & 1 & 0 & 0 \\ 0 & 1 & 0 & 1 & 0 \\ 1 & 0 & 1 & 0 & 1 \\ 1 & 0 & 0 & 1 & 0 \end{bmatrix}$

   c

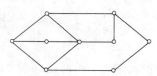

   d

9-29   Determine an algorithm that determines whether or not a graph is bipartite.

9-30   Prove that any tree is bipartite.

9-31   Determine which of the graphs in Exercise 9-28 satisfy $D(a < b)$ is closed for all adjacent a and b.

9-32   Determine the equivalence classes of edges, as defined in Theorem 9.4, for the graphs in Exercise 9-28.

9-33   Prove or disprove that a connected bipartite graph satisfies $D(a < b)$ closed for all adjacent a and b if and only if the relation on edges given in Theorem 9.4 is an equivalence relation.

9-34 Determine an addressing for the following city street system.

9-35 Determine an addressing in S^n for the following graph.

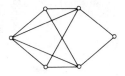

Finite Fields

10.1 INTRODUCTION

Finite fields are introduced in Chapter 8, and examples of finite fields containing p elements, for each prime p, are given. However, many applications use finite fields different from $Z/(p)$, p a prime. If the elements of a set are assigned elements of a finite field, then there is an addition and multiplication of set elements, and systems of linear equations over this finite set can be solved. We see in Section 10.4 how finite fields are used to construct orthogonal latin squares for use in the efficient design of experiments, and in Section 10.7 how finite fields are used to design multiple-error-correcting codes.

This chapter analyzes the structure of finite fields and determines all possible finite fields. There is exactly one (up to isomorphism) finite field of each size p^n, where n is a positive integer and p is a prime. Furthermore, these finite fields are obtained from polynomial rings with coefficients from $Z/(p)$ using a method quite analogous to obtaining $Z/(p)$ from the integers.

10.2 STRUCTURE OF FINITE FIELDS

Finite fields are fields with a finite number of elements. The rings $Z/(p)$, for p a prime, are examples of finite fields. This section determines the structure of all finite fields and shows the relationship between an arbitrary finite field and the ring of polynomials with coefficients from the integers modulo p, where p is a certain prime. To make this relationship clear, several definitions are needed. We first define F to be a *subfield* of K if F is a nonempty subset of K and under the operations of K, F is a field. The field K is called an *extension* of the field F. These definitions are appropriate for arbitrary fields, and many of the results of this section apply to arbitrary fields as stated.

To understand the relationship between the integers modulo p for a prime p and certain finite fields, we use the concept of isomorphism. Two fields are isomorphic if there is a relabeling of the elements of one field that yields the second field and preserves the field operations. Recall from Section 8.5 the following.

Definition The field F is said to be isomorphic to the field K if there exists a one-to-one mapping ϕ from F onto K such that $\phi(a + b) = \phi(a) + \phi(b)$ and $\phi(a \circ b) = \phi(a) \circ \phi(b)$ for all a and b in F. The mapping ϕ is called an isomorphism.

Later in this section, an example of an isomorphism between two fields is given. The first proposition shows that every finite field contains a field isomorphic to the integers modulo p for some prime p.

Proposition 10.1 A field F contains a subfield isomorphic to either $Z/(p)$, where p is a certain prime integer, or the field of rational numbers.

Proof Let e be the multiplicative identity of F. For a positive integer n, define $n \circ e$ to be the element of the field $e + e + \cdots + e$, where e is taken n times. If n is a negative integer, define $n \circ e = -[(-n) \circ e]$. Since multiplication distributes over addition, it is not difficult to check by induction that $(i \circ e) \circ (j \circ e) = (ij) \circ e$ and $(i \circ e) + (j \circ e) = (i + j) \circ e$ for all integers i and j. In F, either $n \circ e$ is never 0 for any positive integer n, or there exists a smallest positive integer p such that $p \circ e = 0$. In the latter case p must be prime, since $p = a \circ b$, with a and b positive integers, and $a < p$ and $b < p$ implies $p \circ e = (a \circ e) \circ (b \circ e) = 0$, so that either $a \circ e$ or $b \circ e$ is 0. This contradicts the fact that p is the smallest integer with $p \circ e = 0$. Hence p is prime. For $[i]$ in $Z/(p)$, the mapping $\phi([i]) = i \circ e$ is well defined, since

$(i + rp) \circ e = i \circ e + r \circ (p \circ e) = i \circ e + 0 = i \circ e$. Since $(i \circ e) \circ (j \circ e) = (ij) \circ e$ and $(i \circ e) + (j \circ e) = (i + j) \circ e$, ϕ is an isomorphism from $Z/(p)$ into F. Thus F contains a subfield isomorphic to the integers modulo p, unless of course $n \circ e$ is never 0 for any positive integer n. In this case $(n \circ e)^{-1}$ exists in F for each positive integer n. For the rational number n/m, the mapping $\phi(n/m) = (n \circ e)(m \circ e)^{-1}$ is well defined for each positive integer m. Furthermore, as above, this is easily found to be an isomorphism from the field of rational numbers into F, proving the proposition.

The subfield of F determined in Proposition 10.1 is called the *prime subfield* of F. Furthermore, if e is the multiplicative identity of a ring R, the *characteristic* of R is defined to be the smallest positive integer n such that $n \circ e = 0$ if such an integer exists, or 0 if no such integer exists.

If F is a finite field, then the rational numbers cannot be a subfield, since the set of rational numbers contains an infinite number of elements. Thus a finite field contains the subfield $Z/(p)$ for some prime p. Since F forms an Abelian group under addition, and multiplication by elements in the prime subfield is allowed, the field F is a vector space over the prime subfield. Thus, in the case in which F is a finite field, F is a finite-dimensional vector space over $Z/(p)$ for p the characteristic of F. The field F thus has a finite basis of n elements over $Z/(p)$. Hence there are p^n possible linear combinations of the basis elements, which implies that $|F| = p^n$. Thus we have shown that the number of elements in a finite field F is a power of a prime. Later in this section it is shown that there exists a finite field containing p^n elements for each p and each positive integer n.

The integers modulo p are constructed by taking equivalence classes of integers, where integers a and b are equivalent if $a - b$ is divisible by p. An analogous procedure can be defined to construct the polynomial ring modulo a fixed polynomial. Let F be a field and $F[x]$ the polynomial ring. Suppose $p(x) \in F[x]$. Define the polynomial $a(x)$ to be equivalent to $b(x)$ modulo $p(x)$ if $a(x) - b(x)$ is divisible by $p(x)$. As in the case of the integers, this relation is easily seen to be an equivalence relation. The equivalence class containing the polynomial $a(x)$ is denoted by $[a(x)]$. An addition and multiplication can be defined for equivalence classes by $[a(x)] + [b(x)] = [a(x) + b(x)]$ and $[a(x)] \circ [b(x)] = [a(x) \circ b(x)]$. These operations are well defined, since $a(x)$ equivalent to $a_1(x)$ implies $a(x) - a_1(x) = p(x)s(x)$ for some $s(x)$ in $F[x]$, and $b(x)$ equivalent to $b_1(x)$ implies $b(x) - b_1(x) = p(x)t(x)$ for some $t(x)$ in $F[x]$. Thus $(a(x) + b(x)) - (a_1(x) + b_1(x)) = p(x)(s(x) + t(x))$ and $a(x) \circ b(x) - a_1(x) \circ b_1(x) = p(x) \cdot (a_1(x)t(x) + b_1(x)s(x) + p(x)s(x)t(x))$. This implies $[a(x) + b(x)] = [a_1(x) + b_1(x)]$ and $[a(x) \circ b(x)] = [a_1(x) \circ b_1(x)]$, so that addition and multiplication are well defined. It is now straightforward to check that the set of equivalence classes forms an Abelian group under addition, multiplication is commutative and associative, there is a multiplicative identity, namely, [1], and multiplication distributes over addition. The set of equivalence classes with the above-defined addition and multiplication is denoted by $F[x]/(p(x))$. Exactly as in the case of integers, we have the following theorem.

Theorem 10.1 Let F be a field with $p(x)$ a polynomial of degree at least 1 in $F[x]$. The ring $F[x]/(p(x))$ is a field if and only if $p(x)$ is a prime polynomial.

Proof Since $F[x]/(p(x))$ is a commutative ring, it remains only to show that each nonzero element has an inverse if and only if $p(x)$ is a prime polynomial. If $p(x)$ is not a prime polynomial, then there exist polynomials $f(x)$ and $g(x)$ such that $p(x) = f(x) \circ g(x)$ and, furthermore, deg $f(x)$ and deg $g(x)$ are both less than deg $p(x)$. Thus neither $f(x)$ nor $g(x)$ is divisible by $p(x)$, so $[f(x)] \neq [0] \neq [g(x)]$, but $[f(x)] \circ [g(x)] = [0]$, which shows that a product of nonzero elements yields 0. Thus the ring is not a field. To show the implication in the other direction, assume $p(x)$ is a prime polynomial. Let $[a(x)]$ be a nonzero element in $F[x]/(p(x))$. Thus $p(x)$ being prime and not dividing $a(x)$ implies the gcd of $p(x)$ and $a(x)$ is an invertible element u. By the Euclidean algorithm there exist elements $s(x)$ and $t(x)$ such that $u = a(x)s(x) + p(x)t(x)$, which yields

$$[1] = [a(x)][s(x)u^{-1}] + [p(x)t(x)u^{-1}]$$
$$= [a(x)] \circ [s(x)u^{-1}],$$

and $[a(x)]$ has a multiplicative inverse.

As an example, let us calculate the prime polynomials in $[Z/(2)][x]$ of degree less than or equal to 4. All polynomials of degree 1 are prime. Any polynomial (different from x and 0) with a constant term 0 is not prime, since x is a factor. Thus list the polynomials of $[Z/(2)][x]$ of degree d, $1 \leq d \leq 4$, with a nonzero constant term. In binary notation, with the highest degree first, these polynomials are 00011, 00101, 00111, 01001, 01011, 01101, 01111, 10001, 10011, 10101, 11001, 11011, 11101, 10111, and 11111. As in the sieve of Eratosthenes, we cross off multiples of primes. In other words, first multiply 00011 by each member in the list and cross off the result. In this particular case, dividing $f(x)$ by $x + 1$ gives a zero remainder if and only if $f(1) = 0$, and thus if and only if $f(x)$ has an even number of 1's in its binary representation. Thus the list becomes 00011, 00111, 01011, 01101, 10011, 10101, 11001, and 11111. Continue this process with the remainder of the list. Thus $(00111)^2 = 10101$ and all other products have degree greater than 4. Thus the primes of degree ≤ 4 in $[Z/(2)][x]$ are 00010, 00011, 00111, 01011, 01101, 10011, 11001, and 11111.

Theorem 10.1 shows us that the polynomial ring in one variable with coefficients in $Z/(2)$, modulo any of the prime polynomials determined in the previous paragraph, is a field. However, the theorem does not indicate that these fields are distinct. Some of the fields are easily seen to be distinct, since they contain different numbers of elements. If F is a field and $p(x)$ is a prime polynomial of degree n, then the equivalence classes $[x^i]$, for $i = 0$, $1, \ldots, n - 1$, form a basis for $F[x]/(p(x))$ as a vector space over F. This follows since

$$\left[\sum_{i=0}^{n-1} a_i x^i \right] = \sum_{i=0}^{n-1} a_i [x^i], \qquad a_i \in F$$

which implies that the given set of vectors span the set of equivalence classes containing a representative of degree less than n. However, each equivalence class contains a representative of degree less than n, since any representative minus an appropriate polynomial multiple of $p(x)$ yields a remainder in that class and this remainder has degree less than n. If

$$\sum_{i=0}^{n-1} b_i [x^i] = [0], \qquad \text{then} \qquad \left[\sum_{i=0}^{n-1} b_i x^i \right] = [0], \qquad b_i \in F$$

which implies

$$p(x) \left| \sum_{i=0}^{n-1} b_i x^i \right.,$$

which is impossible unless all $b_i = 0$. Thus $\{[x^i] : i = 0, 1, \ldots, n - 1\}$ forms a basis for $F[x]/(p(x))$ over F. If F is finite, then $|F(x)/(p(x))| = |F|^n$. Hence the fields $F[x]/(p(x))$ are distinct if the degrees of the polynomial $p(x)$ are distinct. Since we have determined prime polynomials of degree 1, 2, 3, and 4 over $Z/(2)$, there exist finite fields of order 2, 4, 8, and 16. We will show that there exists exactly one finite field of each order p^n, where p is a positive prime and n is a positive integer. If this can be shown, then the fields

$$F_1 = \frac{[Z/(2)][x]}{(x^3 + x^2 + 1)} \qquad \text{and} \qquad F_2 = \frac{[Z/(2)][x]}{(x^3 + x + 1)}$$

are isomorphic. We now find an isomorphism between F_1 and F_2. Since the identity in F_1 must be mapped to the identity in F_2, the integers modulo 2 must be mapped onto the integers modulo 2. Since $\{[1], [x], [x][x]\}$ forms a basis of F_1 over $Z/(2)$, and since an isomorphism ϕ satisfies $\phi(\sum_{i=0}^{2} b_i [x]^i) = \sum_{i=0}^{2} b_i [\phi([x])]^i$, $b_i \in Z/(2)$, $i = 0, 1, 2$, the isomorphism is determined by the image of $[x]$. However, $[x]^3 + [x]^2 + [1] = [0]$ in F_1, hence the image of $[x]$ must satisfy the same equation in F_2. The only elements in F_2 that satisfy this equation are $[x + 1]$, $[x^2 + 1]$, and $[x^2 + x + 1]$, so we chose one of these for the image of $[x]$. The mapping ϕ induced by $\phi([x]) = [x + 1]$ is given in Figure 10.1.

Elements in $F_1 = (Z/(2))[x]/(x^3 + x^2 + 1)$	Mapping	Elements in $F_2 = (Z/(2))[x]/(x^3 + x + 1)$
0	$\longrightarrow$	0
1	$\longrightarrow$	1
$[x]$	$\longrightarrow$	$[x + 1]$
$[x + 1] = [x] + 1$	$\longrightarrow$	$[x + 1] + 1 = [x]$
$[x^2] = [x][x]$	$\longrightarrow$	$[x + 1][x + 1] = [x^2 + 1]$
$[x^2 + x] = [x][x] + [x]$	$\longrightarrow$	$[x + 1][x + 1] + [x + 1] = [x^2 + x]$
$[x^2 + 1] = [x][x] + 1$	$\longrightarrow$	$[x + 1][x + 1] + 1 = [x^2]$
$[x^2 + x + 1] = [x][x] + [x] + 1$	$\longrightarrow$	$[x + 1][x + 1] + [x + 1] + 1 = [x^2 + x + 1]$

Figure 10.1 Mapping from $(Z/(2))[x]/(x^3 + x^2 + 1)$ onto $(Z/(2))[x]/(x^3 + x + 1)$.

$\circ$	1	α	$\alpha + 1$	α^2	$\alpha^2 + \alpha$	$\alpha^2 + 1$	$\alpha^2 + \alpha + 1$
1	1	α	$\alpha + 1$	α^2	$\alpha^2 + \alpha$	$\alpha^2 + 1$	$\alpha^2 + \alpha + 1$
α	α	α^2	$\alpha^2 + \alpha$	$\alpha^2 + 1$	1	$\alpha^2 + \alpha + 1$	$\alpha + 1$
$\alpha + 1$	$\alpha + 1$	$\alpha^2 + \alpha$	$\alpha^2 + 1$	1	$\alpha^2 + \alpha + 1$	α	α^2
α^2	α^2	$\alpha^2 + 1$	1	$\alpha^2 + \alpha + 1$	α	$\alpha + 1$	$\alpha^2 + \alpha$
$\alpha^2 + \alpha$	$\alpha^2 + \alpha$	1	$\alpha^2 + \alpha + 1$	α	$\alpha + 1$	α^2	$\alpha^2 + 1$
$\alpha^2 + 1$	$\alpha^2 + 1$	$\alpha^2 + \alpha + 1$	α	$\alpha + 1$	α^2	$\alpha^2 + \alpha$	1
$\alpha^2 + \alpha + 1$	$\alpha^2 + \alpha + 1$	$\alpha + 1$	α^2	$\alpha^2 + \alpha$	$\alpha^2 + 1$	1	α

Figure 10.2 Multiplication table for $(Z/(2))[x]/(x^3 + x^2 + 1)$.

We now adopt the standard convention of denoting the equivalence class containing the variable x by α. The multiplication table for $[Z/(2)][x]/(x^3 + x^2 + 1)$ is given in Figure 10.2. If the mapping ϕ is applied to every entry in this table, the result is Figure 10.3. Figure 10.3 is also a multiplication table for $[Z/(2)][x]/(x^3 + x + 1)$. Thus the condition $\phi(a \circ b) = \phi(a) \circ \phi(b)$ is satisfied. Since 1, α, and α^2 form a basis for the first field as a vector space over the integers modulo 2, and the image of a linear combination is simply the linear combination of the images, the mapping ϕ is a linear transformation, so that $\phi(a + b) = \phi(a) + \phi(b)$. This makes ϕ an isomorphism between the two fields.

In determining the above isomorphism, we used the fact that $[x]$ satisfies $[x]^3 + [x]^2 + [1] = [0]$ to help us in determining the image of $[x]$. In general, if $p(x)$ is a polynomial in $F[x]$, where F is a field, and if β is an element of an extension field K of F, with $p(\beta) = 0$, then β is called a *root* of the polynomial $p(x)$. If β is a root of $p(x)$, then $x - \beta$ divides the polynomial $p(x)$ in $K[x]$, since in $K[x]$ we have $p(x) = q(x)(x - \beta) + r(x)$ with deg $r(x) < 1$. Thus $r(x)$ is a constant, say r_0, and $p(\beta) = q(\beta) \cdot (\beta - \beta) + r_0 = r_0 = 0$, and $x - \beta$ divides $p(x)$. Theorem 10.1 not only shows that $F[x]/(p(x))$ is a field for F a field and $p(x)$ a prime polynomial but actually shows that, in this extension field of F, $p(x)$ has a root, namely, $[x]$. Hence we have the following corollary.

∘	1	α + 1	α	α² + 1	α² + α	α²	α² + α + 1
1	1	α + 1	α	α² + 1	α² + α	α²	α² + α + 1
α + 1	α + 1	α² + 1	α² + α	α²	1	α² + α + 1	α
α	α	α² + α	α²	1	α² + α + 1	α + 1	α² + 1
α² + 1	α² + 1	α²	1	α² + α + 1	α + 1	α	α² + α
α² + α	α² + α	1	α² + α + 1	α + 1	α	α² + 1	α²
α²	α²	α² + α + 1	α + 1	α	α² + 1	α² + α	1
α² + α + 1	α² + α + 1	α	α² + 1	α² + α	α²	1	α + 1

Figure 10.3   The result of applying ϕ to each element in Figure 10.2.

Corollary 10.1   If F is a field and $f(x)$ is a polynomial in $F[x]$, then there exists an extension field K of F which contains a root of $f(x)$.

Proof   Since $F[x]$ is a Euclidean domain, $f(x)$ can be factored into a product of prime polynomials. Suppose $p(x)$ is a prime factor of $f(x)$, so that in the extension field $F[x]/(p(x))$ of F, $p(x)$ has a root α and thus $f(x)$ has the root α.

It is important to note that the number of roots of $p(x) \in F[x]$, F a field, is limited by the degree of the polynomial. $F[x]$ is a Euclidean domain. Each root α of $p(x)$ yields a prime factor $x - \alpha$ of $p(x)$. Since the degree of the product of polynomials is the sum of the degrees of the factors, there can be at most $\deg(p(x))$ factors of the form $x - \alpha$, where α is some root. This observation, plus the next theorem on groups, yield the structure of the group of nonzero elements of F.

The next theorem is a direct result of Lagrange's theorem (7.4).

Theorem 10.2   Let G be an Abelian group of finite order n, which is not cyclic. Then there exists $k < n$, with $n = mk$ and $g^k = e$ for all g in G.

Proof   We first need the fact that, if $g \in G$ has order t and s is a positive integer with $\gcd\{s, t\} = 1$, then g^s has order t. Certainly, $(g^s)^t = (g^t)^s = e^s = e$, where e is the identity of G, so the order of g^s divides t. If $(g^s)^r = g^{sr} = e$ for some integer r, then t divides sr. Since $\gcd\{t, s\} = 1$, t must divide r, and the order of g is t. By the fundamental theorem of arithmetic, $n = p_1^{\alpha_1} \cdots p_l^{\alpha_l}$, where $p_1, \ldots, p_l$ are distinct prime factors of n and $\alpha_1, \ldots, \alpha_l$ are positive integers. For each i, $1 \le i \le l$, let β_i be the largest integer in $T_i = \{r \in Z:$ there exists g in G of order $p_i^r\}$. Since e has order p_i^0, each T_i contains 0, and since the order of any g in G divides $|G|$, each r in T_i satisfies $r \le \alpha_i$. Thus β_i exists for each i, $1 \le i \le l$. If $\beta_i = \alpha_i$ for all i, $1 \le i \le l$, then we claim $h = g_1 \circ g_2 \circ \cdots \circ g_l$ has order n. Since the g_i's commute, we certainly have $(g_1 \circ g_2 \circ \cdots \circ g_l)^n = g_1^n \circ g_2^n \circ \cdots \circ g_l^n = e$. Suppose now that the order of h

is $p_1^{\delta_1} \cdots p_l^{\delta_l}$ with $\delta_i \le \alpha_i$ for $1 \le i \le l$. Define $n_i = p_1^{\alpha_1} \cdots p_{i-1}^{\alpha_{i-1}} p_{i+1}^{\alpha_{i+1}} \cdots p_l^{\alpha_l}$. Thus

$$e = h^{n_i p_i^{\delta_i}} = g_1^{n_i p_i^{\delta_i}} \circ \cdots \circ g_{i-1}^{n_i p_i^{\delta_i}} \circ g_i^{n_i p_i^{\delta_i}} \circ \cdots \circ g_l^{n_i p_i^{\delta_i}}$$

$$= e \circ \cdots \circ e \circ g_i^{n_i p_i^{\delta_i}} \circ e \circ \cdots \circ e = (g_i^{n_i})^{p_i^{\delta_i}}.$$

Since $\gcd\{n_i, p_i^{\alpha_i}\} = 1$, the order of $g_i^{n_i}$ is $p_i^{\alpha_i} = p_i^{\beta_i}$. Hence $\delta_i = \alpha_i$ and h has order n. In this case, the subgroup generated by h has order n and must be all of G. This contradicts the assumption that G is not cyclic. Thus there must be some integer j, $1 \le j \le l$, with $\beta_j < \alpha_j$. Let $k = p_1^{\beta_1} \cdots p_l^{\beta_l}$, so that $k = p_1^{\beta_1} \cdots p_l^{\beta_l} < p_1^{\alpha_1} \cdots p_l^{\alpha_l} = n$ and $n = mk$. If g is an element of G then by Lagrange's theorem, g has order $p_1^{\gamma_1} \cdots p_l^{\gamma_l}$, γ_i integers. If $u_i = p_1^{\gamma_1} \cdots p_{i-1}^{\gamma_{i-1}} p_{i+1}^{\gamma_{i+1}} \cdots p_l^{\gamma_l}$, then g^{u_i} has order $p_i^{\gamma_i}$, which implies $\gamma_i \le \beta_i$. Thus $p_1^{\gamma_1} \cdots p_l^{\gamma_l} \le p_1^{\beta_1} \cdots p_l^{\beta_l}$ and

$$g^k = \left(g^{p_1^{\gamma_1} \cdots p_l^{\gamma_l}}\right)^{p_1^{\beta_1 - \gamma_1} \cdots p_l^{\beta_l - \gamma_l}} = e^{p_1^{\beta_1 - \gamma_1} \cdots p_l^{\beta_l - \gamma_l}} = e,$$

proving the theorem.

We denote the nonzero elements of a field F by F^*.

Theorem 10.3 Let F be a finite field. The group F^* is cyclic.

Proof Let F contain m elements. F^* contains $m - 1$ elements and is a finite Abelian group. If F^* is not cyclic, then Theorem 10.2 guarantees that there exists an integer k dividing $m - 1$, with $0 < k < m - 1$, such that $a^k - 1 = 0$ for all a in F^*. Thus F contains $m - 1$ distinct roots of $x^k - 1$. This is impossible, since $x^k - 1$ has at most k roots. Thus F^* must be cyclic.

The proof of Theorem 10.3 actually embodies a stronger result: namely, any finite subgroup of the group of invertible elements of a field must be cyclic. However, the full generality of this result is not needed.

Exercises

10-1 Determine all prime polynomials of degree 5 in $[Z/(2)][x]$.

10-2 Determine a prime polynomial of degree 3 in $[Z/(5)][x]$.

10-3 Calculate $[x + 2]^{-1}$ in $[Z/(3)][x]/(x^2 + 1)$.

10-4 Write out the multiplication table for $[Z/(3)][x]/(x^2 + x + 2)$.

10-5 Determine a generator of the cyclic subgroup
  a $[Z/(2)][x]/(x^4 + x + 1)^*$
  b $[Z/(2)][x]/(x^4 + x^3 + x^2 + x + 1)^*$.

10-6 Prove that, if a and b are elements in a field of characteristic p, then $(a + b)^{p^n} = a^{p^n} + b^{p^n}$.

10-7 Prove that, if $a_1, \ldots, a_k$ are elements in a field of characteristic p, then $(a_1 + \cdots + a_k)^{p^n} = a_1^{p^n} + \cdots + a_k^{p^n}$.

10-8 If ϕ is an isomorphism from F_1 to F_2 and ψ is an isomorphism from F_2 to F_3, prove $\psi \circ \phi$ is an isomorphism from F_1 to F_3.

10-9 Describe an algorithm that determines all prime polynomials of degree less than n in $[Z/(p)][x]$, where p and n are positive integers and p is a prime.

10-10 Use the Euclidean algorithm to determine the inverse (if it exists) of $x^2 + x + 1$ in $[Z/(2)][x]/(x^4 + x + 1)$.

10-11 Find all integers n such that $x^5 - 10x + 12$ is divisible by $x^2 + 2$ in $[Z/(n)][x]$.

10-12 Determine all monic prime polynomials of degree 3 in $F[x]$, where F is $Z/(3)$. (A monic polynomial $p(x)$ is one in which the coefficient of x^k, $k = \deg p(x)$, is 1.)

10-13 Formulate and prove for polynomials in $F[x]$, F a field, a version of the Chinese remainder theorem.

10.3 EXISTENCE OF FINITE FIELDS

This section shows that exactly one finite field of order p^n exists for each prime p and each positive integer n. In the process of proving this, we closely examine the roots of a polynomial in extension fields. Much of what we do is applicable to arbitrary fields. Let K be an extension field of the field F and suppose the element β in K is a root of some polynomial in $F[x]$. The next proposition determines those polynomials that have β as a root. To describe these polynomials, first define a polynomial in $F[x]$ to be monic if

$$f(x) = x^n + \sum_{i=0}^{n-1} a_i x^i,$$

with a_i in F.

Proposition 10.2 Let K be an extension field of the field F and suppose β in K is a root of some polynomial in $F[x]$. The element β is then the root of a unique monic prime polynomial in $F[x]$ that divides every other polynomial of $F[x]$ having β as a root.

Proof Take a polynomial in $F[x]$ of minimal degree, which has β as a root. Multiply the polynomial by the inverse of the leading coefficient to obtain a monic polynomial with β as a root. If β is a root of any polynomial $g(x)$, then by the division algorithm in $F[x]$ there exists $q(x)$ and $r(x)$ with $g(x) = q(x) \circ f(x) + r(x)$, where $r(x) = 0$ or the degree of $r(x) <$ the degree of $f(x)$. However, $0 = g(\beta) = q(\beta) \circ f(\beta) + r(\beta) = 0 + r(\beta) = r(\beta)$ implies β is a root of $r(x)$. This contradicts the fact that $f(x)$ is of minimal degree, so that $r(x)$ must be 0. Thus $g(x)$ is divisible by $f(x)$. If $f(x) = a(x)b(x)$ with deg $a(x) <$ deg $f(x)$, deg $b(x) <$ deg $f(x)$, and both $a(x)$ and $b(x)$ in $F[x]$, then $f(\beta) = a(\beta) \circ b(\beta) = 0$, so one of $a(\beta)$ or $b(\beta)$ is 0. Thus β is a root of a polynomial in $F[x]$ of degree less than the degree of $f(x)$. This contradicts the fact that $f(x)$ is a polynomial in $F[x]$ of minimal degree. Thus $f(x)$ is prime in $F[x]$. Furthermore, $f(x)$ is unique, since $h(x)$, another polynomial with the same properties, implies $f(x) = c \circ h(x)$, where c is in F. The leading coefficients of $f(x)$ and $h(x)$ are both 1, so $c = 1$.

The polynomial $f(x)$ in Proposition 10.2 is called the *minimal polynomial* of β. If F is a finite field of order p^n, any nonzero element β of F satisfies $x^{p^n - 1} = 1$, since F^* is a cyclic group of order $p^n - 1$ by Theorem 10.3. Thus, if $\beta = \alpha + 1$ in the field $[Z/(2)][x]/(x^3 + x + 1)$ when $\alpha = [x]$, then β is a root of $x^7 - 1$. However, β also satisfies $x^3 + x^2 + 1$, which indeed is the minimal polynomial of β. Furthermore, $x^7 - 1 = (x^3 + x^2 + 1)(x^3 + x + 1)(x + 1)$ in $[Z/(2)][x]$.

If K is an extension field of the field F and $\beta_1, \beta_2, \ldots, \beta_k$ are elements in K, denote the smallest subfield of K containing F and the elements $\beta_1, \ldots, \beta_k$ by $F(\beta_1, \ldots, \beta_k)$. It is not difficult to check that such a smallest subfield exists, since there is certainly some subfield, namely, K, that contains F and all the elements $\beta_1, \ldots, \beta_k$, and the intersection of all subfields of K containing F and $\beta_1, \ldots, \beta_k$ is again a field. The proof of this is left as an exercise. More generally, the intersection of a nonempty set of subfields of the field K is again a field, since it is easily found to be closed under subtraction, closed under multiplication, and closed under multiplicative inverses.

The next proposition determines the structure of $F(\beta)$ when β is a root of a polynomial in $F[x]$. As an illustration, let C be the field of complex numbers and R the field of real numbers. The element $i = \sqrt{-1}$ is in C, and $R(i)$ is all of C. Furthermore, i is a root of the polynomial $x^2 + 1$. Since $x^2 + 1$ is prime in $R[x]$, $R[x]/(x^2 + 1)$ is a field. Since $i^2 = -1$ in $R(i)$ and $[x]^2 = -1$ in $R[x]/(x^2 + 1)$, $\pm[x]$ and $\pm i$ are roots of $x^2 + 1$ in $R[x]$. In fact, i corresponds to $[x]$, and the map $r_0 + r_1 i \to [r_0 + r_1 x]$ is an isomorphism between the two fields.

Proposition 10.3 Let K be an extension field of the field F and let β in K be a root of a polynomial in $F[x]$. The field $F(\beta)$ is then isomorphic to $F[x]/(f(x))$, where $f(x)$ is the minimal polynomial of β.

Proof Suppose

$$f(x) = x^n + \sum_{i=0}^{n-1} a_i x^i,$$

so that

$$\beta^n = -\sum_{i=0}^{n-1} a_i \beta^i.$$

The set $\{1, \beta, \ldots, \beta^{n-1}\}$ is linearly independent over F, since a dependency would imply that β is the root of a polynomial of degree less than deg $(f(x))$. We claim that the subspace V of K, spanned by $\{1, \beta, \ldots, \beta^{n-1}\}$ as a vector space over F, is closed under multiplication. Since multiplication distributes over addition, it is sufficient to show that $\beta^k \circ v \in V$ for $v \in V$, $0 \le k \le n-1$. Certainly, $\beta^0 \circ v = 1 \cdot v = v \in V$, so assume $\beta^k \circ v \in V$. Then

$$\beta^{k+1} \circ v = \beta(\beta^k v) = \beta \circ v_1 = \beta \circ \sum_{i=0}^{n-1} c_i \beta^i = c_{n-1}\beta^n + \sum_{i=1}^{n-1} c_{i-1}\beta^i$$

$$= -c_{n-1}a_0 + \sum_{i=1}^{n-1}(-c_{n-1}a_i + c_{i-1})\beta^i, \qquad c_i \in F,$$

is in V, so that by induction V is closed under multiplication. Since $\{1, \beta, \ldots, \beta^{n-1}\}$ is linearly independent, the map

$$\phi\left(\left[\sum_{i=0}^{n-1} b_i x^i\right]\right) = \sum_{i=0}^{n-1} b_i \beta^i, \qquad b_i \in F,$$

is one-to-one from $F[x]/(f(x))$ onto V. The map ϕ is easily found to be additive and, if

$$\left(\sum_{i=0}^{n-1} b_i x^i\right)\left(\sum_{i=0}^{n-1} d_i x^i\right) = \sum_{i=0}^{n-1} e_i x^i + s(x)f(x), \qquad d_i, e_i \in F$$

then

$$\phi\left(\left[\sum_{i=0}^{n-1} b_i x^i\right]\left[\sum_{i=0}^{n-1} d_i x^i\right]\right) = \sum_{i=0}^{n-1} e_i \beta^i$$

and

$$\phi\left(\left[\sum_{i=0}^{n-1} b_i x^i\right]\right) \circ \phi\left(\left[\sum_{i=0}^{n-1} d_i x^i\right]\right) = \left(\sum_{i=0}^{n-1} b_i \beta^i\right)\left(\sum_{i=0}^{n-1} d_i \beta^i\right)$$

$$= \sum_{i=0}^{n-1} e_i \beta^i + s(\beta)f(\beta)$$

$$= \sum_{i=0}^{n-1} e_i \beta^i.$$

Thus ϕ is an isomorphism from $F[x]/(f(x))$ onto V. This also shows that V is a field, and $F[x]/(f(x))$ is thus isomorphic to $F(\beta)$.

The first application of Proposition 10.3 shows how to extend an isomorphism between two fields to an isomorphism between two extension fields if the extension fields are of a certain type. In order to do this we need to examine the action of an isomorphism on a polynomial. Suppose ϕ is an isomorphism from the field F_1 onto the field F_2. It is not difficult to check that the map

$$\phi\left(\sum_{i=0}^{n} a_i x^i\right) = \sum_{i=0}^{n} \phi(a_i)x^i$$

is actually an isomorphism from $F_1[x]$ onto $F_2[x]$. An important fact about this mapping is, if

$$\sum_{i=0}^{n} a_i x^i = \left(\sum_{i=0}^{m} b_i x^i\right)\left(\sum_{i=0}^{n-m} d_i x^i\right), \qquad d_i, e_i \in F$$

with a_i, b_i, d_i in F_1 so that

$$a_j = \sum_{i=0}^{j} b_i d_{j-1},$$

then

$$\phi(a_j) = \sum_{i=0}^{j} \phi(b_i)\phi(d_{j-i}),$$

which implies

$$\sum_{i=0}^{n} \phi(a_i)x^i = \left(\sum_{i=0}^{m} \phi(b_i)x^i\right)\left(\sum_{i=0}^{m-n} \phi(d_i)x^i\right).$$

Thus, if a polynomial in $F_1[x]$ can be factored, then the image of that polynomial can be factored in $F_2[x]$. The converse also holds, since ϕ has an inverse mapping, which takes

$$\sum_{i=0}^{k} c_i x^i, \text{ with } c_i \text{ in } F_2, \text{ to } \sum_{i=0}^{k} \phi^{-1}(c_i)x^i.$$

As a result prime polynomials are mapped to prime polynomials.

Proposition 10.4 Let ϕ be an isomorphism from the field F_1 onto the field F_2, which maps the monic prime polynomial $f(x)$ to $g(x)$. If α is a root of $f(x)$ in some extension field K of F_1, and β is a root of the polynomial $g(x)$ in an extension field L of F_2, then $F_1(\alpha)$ is isomorphic to $F_2(\beta)$.

Proof By Proposition 10.3, $F_1(\alpha)$ is isomorphic to $F[x]/(f(x))$. Furthermore, $F_2(\beta)$ is isomorphic to $F[x]/(g(x))$, since $g(x)$ is prime, and β is a root of $g(x)$. Thus the proposition follows if we can show that $F_1[x]/(f(x))$ is isomorphic to $F_2[x]/(g(x))$. The function ψ, where

$$\psi\left(\left[\sum_{i=0}^{n-1} a_i x^i\right]\right) = \left[\sum_{i=0}^{n-1} \phi(a_i)x^i\right],$$

is easily found to be defined, one-to-one, onto, and additive. To show that ψ is multiplicative simply note that

$$\left(\sum_{i=0}^{n-1} a_i x^i\right)\left(\sum_{i=0}^{n-1} b_i x^i\right) = \sum_{i=0}^{n-1} e_i x^i + \left(\sum s_i x^i\right)f(x)$$

implies that

$$\left(\sum_{i=0}^{n-1} \phi(a_i)x^i\right)\left(\sum_{i=0}^{n-1} \phi(b_i)x^i\right) = \sum_{i=0}^{n-1} \phi(e_i)x^i + \left(\sum \phi(s_i)x^i\right)g(x).$$

Hence ψ is an isomorphism, and the proposition is proved.

Let $f(x)$ be a polynomial in $F[x]$. Since $F[x]$ is a Euclidean domain, $f(x)$ is a product of, say n_1, prime factors in $F[x]$. If $p_1(x)$ is a prime factor of degree greater than 1 then, by Corollary 1.1, $p_1(x)$ has a root α_1 in $F[x]/(p_1(x)) = K_1$. Thus $f(x)$ has a new root α_1 in K_1, and $f(x)$ factors in $K_1[x]$ into a product of $n_2 \geq n_1 + 1$ prime factors. Continue this process of enlarging the field by roots of $f(x)$ until $f(x)$ is a product of linear factors in $K_n[x]$. Thus we have

$$F \subset K_1 = F(\alpha_1) \subset K_2 = F(\alpha_1)(\alpha_2) \subset \cdots \subset K_n = F(\alpha_1)(\alpha_2) \cdots (\alpha_n),$$

where

$$f(x) = c(x - \alpha_1)(x - \alpha_2) \cdots (x - \alpha_n).$$

It is left to the exercises to show that $F(\alpha_1) \cdots (\alpha_k) = F(\alpha_1, \ldots, \alpha_k)$, so that $F \subset F(\alpha_1) \subset F(\alpha_1, \alpha_2) \subset \cdots \subset F(\alpha_1, \alpha_2, \ldots, \alpha_n)$. Fields obtained in this manner have a special name and will be shown to be unique. To be precise let $f(x)$ be a monic polynomial in $F[x]$, where F is a field. An extension field D of F is called a *splitting field* of $f(x)$ over F if $f(x) = (x - \alpha_1) \cdot (x - \alpha_2) \cdots (x - \alpha_n)$ in $D[x]$ and $D = F(\alpha_1, \alpha_2, \ldots, \alpha_n)$.

Theorem 10.4 Let $f(x)$ be a monic polynomial in $F[x]$, where F is a field. If D_1 and D_2 are splitting fields for $f(x)$ over F, then D_1 is isomorphic to D_2.

Proof   The proof is simply repeated applications of Proposition 10.4. If α is a root of $f(x)$ in D_1, then α is a root of some prime factor of $f(x)$, where the factorization is in $F[x]$. Since $f(x)$ factors into a product of factors of degree 1 in $D_2[x]$, the prime polynomial has a root β in D_2. Thus there is an isomorphism from $F(\alpha)$ onto $F(\beta)$. The isomorphism extends to a mapping of the prime factors of $f(x)$ in $F(\alpha)[x]$ to the prime factors of $f(x)$ in $F(\beta)[x]$. Thus we can continue adding the roots of $f(x)$ in D_1 until we obtain an isomorphism $F(\alpha_1, \ldots, \alpha_n)$ onto $F(\beta_1, \ldots, \beta_n)$.

Since D_1 is equal to $F(\alpha_1, \ldots, \alpha_n)$ and D_2 is equal to $F(\beta_1, \ldots, \beta_n)$ we find that D_1 is isomorphic to D_2.

Theorem 10.4 tells us that the splitting field of a polynomial is unique. This fact is now used to show that there exists exactly one finite field of order p^n for prime p and a positive integer n. An important step in showing this result is to determine when a polynomial $f(x)$ in $F[x]$, where F is a field, will have distinct roots in an extension field K of F. In other words, a factorization of $f(x)$ into linear factors cannot contain $(x - \alpha)^2$ for some α. If $f(x)$ does not contain $(x - \alpha)^2$ for any α in a factorization into linear factors, then $f(x)$ is called square-free. For $f(x) = \sum_{i=0}^{k} a_i x^i$ in $F[x]$, F a field, define $f'(x) = \sum_{i=1}^{k} a_i i x^{i-1}$. The mapping $f(x) \to f'(x)$ has many of the properties of differentiation of polynomials with complex coefficients. Thus $(f + cg)' = f' + cg'$ and $(fg)' = f'g + fg'$ for f and g in $F[x]$ and c in F. These facts are left as exercises. Thus if $f(x) = (x - \alpha)^2 f_1(x)$, then

$$f'(x) = 2(x - \alpha)f_1(x) + (x - \alpha)^2 f'_1(x)$$
$$= (x - \alpha)(2f_1(x) + (x - \alpha)f'_1(x)).$$

Conversely, if $x - \alpha$ divides both $f(x)$ and $f'(x)$, then $f(x) = (x - \alpha)h(x)$ and $f'(x) = h(x) + (x - \alpha)h'(x)$, so that $x - \alpha$ divides $f'(x) - (x - \alpha)h'(x) = h(x)$. This shows $f(x)$ is divisible by $(x - \alpha)^2$. The conclusion is that $f(x)$ is square-free in $K[x]$, where K is its splitting field, if and only if no linear factor divides both $f(x)$ and $f'(x)$ in $K[x]$. In other words, $f(x)$ is square-free if and only if $\gcd\{f(x), f'(x)\}$ is invertible. We are now ready to prove Theorem 10.5.

Theorem 10.5   There exists exactly one finite field of order p^n, where p is a prime and n a positive integer.

Proof   Let K be the splitting field of $x^{p^n} - x$ in $(Z/(p))[x]$. The field K is finite, since it takes only a finite number of steps to construct a field containing the roots of $x^{p^n} - x$ and at each step the extension field is finite. The polynomial $x^{p^n} - x$ has at most p^n roots and, since $(x^{p^n} - x)' = p^n x^{p^n - 1} - 1 = -1$ in $[Z/(p)][x]$, all the roots are distinct. Thus K contains at least p^n

elements. However, every element in K satisfies $x^{p^n} - x$. To see this let us examine the construction of K more closely. If a is a nonzero in $Z/(p)$, then $a^{p-1} = 1$ and $a^p = a$. Thus $a^{p^n} = a$ and every element in $Z/(p)$ is a root of $x^{p^n} - x$. If every element of F is a root of $x^{p^n} - x$ and α is an additional root, then every element in $F(\alpha)$ is a root. This follows, since b in $F(\alpha)$ implies $b = \sum f_i \alpha^i$ and $b^{p^n} = (\sum f_i \alpha^i)^{p^n} = \sum f_i^{p^n} \alpha^{ip^n} = \sum f_i \alpha^i = b$ by the exercises in Section 10.2. Hence every element of K is a root of $x^{p^n} - x$, and $|K| = p^n$. The field K is unique, since if D is a field of order p^n, then $d^{p^n-1} = 1$ for every element in the group D^*, which implies $d^{p^n} = d$ for every element in D. Thus D is also a splitting field of $x^{p^n} - x$, and by Theorem 10.4 there is an isomorphism from K onto D.

Although Theorem 10.5 shows that a finite field F of order p^n, where p is a prime, is simply the splitting field of $x^{p^n} - x$, it does not indicate the number of steps necessary in the construction of the splitting field, nor does it give a simple form for the splitting field. However, a finite field F has the form $[Z/(p)][x]/(f(x))$, where p is a suitable prime integer and $f(x)$ is a suitable prime polynomial. To see this, observe that the group of invertible elements of F is cyclic, say with generator α, so that the powers of α are all the nonzero elements of F. Thus $[Z/(p)](\alpha) = F$ and by Proposition 10.3 $[Z/(p)](\alpha)$ is isomorphic to $[Z/(p)][x]/(f(x))$, where $f(x)$ is the minimum polynomial of α. Thus F is isomorphic to $[Z/(p)][x]/(f(x))$, and every finite field is one of the fields determined in Section 10.2. The polynomial $f(x)$ associated with the element α is called a *primitive* polynomial. The degree of $f(x)$ is n, and $f(x)$ is a prime polynomial which divides $x^{p^n} - x$. Since $\alpha^{p^m} \neq \alpha$ for $m < n$, $f(x)$ does not divide $x^{p^m} - x$ for any integer m less than n. This in fact is an equivalent definition of a primitive polynomial.

Exercises

10-14 Factor $x^{16} + x$ into a product of primes over $[Z/(2)][x]$. (*Hint:* Since $16 = 2^4$, try dividing the product of the prime polynomials of degree 4 into $x^{16} + x$.)

10-15 Prove that a monic prime polynomial of degree n in $[Z/(p)][x]$ is a factor of $x^{p^n} - x$.

10-16 Let S be a nonempty set of subfields of a field L. Prove $\cap\ F$, where F ranges over S, is a field.

10-17 Let L be an extension field of F and $\alpha_1, \ldots, \alpha_k$ be elements of L. Prove that $F(\alpha_1) \cdots (\alpha_k) = F(\alpha_1, \ldots, \alpha_k)$.

10-18 Find an example of a prime polynomial that is not primitive.

10-19 Prove that $(f + cg)' = f' + cg'$ for f and g in $F[x]$, c in F, F a field.

10-20 Prove that $(fg)' = f'g + fg'$ for f and g in $F[x]$, F a field.

*10.4 LATIN SQUARES

In many types of experiments, different factors may affect the experiment, and the experiment must relate the effects of each factor. For example, an agriculturist may wish to test several strains of wheat to determine their yield. The fertility of the land significantly affects the harvest. In fact, one strain of wheat may do better under a heavy application of fertilizer and poorer under no application of fertilizer than another strain of wheat. Thus the experimenter may wish to test each strain of wheat with applications of different amounts of fertilizer. Suppose that there are three strains of wheat and three amounts of fertilizer application to be tested, that the agriculturist has three fields available for the testing, and that each field is large enough to be divided into three small plots. Since soil conditions can vary considerably from field to field, the experimenter has a problem in differentiating the effects of strain and amount of fertilizer applied from the effects due to soil characteristics. Ideally, all nine combinations of strain and amount of fertilizer should be tested on the same field but, in this example, this is not possible. To minimize the effects due to differences in the fields, each strain of wheat should be grown on each field and each fertilizer application should be made on each field.

Let F_1, F_2, and F_3 denote the fields and let P_1, P_2, and P_3 denote the plots into which each field is divided. Figure 10.4 shows the strains of wheat grown on each plot, where the strains are denoted by 1, 2, and 3. In Figure 10.4 a row corresponds to the field and a column corresponds to the three plots. Since each strain is grown on each field, each row consists of 1, 2, and 3 in some order. Figure 10.5 shows the amount of fertilizer applied to each plot, where the amounts are denoted by 1, 2, and 3. Again each row consists of 1, 2, and 3 in some order, but the order is such that each combination of wheat strain and fertilizer is tested. Thus, if Figure 10.4 is the matrix

$$A = (a_{ij}) = \begin{bmatrix} 1 & 2 & 3 \\ 3 & 1 & 2 \\ 2 & 3 & 1 \end{bmatrix},$$

and Figure 10.5 is the matrix

$$B = (b_{ij}) = \begin{bmatrix} 1 & 2 & 3 \\ 2 & 3 & 1 \\ 3 & 1 & 2 \end{bmatrix},$$

then the matrix

$$(a_{ij}, b_{ij}) = \begin{bmatrix} (1, 1) & (2, 2) & (3, 3) \\ (3, 2) & (1, 3) & (2, 1) \\ (2, 3) & (3, 1) & (1, 2) \end{bmatrix}$$

	P_1	P_2	P_3
F_1	1	2	3
F_2	3	1	2
F_3	2	3	1

Figure 10.4 Strains of wheat grown on each plot.

	P_1	P_2	P_3
F_1	1	2	3
F_2	2	3	1
F_3	3	1	2

Figure 10.5 Amounts of fertilizer applied to each plot.

contains all nine elements of $\{(i, j) : i = 1, 2, 3 \text{ and } j = 1, 2, 3\}$, corresponding to the nine possible combinations of wheat strain and fertilizer.

Definition An $n \times n$ matrix $A = (a_{ij})$ is a latin square if each row consists of $1, 2, \ldots, n$ in some order, and each column consists of $1, 2, \ldots, n$. That is, $R_i = \{a_{ij} : j = 1, 2, \ldots, n\} = \{1, 2, \ldots, n\}$ for each i, $1 \le i \le n$, and $C_j = \{a_{ij} : i = 1, 2, \ldots, n\} = \{1, 2, \ldots, n\}$ for each j, $1 \le j \le n$.

Definition $\{A_1, A_2, \ldots, A_k : A_l = (a_{ij}^{(l)})$ is an $n \times n$ latin square, $1 \le l \le k\}$ is a set of orthogonal latin squares if for each $l \ne m$, $1 \le l \le k$, $1 \le m \le k$,

$$\{(a_{ij}^{(l)}, a_{ij}^{(m)}) : 1 \le i \le n \text{ and } 1 \le j \le n\} = \{(i, j) : 1 \le i \le n \text{ and } 1 \le j \le n\}.$$

In the agricultural experiment just described,

$$\left\{ \begin{bmatrix} 1 & 2 & 3 \\ 3 & 1 & 2 \\ 2 & 3 & 1 \end{bmatrix}, \begin{bmatrix} 1 & 2 & 3 \\ 2 & 3 & 1 \\ 3 & 1 & 2 \end{bmatrix} \right\}$$

is a set of two orthogonal latin squares, and their determination is desirable for the completion of the experiment. There are numerous experiments that involve the testing of several different factors and which can be optimally carried out by using a set of orthogonal latin squares to determine the combination of factors to be used on each run. In the case of the experiment involving the strains of wheat, the use of orthogonal latin squares reduces the effect of extraneous factors (namely, soil conditions in the different fields). In other types of experiments, the use of orthogonal latin squares reduces the number of runs of the experiment, and this may be important if the cost of each run is high. An examination of these applications in detail, and a statistical justification for the use of orthogonal latin squares, is beyond the scope of this book, but we do investigate some of their properties.

Theorem 10.6 If $\{A_1, A_2, \ldots, A_k\}$ is a set of orthogonal $n \times n$ latin squares, then $k < n$.

Proof Let $A_l = (a_{ij}^{(l)})$. Let π be a permutation of $\{1, 2, \ldots, n\}$. Define $\pi(A_l) = (\pi(a_{ij}^{(l)}))$. In other words, $\pi(A_l)$ is the $n \times n$ matrix whose i, j entry is $\pi(a_{ij}^{(l)})$. Since $\{\pi(1), \pi(2), \ldots, \pi(n)\} = \{1, 2, \ldots, n\}$, $\pi(A_l)$ is a latin square. If $\pi_1, \pi_2, \ldots, \pi_k \in S_n$, then $T = \{\pi_1(A_1), \pi_2(A_2), \ldots, \pi_k(A_k)\}$ is a set of $n \times n$ latin squares. Furthermore, T is a set of orthogonal latin squares, since for $l \neq m$, $(\pi_l(a_{ij}^{(l)}), \pi_m(a_{ij}^{(m)})) = (\pi_l(a_{pq}^{(l)}), \pi_m(a_{pq}^{(m)}))$ implies $\pi_l(a_{ij}^{(l)}) = \pi_l(a_{pq}^{(l)})$ and $\pi_m(a_{ij}^{(m)}) = \pi_m(a_{pq}^{(m)})$. Since π_l and π_m are both one-to-one mappings, we have $a_{ij}^{(l)} = a_{pq}^{(l)}$ and $a_{ij}^{(m)} = a_{pq}^{(m)}$. This contradicts the orthogonality of A_l and A_m. Thus the matrices $\pi_l(A_l)$ and $\pi_m(A_m)$ are orthogonal for $l \neq m$. Choose π_1, $\pi_2, \ldots, \pi_k$ such that the first row of $\pi_l(A_l)$ is $1, 2, \ldots, n$, in that order, for each l. That is, $\pi_l(a_{1j}^{(l)}) = j$, $1 \leq j \leq n$, for each l. Since 1 occurs in the first column of each latin square exactly once, 1 cannot occur in the 2, 1 component of any $\pi_l(A_l)$. Furthermore, since $\{(\pi_l(a_{1j}^{(l)}), \pi_m(a_{1j}^{(m)})) : 1 \leq j \leq n\} = \{(i, i) : 1 \leq i \leq n\}$ and $\pi_l(A_l)$ and $\pi_m(A_m)$ are orthogonal, the 2, 1 components of $\pi_l(A_l)$ and $\pi_m(A_m)$ must be different. Thus there are at most $n - 1$ possible matrices $\pi_l(A_l)$, hence $k < n$.

Theorem 10.6 shows that the number of elements in a set of orthogonal $n \times n$ latin squares is bounded by $n - 1$. We use the existence of a finite field of order $n = p^r$ for each prime p to show that there exist $n - 1$ orthogonal $n \times n$ latin squares for $n = p^r$. It is not known, for general n, even when there exists a set of two orthogonal $n \times n$ latin squares.

Theorem 10.7 Let p be a prime and $n = p^r$. There exists a set of $n - 1$ orthogonal $n \times n$ latin squares for each positive integer r.

Proof Let $\{\alpha_1 = 1, \alpha_2, \ldots, \alpha_{n-1}, \alpha_n = 0\}$ be the finite field containing n elements. Define $A_l = (\alpha_l \alpha_i + \alpha_j)$, $1 \leq i \leq n$, $1 \leq j \leq n$, for each l, $1 \leq l \leq n - 1$. Each A_l is a latin square, since $\alpha_l \alpha_i + \alpha_j = \alpha_l \alpha_i + \alpha_t$, $1 \leq i \leq n$, $1 \leq j \leq n$, $1 \leq l \leq n - 1$, $1 \leq t \leq n$ implies $\alpha_j = \alpha_t$ and $j = t$. Also, $\alpha_l \alpha_i + \alpha_j = \alpha_l \alpha_t + \alpha_j$ implies $\alpha_l \alpha_i = \alpha_l \alpha_t$, and since $\alpha_l \neq 0$, $(\alpha_l)^{-1}$ exists so that $\alpha_i = \alpha_t$ and $i = t$. If, furthermore, $l \neq m$, then we claim A_l and A_m are orthogonal. Suppose $(\alpha_l \alpha_i + \alpha_j, \alpha_m \alpha_i + \alpha_j) = (\alpha_l \alpha_x + \alpha_y, \alpha_m \alpha_x + \alpha_y)$, $1 \leq l \leq n - 1$, $1 \leq m \leq n - 1$, $1 \leq i \leq n$, $1 \leq j \leq n$, $1 \leq x \leq n$, $1 \leq y \leq n$. Thus

$$\alpha_l \alpha_i + \alpha_j = \alpha_l \alpha_x + \alpha_y \tag{1}$$

and

$$\alpha_m \alpha_i + \alpha_j = \alpha_m \alpha_x + \alpha_y. \tag{2}$$

Subtracting Eq. (2) from Eq. (1) we obtain $(\alpha_l - \alpha_m)\alpha_i = (\alpha_l - \alpha_m)\alpha_x$. Since $\alpha_l \neq \alpha_m$, $(\alpha_l - \alpha_m)^{-1}$ exists and $\alpha_i = \alpha_x$. This furthermore implies that $\alpha_j = \alpha_y$. Thus $i = x$ and $j = y$, showing that A_l and A_m are orthogonal.

Exercises

10-21   Determine a set of three orthogonal 4×4 latin squares.

10.5   FIELDS OF FRACTIONS

This section shows how to generalize the construction of the field of rational numbers as fractions with numerator and denominator integers and denominator nonzero. Although this process of constructing fractions for arbitrary integral domains is important in understanding the structure of general fields, we apply it only once in Section 10.7, where fractions with numerators and denominators from polynomial rings are needed.

Let R be an integral domain. Define $S = \{r/s : r, s \in R \text{ and } s \neq 0\}$. Thus, if R is Z, then S is just the set of what is normally called fractions. As in the case of $R = Z$, we define two elements r_1/s_1 and r_2/s_2 to be equivalent if $r_1 s_2 = r_2 s_1$. This is easily found to be an equivalence relation, and we define $Q(R)$ to be the set of equivalence classes of S under this relation. In the case of Z, for example, the class $[1/2]$ contains $2/4$, $3/6$, $-5/-10$ and, in general, $n/2n$ for all nonzero integers n.

Binary operations are defined on $Q(R)$ now, by putting

$$\left[\frac{r_1}{s_1}\right] + \left[\frac{r_2}{s_2}\right] = \left[\frac{r_1 s_2 + r_2 s_1}{s_1 s_2}\right] \quad \text{and} \quad [r_1/s_1][r_2/s_2] = [r_1 r_2/s_1 s_2].$$

In order to be sure that $+$ and $\circ$ are truly binary operations, we must make sure that $+$ and $\circ$ are well defined. Thus suppose $r_1'/s_1' \in [r_1/s_1]$ and $r_2'/s_2' \in [r_2/s_2]$. Thus $r_1' s_1 = r_1 s_1'$ and $r_2' s_2 = r_2 s_2'$. Thus

$$(r_1 s_2 + r_2 s_1)s_1' s_2' = r_1 s_2 s_1' s_2' + r_2 s_1 s_1' s_2' = r_1' s_2' s_1 s_2 + r_2' s_1' s_1 s_2$$

$$= (r_1' s_2' + r_2' s_1')s_1 s_2,$$

so that

$$\left[\frac{r_1' s_2' + r_2' s_1'}{s_1' s_2'}\right] = \left[\frac{r_1 s_2 + r_2 s_1}{s_1 s_2}\right].$$

Similarly, multiplication is well defined.

Since R is an integral domain, associativity and commutativity of addition and multiplication of R pass easily on to $Q(R)$, as does distributivity. The classes $[0/1]$ and $[1/1]$ act as additive and multiplicative identities. The additive inverse of $[r/s]$ is $[-r/s]$ and, if $r \neq 0$, the multiplicative inverse of $[r/s]$ is $[s/r]$. Thus $Q(R)$ forms a field, called the field of fractions of R.

Exercises

10-22 If $r_1/s_1 \sim r_2/s_2$, when $r_1 s_2 = r_2 s_1$, where all r_i and s_i are in the integral domain R, with $s_1 \neq 0 \neq s_2$, then prove that $\sim$ is an equivalence relation.

10-23 Prove that $Q(R)$ satisfies the distributive law.

10.6 POLYNOMIAL CODES

Polynomial codes are a special type of matrix code. Let $v = (c_0, c_1, \ldots, c_{k-1})$ be a vector in F^k, where F is a field. Define a $(m, m + k)$ encoding over F by

$$(a_0, a_1, \ldots, a_{m-1}) \rightarrow \left(a_0 c_0, a_0 c_1 + a_1 c_0, \ldots, \sum_{i=0}^{j} a_i c_{j-i}, \ldots, a_{m-1} c_{k-1} \right),$$

with the convention that $c_j = 0$ for all $j > k - 1$. This encoding is called a polynomial encoding, because it can be represented by polynomial multiplication. The vector $(a_0, \ldots, a_{m-1})$ corresponds to the polynomial

$$a(x) = \sum_{i=0}^{m-1} a_i x^i,$$

while

$$g(x) = \sum_{i=0}^{k-1} c_i x^i$$

is the encoding polynomial. The polynomial $a(x)$ is then mapped to $a(x) \circ g(x)$, which is represented as the corresponding $(m + k)$-tuple. A polynomial code is a linear transformation, since $(a(x) + b(x)) \circ g(x) = a(x) \circ g(x) + b(x) \circ g(x)$. A basis of the message space is $\{x^i\}_{i=0}^{m-1}$, so that $x^i \rightarrow x^i g(x)$, which is just $g(x)$ shifted i places to the right. Thus the encoding matrix is

$$\begin{bmatrix} c_0 & c_1 & c_2 & \cdots & c_{k-1} & 0 & \cdots & 0 & 0 \\ 0 & c_0 & c_1 & \cdots & c_{k-2} & c_{k-1} & \cdots & 0 & 0 \\ \vdots & \vdots & \ddots & & & \ddots & \ddots & & \\ & & & & & & \ddots & c_{k-1} & 0 \\ 0 & 0 & \cdots & 0 & c_0 & \cdots & \cdots & c_{k-2} & c_{k-1} \end{bmatrix}.$$

As an example, let the encoding polynomial be $1 + x + x^2$ and let the message space be $[Z/(2)]^3$. The encoding function is

$$000 \to 0 \circ (1 + x + x^2) \sim 00000$$

$$001 \to x^2(1 + x + x^2) = x^2 + x^3 + x^4 \sim 00111$$

$$010 \to x(1 + x + x^2) = x + x^2 + x^3 \sim 01110$$

$$011 \to (x + x^2)(1 + x + x^2) = x + x^4 \sim 01001$$

$$100 \to 1(1 + x + x^2) = 1 + x + x^2 \sim 11100$$

$$101 \to (1 + x^2)(1 + x + x^2) = 1 + x + x^3 + x^4 \sim 11011$$

$$110 \to (1 + x)(1 + x + x^2) = 1 + x^3 \sim 10010$$

$$111 \to (1 + x + x^2)(1 + x + x^2) = 1 + x^2 + x^4 \sim 10101.$$

The matrix associated with this linear transformation is

$$\begin{bmatrix} 1 & 1 & 1 & 0 & 0 \\ 0 & 1 & 1 & 1 & 0 \\ 0 & 0 & 1 & 1 & 1 \end{bmatrix}.$$

The algebraic structure of polynomial codes yields powerful tools for analyzing the distance properties of these codes. In the next section, we show how this structure can be used to give a polynomial code of an arbitrary error correction capability.

Exercises

10-24   List the set of encoded vectors of the $(4, 7)$ polynomial code over $Z/(2)$ with encoding polynomial $x + x^3$. What is the minimum distance between the encoded vectors?

10-25   Let $g(x)$ be a polynomial in $[Z/(2)][x]$ with a nonzero constant coefficient. Prove that, if $g(x)$ does not divide $x^m - 1$ for all $m < n$, then the $[n - \deg g(x), n]$ code with encoding polynomial $g(x)$ has a minimum distance of at least 3.

10-26   Let $g(x) = x^4 + x^3 + 2$ in $[Z/(3)][x]$ be the encoding polynomial for a $(6, 10)$ polynomial code. Determine if the received word 2101010011 is a code word.

10.7   BCH CODES

Bose and Chaudhuri in 1960 and Hocquenghem in 1959 constructed a special class of polynomial codes (BCH codes), which is closely related to the structure of finite fields. Let $GF(2^k)$ be the finite field of order 2^k. Let α be a generator of the cyclic group $(GF(2^k))^*$ and denote the minimal polynomial of α^i by $f_i(x)$, $i = 1, 2, \ldots, 2^k - 2$. Fix an integer d with $2 \leq d \leq 2^k - 1$. The BCH code associated with α and d is the $[(2^k - 1) - \deg g(x), 2^k - 1]$ polynomial code with encoding polynomial $g(x) = \mathrm{lcm}\{f_1(x), f_2(x), \ldots, f_{d-1}(x)\}$.

As an example, take $GF(2^4) \cong [Z/(2)][x]/(x^4 + x + 1)$. Let $\alpha = [x]$ be a root of $x^4 + x + 1$, so that $\alpha^4 = \alpha + 1$ and $\alpha^5 = \alpha \circ \alpha^4 = \alpha(\alpha + 1) = \alpha^2 + \alpha$. Since $|(GF(2^4))^*| = 2^4 - 1 = 15$, α must have order 1, 3, 5, or 15. Since none of α, α^3, or α^5 equals the identity, the order of α is 15 and α is a generator of the cyclic group $(GF(2^4))^*$. The minimal polynomial of α is $x^4 + x + 1$, so $f_1(x) = x^4 + x + 1$. In general, to determine the minimal polynomial of $f_i(x)$, successively take powers of α^i, say $1, \alpha^i, (\alpha^i)^2, (\alpha^i)^3, \ldots,$ $(\alpha^i)^j$, until there is a dependency over $Z/(2)$ of the vectors $1, \alpha^i, \ldots, (\alpha^i)^j$. This yields a polynomial with α^i as a root and, if j is the smallest power of α^i such that a dependency of $\{1, \alpha^i, \ldots, (\alpha^i)^j\}$ exists, then this polynomial is the minimal polynomial of α^i. Thus to determine $f_3(x)$, observe that

$$\{1, \alpha^3, (\alpha^3)^2 = \alpha^6 = \alpha^2 \circ \alpha^4 = \alpha^2 \circ (\alpha + 1) = \alpha^3 + \alpha^2, (\alpha^3)^3 = \alpha \circ (\alpha^4)^2$$

$$= \alpha \circ (\alpha + 1)^2 = \alpha \circ (\alpha^2 + 1) = \alpha^3 + \alpha\}$$

is linearly independent, since

$$c_0 \circ 1 + c_1 \circ (\alpha^3) + c_2(\alpha^3)^2 + c_3(\alpha^3)^3 = 0$$

if and only if

$$c_0 \circ 1 + c_1 \circ \alpha^3 + c_2(\alpha^3 + \alpha^2) + c_3(\alpha^3 + \alpha) = 0$$

if and only if

$$c_0 \circ 1 + c_3 \circ \alpha + c_2 \circ \alpha^2 + (c_1 + c_2 + c_3)\alpha^3 = 0.$$

Since the minimal polynomial of α is $x^4 + x + 1$, α is not a root of a nonzero polynomial of smaller degree. Hence $0 = c_0 = c_3 = c_2 = (c_1 + c_2 + c_3)$, which shows $0 = c_0 = c_1 = c_2 = c_3$ and the vectors are independent. However, $\{1, \alpha^3, (\alpha^3)^2 = \alpha^3 + \alpha^2; (\alpha^3)^3 = \alpha^3 + \alpha; (\alpha^3)^4 = (\alpha + 1)^3 = \alpha^3 + \alpha^2 + \alpha + 1\}$ is linearly dependent. In fact, $1 + \alpha^3 + (\alpha^3)^2 + (\alpha^3)^3 + (\alpha^3)^4 = 0$, so that α^3 is a root of $x^4 + x^3 + x^2 + x + 1$. Thus $f_3(x) = x^4 + x^3 + x^2 + x + 1$.

The same procedure can be used to calculate $f_2(x)$, but it is much simpler to observe that $\sum_{j=0}^{l} a_j \alpha^j = 0$ implies

$$0 = \left(\sum_{j=0}^{l} a_j \alpha^j\right)^2 = \sum_{j=0}^{l} a_j^2 (\alpha^2)^j = \sum_{j=0}^{l} a_j (\alpha^2)^j$$

by Exercise 10.6 and the fact that a_j is either 0 or 1. Thus α^2 is also a root of $f_1(x)$. Since $f_1(x)$ is prime, $f_2(x) = f_1(x)$. In fact, since $0 = [f_i(\alpha^i)]^2 = f_i(\alpha^{2i})$, we have $f_{2i}(x) = f_i(x)$ for all positive integers i. Thus $x^4 + x + 1 = f_1(x) = f_2(x) = f_4(x)$ and $x^4 + x^3 + x^2 + x + 1 = f_3(x) = f_6(x)$. We determine one further minimal polynomial $f_5(x)$. First calculate

$$\alpha^5 = \alpha \circ \alpha^4 = \alpha^2 + \alpha, \ (\alpha^5)^2 = (\alpha^2 + \alpha)^2 = \alpha^4 + \alpha^2 = \alpha^2 + \alpha + 1.$$

Thus $1 + \alpha^5 + (\alpha^5)^2 = 0$, and $x^2 + x + 1 = f_5(x)$. The polynomial

$$\begin{aligned} g(x) &= \text{lcm}\{f_1(x), f_2(x), f_3(x), f_4(x), f_5(x), f_6(x)\} \\ &= \text{lcm}\{x^4 + x + 1, \ x^4 + x^3 + x^2 + x + 1, \ x^2 + x + 1\} \\ &= x^{10} + x^8 + x^5 + x^4 + x^2 + x + 1, \end{aligned}$$

since $x^4 + x + 1$, $x^4 + x^3 + x^2 + x + 1$, and $x^2 + x + 1$ are all prime. Thus $g(x)$ is the encoding polynomial of a $(16 - 1 - 10, 16 - 1) = (5, 15)$ BCH code with $d = 7$.

The importance of BCH codes stems from the following theorem.

Theorem 10.8   Let α be a generator of $(GF(2^k))^*$. If $g(x) \in [Z/(2)][x]$ has $\alpha, \alpha^2, \ldots, \alpha^{d-1}$ as roots, $d \leq 2^k$, then the polynomial code with $g(x)$ as encoding polynomial has a minimum distance of at least d between encoded vectors.

Proof   The polynomial $g(x)$ has $\alpha, \ \alpha^2, \ \alpha^3, \ldots, \alpha^{d-1}$ as roots, hence $a(x) \circ g(x)$ also has α^i, $i = 1, \ldots, d - 1$ as roots, where $a(x)$ is a message polynomial. Since the minimum distance between encoded vectors is the minimum weight of an encoded vector, it is sufficient to show that a polynomial with $\alpha, \alpha^2, \ldots, \alpha^{d-1}$ as roots must have a weight of at least d. If an encoded polynomial has a weight less than d, then it can be written

$$c_1 x^{n_1} + c_2 x^{n_2} + \cdots + c_{d-1} x^{n_{d-1}},$$

where not all c_i are zero and $0 \leq n_1 < n_2 < \cdots < n_{d-1} \leq 2^k - 1$. Since $\alpha, \alpha^2, \ldots, \alpha^{d-1}$ are roots, we have the system of equations

$$\begin{aligned} c_1 \alpha^{n_1} + \cdots + c_{d-1} \alpha^{n_{d-1}} &= 0 \\ c_1 (\alpha^2)^{n_1} + \cdots + c_{d-1}(\alpha^2)^{n_{d-1}} &= 0 \\ \vdots \qquad \cdots \qquad \vdots \qquad \qquad &\vdots \\ c_1 (\alpha^{d-1})^{n_1} + \cdots + c_{d-1}(\alpha^{d-1})^{n_{d-1}} &= 0, \end{aligned}$$

which gives

$$\begin{aligned} c_1 \alpha^{n_1} + \cdots + c_{d-1} \alpha^{n_{d-1}} &= 0 \\ c_1 (\alpha^{n_1})^2 + \cdots + c_{d-1}(\alpha^{n_{d-1}})^2 &= 0 \\ \vdots \qquad \cdots \qquad \vdots \qquad \qquad &\vdots \\ c_1 (\alpha^{n_1})^{d-1} + \cdots + c_{d-1}(\alpha^{n_{d-1}})^{d-1} &= 0. \end{aligned}$$

Denote α^{n_i} by β_i. Thus in matrix notation:

$$(c_1, \ldots, c_{d-1}) \begin{bmatrix} \beta_1 & \beta_1^2 & \cdots & \beta_1^{d-1} \\ \beta_2 & \beta_2^2 & \cdots & \beta_2^{d-1} \\ \vdots & \vdots & \cdots & \vdots \\ \beta_{d-1} & \beta_{d-1}^2 & \cdots & \beta_{d-1}^{d-1} \end{bmatrix} = (00 \cdots 0).$$

If

$$M = \begin{bmatrix} \beta_1 & \beta_1^2 & \cdots & \beta_1^{d-1} \\ \vdots & \vdots & \cdots & \vdots \\ \beta_{d-1} & \beta_{d-1}^2 & \cdots & \beta_{d-1}^{d-1} \end{bmatrix}$$

is invertible, then $c_i = 0$ for all i, and the only encoded vector of weight less than d is zero. However, M is invertible by the following argument. Define

$$N = \begin{bmatrix} 1 & y_1 & \cdots & y_1^{d-2} \\ 1 & y_2 & \cdots & y_2^{d-2} \\ \vdots & \vdots & \cdots & \vdots \\ 1 & y_{d-1} & \cdots & y_{d-1}^{d-2} \end{bmatrix}.$$

The matrix N is called the Vandermonde matrix, and the determinant of N is $\prod_{i>j} (y_i - y_j)$, where $y_1, \ldots, y_{d-1}$ are variables. To see this, replace y_j by y_i in N for $i > j$ to obtain a matrix with two identical rows, which thus has determinant zero. In $F[y_i]$, where F is the field of fractions of the integral domain $[Z/(2)][y_1, y_2, \ldots, y_{i-1}, y_{i+1}, \ldots, y_{d-1}]$ of polynomials in indeterminates $y_1, y_2, \ldots, y_{i-1}, y_{i+1}, \ldots, y_{d-1}$ with coefficients from $Z/(2)$, the determinant is a polynomial in y_i and must therefore be divisible by $y_i - y_j$, since y_j is a root of the polynomial in $F[y_i]$. Thus $\prod_{i>j} (y_i - y_j)$ divides det N. Since the total degree of $\prod_{i>j} (y_i - y_j)$ is $(d-1)(d-2)/2$ and the degree of det N is $0 + 1 + 2 + \cdots + d - 2 = (d-1)(d-2)/2$, det N is a scalar multiple of $\prod_{i>j} (y_i - p_j)$. Since the coefficient of $y_{d-1}^{d-2} y_{d-2}^{d-3} \cdots y_2\, 1$ is 1 in det N, we have det $N = \prod_{i>j} (y_i - y_j)$. Hence det $M = \beta_1 \beta_2 \cdots \beta_{d-1} \prod_{i>j} (\beta_i - \beta_j) \neq 0$, since β_i are all distinct, which proves the theorem.

Theorem 10.8 shows that the (5, 15) BCH code, given as an example, has a minimum distance between encoded words of at least 7. Thus the code can correct all sets of three or fewer errors which might occur in the transmission of a vector. The theorem does not give an error correction procedure. Since the minimum distance between encoded words is large enough, a search through a list of all encoded words to find the closest encoded word would yield an error-correcting procedure. This is extremely unsatisfactory, since even for message vectors of the small block size 20, there are well over 1 million encoded vectors through which to search. Thus more efficient methods must be found.

One error-correcting method for BCH codes is the following. Suppose $v(x)$ is an encoded vector, and $r(x) = v(x) + e(x)$ is received during a transmission of $v(x)$, where $e(x)$ is the error pattern. If we can determine $e(x)$ from $r(x)$, then $v(x) = r(x) - e(x)$ can be recovered. Since $\alpha, \alpha^2, \ldots, \alpha^{d-1}$ are roots of every encoded vector, $r(\alpha^i) = v(\alpha^i) + e(\alpha^i) = 0 + e(\alpha^i) = e(\alpha^i)$, the values that $e(x)$ takes at α^i, $i = 1, \ldots, d-1$, are known. Suppose $e(x) = x^{m_1} + \cdots + x^{m_s}$, where $0 \le m_1 < m_2 < \cdots < m_s \le 2^k - 1$ and $2s + 1 \le d = 2t + 1$. Thus $e(x)$ is known once $m_1, \ldots, m_s$ are determined. Since $e(\alpha^i) = (\alpha^{m_1})^i + \cdots + (\alpha^{m_s})^i$ for $1 \le i \le d-1$, a solution of the system of equations

$$
\begin{aligned}
r(\alpha) &= e(\alpha) &= X_1 &+ \cdots + X_t \\
r(\alpha^2) &= e(\alpha^2) &= X_1^2 &+ \cdots + X_t^2 \\
&\;\;\vdots & \vdots &\quad\cdots \\
r(\alpha^{d-1}) &= e(\alpha^{d-1}) &= X_1^{d-1} &+ \cdots + X_t^{d-1}
\end{aligned}
$$

in $GF(2^k)$ yields X_i's which can then be expressed as powers of α to determine the m_j. The solutions, if any exist, to this system of equations over $GF(2^k)$ yield a unique $e(x)$, since otherwise there would be two distinct vectors $e_1(x)$ and $e_2(x)$ with $e_j(\alpha^i) = r(\alpha^i)$, $i = 1, \ldots, d-1$, and $j = 1, 2$. Thus $r(x) + e_j(x)$ would have $\alpha, \ldots, \alpha^{d-1}$ as roots, implying $g(x)$ divides $r(x) + e_j(x)$, $j = 1, 2$. Thus two encoded vectors have distance $\le 2t$ which contradicts Theorem 10.8.

As an example suppose the vector $110001001101000 \sim 1 + x + x^5 + x^8 + x^9 + x^{11}$ is received and the code is the (5, 15) BCH code given in the first part of the section. With the use of Figure 10.6, which computes the powers of α, it is simple to calculate $r(\alpha)$, $r(\alpha^3)$, and $r(\alpha^5)$.

Substitution of α, α^3, and α^5 into the received polynomial yields

$$
\begin{aligned}
r(\alpha) &= 1 + \alpha + \alpha^5 + \alpha^8 + \alpha^9 + \alpha^{11} = \alpha^2 \\
r(\alpha^3) &= 1 + \alpha^3 + \alpha^{15} + \alpha^{24} + \alpha^{27} + \alpha^{33} = 1 + \alpha^2 \\
r(\alpha^5) &= 1 + \alpha^5 + \alpha^{25} + \alpha^{40} + \alpha^{45} + \alpha^{55} = 1.
\end{aligned}
$$

Thus

$$
\begin{aligned}
X_1 + X_2 + X_3 &= \alpha^2 \\
X_1^3 + X_2^3 + X_3^3 &= 1 + \alpha^2 \\
X_1^5 + X_2^5 + X_3^5 &= 1.
\end{aligned}
$$

Since $(GF(2^4))^* = 15$, the only possibilities for X_i^5 are $0, 1, \alpha^5$, and α^{10}. However, $\alpha^5 = \alpha^2 + \alpha$ and $\alpha^{10} = \alpha^2 + \alpha + 1$, so that the only possible solution is $\{X_1^5, X_2^5, X_3^5\} = \{0, \alpha^{10}, \alpha^5\}$. Thus assume $X_1^5 = 0$, so that $X_1 = 0$;

$1 = 1$	$\alpha^4 = \alpha + 1$	$\alpha^8 = \alpha^2 + 1$	$\alpha^{12} = \alpha^3 + \alpha^2 + \alpha + 1$
$\alpha = \alpha$	$\alpha^5 = \alpha^2 + \alpha$	$\alpha^9 = \alpha^3 + \alpha$	$\alpha^{13} = \alpha^3 + \alpha^2 + 1$
$\alpha^2 = \alpha^2$	$\alpha^6 = \alpha^3 + \alpha^2$	$\alpha^{10} = \alpha^2 + \alpha + 1$	$\alpha^{14} = \alpha^3 + 1$
$\alpha^3 = \alpha^3$	$\alpha^7 = \alpha^3 + \alpha + 1$	$\alpha^{11} = \alpha^3 + \alpha^2 + \alpha$	$\alpha^{15} = 1$

Figure 10.6 Powers of α in $GF(2^4)$.

$X_2^5 = \alpha^5$, so that X_2 is one of $\{\alpha, \alpha^4, \alpha^7, \alpha^{10}, \alpha^{13}\}$; and $X_3^5 = \alpha^{10}$, so that X_3 is one of $\{\alpha^2, \alpha^5, \alpha^8, \alpha^{11}, \alpha^{14}\}$. Since $X_1 = 0$, the first two equations yield $X_2 + X_3 = \alpha^2$, and

$$X_2^3 + X_3^3 = (X_2 + X_3)(X_2^2 + X_2 X_3 + X_3^2)$$
$$= (X_2 + X_3)((X_2 + X_3)^2 + X_2 X_3)$$
$$= 1 + \alpha^2.$$

Thus

$$1 + \alpha^2 = \alpha^2(\alpha^4 + X_2 X_3)$$

and

$$X_2 X_3 = \alpha^{13} + 1 + \alpha^4$$
$$= \alpha^{12}(\alpha + \alpha^3 + \alpha^7)$$
$$= \alpha^{12} \circ 1 = \alpha^{12}.$$

Thus the possibilities for X_2 and X_3 are as follows. The ordered pair (X_2, X_3) is one of (α, α^{11}), (α^4, α^8), (α^7, α^5), (α^{10}, α^2), and $(\alpha^{13}, \alpha^{14})$. However,

$$\alpha + \alpha^{11} = \alpha + (\alpha + 1)^2 \alpha^3 = \alpha + \alpha^5 + \alpha^3 = \alpha^3 + \alpha^2 \neq \alpha^2$$
$$\alpha^4 + \alpha^8 = (\alpha + 1)(1 + (\alpha + 1)) = \alpha^2 + \alpha \neq \alpha^2$$
$$\alpha^7 + \alpha^5 = (\alpha^2 + \alpha)(\alpha^2 + 1) = \alpha^3 + \alpha^2 + 1 \neq \alpha^2$$
$$\alpha^{10} + \alpha^2 = \alpha^2(\alpha^2 + 1 + 1) = \alpha + 1 \neq \alpha^2$$
$$\alpha^{13} + \alpha^{14} = (\alpha + 1)^3(\alpha + 1)\alpha = (\alpha^4 + 1)\alpha = \alpha^2.$$

Thus $X_2 = \alpha^{13}$ and $X_3 = \alpha^{14}$, so we can assume two errors occurred during transmission and that the errors occurred in the thirteenth and fourteenth components of the vector. Thus the corrected received vector is $110001001101011 \sim 1 + x + x^5 + x^8 + x^9 + x^{11} + x^{13} + x^{14}$. Dividing this vector by the encoding polynomial $1 + x + x^2 + x^4 + x^5 + x^8 + x^{10}$ yields a remainder 0 and a quotient $a(x) = 1 + x^2 + x^3 + x^4$. Thus the message vector is 10111.

   The solution of the system of equations in the above example is ad hoc
and unsatisfactory for any generalization. There is, however, a general error
correction procedure. The basic idea is to let the variables $X_1, \ldots, X_t$ in

$$X_1 \quad + \cdots + X_t \quad = r(\alpha)$$
$$\vdots \qquad \cdots \qquad \vdots \qquad \vdots$$
$$X_1^{d-1} + \cdots + X_t^{d-1} = r(\alpha^{d-1})$$

be found as the roots of an equation of degree t. Thus $X_1, \ldots, X_t$ are the
roots of

$$(Z - X_1)(Z - X_2) \cdots (Z - X_t) = Z^t - \sigma_1 Z^{t-1} + \sigma_2 Z^{t-2} - \cdots + (-1)^t \sigma_n,$$

where

$$\sigma_1 = X_1 + X_2 + \cdots + X_t$$
$$\sigma_2 = \sum_{i<j} X_i X_j$$
$$\vdots \qquad \vdots$$
$$\sigma_l = \sum_{i_1 < i_2 < \cdots < i_l} X_{i_1} X_{i_2} \cdots X_{i_l}$$
$$\vdots \qquad \vdots$$
$$\sigma_t = X_1 X_2 \cdots X_t.$$

The problem is now fixed in terms of determining the coefficients σ_i of this
polynomial in terms of the known $r(\alpha^i)$ and then determining the roots of the
polynomial as powers of α. The polynomial with roots $X_1, \ldots, X_t$ and
coefficients in terms of $r(\alpha^i)$ is called the error locator polynomial. For
example, if $t = 2$,

$$X_1 + X_2 = r(\alpha)$$
$$X_1^3 + X_2^3 = r(\alpha^3)$$

and $(Z - X_1)(Z - X_2) = Z^2 - (X_1 + X_2)Z + X_1 X_2$. Since $X_1^3 + X_2^3 = (X_1 + X_2)([X_1 + X_2]^2 + X_1 X_2)$, we have

$$X_1 X_2 = \frac{r(\alpha^3)}{r(\alpha)} - r^2(\alpha),$$

so that the roots of

$$Z^2 - r(\alpha)Z + \frac{r(\alpha^3) + r^3(\alpha)}{r(\alpha)}$$

expressed as powers of α, give the location of the errors.

To furnish a solution in general, it is sufficient to show that σ_i can be expressed in terms of $r(\alpha^i)$. In fact, define $\gamma_i = \sum_{j=1}^{t} X_j^i$. The relationship between γ_i and σ_j is given by the following proposition.

Proposition 10.5 $\gamma_p - \gamma_{p-1}\sigma_1 + \gamma_{p-2}\sigma_2 - \cdots + (-1)^{p-1}\gamma_1\sigma_{p-1} + (-1)^p\sigma_p = 0$ for $p \leq t$.

Proof The proof follows once we note that

$$\sum_{j=1}^{t} \sum_{\substack{i_1 < \cdots < i_l \\ i_k \neq j, \text{ all } k}} X_{i_1} \cdots X_{i_l} X_j^{p-l}$$

$$= \sum_{j=1}^{t} \left(\sum_{\substack{i_1 < \cdots < i_l \\ i_k \neq j, \text{ all } k}} X_{i_1} \cdots X_{i_l} X_j \right) X_j^{p-l-1} + u - u$$

$$= \sum_{j=1}^{t} \left(\sum_{i_1 < \cdots < i_{l+1}} X_{i_1} \cdots X_{i_{l+1}} \right) X_j^{p-l-1} - u$$

$$= \sigma_{l+1}\gamma_{p-l-1} - u$$

where

$$u = \sum_{j=1}^{t} \left(\sum_{\substack{i_1 < \cdots < i_l \\ i_k \neq j \text{ all } k}} \left(\sum_{\substack{i_{l+1}, i_{l+1} \neq i_k, \\ \text{all } k, i_{l+1} \neq j}} X_{i_1} \cdots X_{i_{l+1}} \right) \right) X_j^{p-l-1}$$

Thus

$$u = \sum_{j=1}^{t} \left(\sum_{\substack{i_1 < \cdots < i_{l+1}, \\ i_k \neq j, \text{ all } k}} X_{i_1} \cdots X_{i_{l+1}} \right) X_j^{p-(l+1)},$$

and by induction

$$u = \sigma_{l+2}\gamma_{p-(l+2)} - \cdots + (-1)^{p-(l+2)}\gamma_1\sigma_{p-1} + (-1)^{p-(l+1)}\sigma_p.$$

Hence, with $l = 0$, we obtain $\gamma_p - \gamma_{p-1}\sigma_1 + \cdots + (-1)^p\sigma_p = 0$.

Corollary 10.2 σ_t can be expressed in terms of γ_i.

Proof We certainly have $\sigma_1 = \gamma_1$. Suppose that $\sigma_i = f_i(\gamma_1, \gamma_2, \ldots, \gamma_t)$ for $i = 1, \ldots, p-1$, where f_i are polynomials in t variables. Thus

$$\sigma_p = \gamma_1\sigma_{p-1} - \gamma_2\sigma_{p-2} + \cdots + (-1)^{p+1}\gamma_p$$

$$= \gamma_1 f_{p-1}(\gamma_1, \ldots, \gamma_t) - \gamma_2 f_{p-2}(\gamma_1, \ldots, \gamma_t) + \cdots + (-1)^{p+1}\gamma_p,$$

which is of the form $f_p(\gamma_1, \ldots, \gamma_t)$.

Thus we see that the roots of the error locator polynomial give the locations of the errors and, furthermore, Proposition 10.5 and its corollary yield methods for determining the coefficients of the error locator polynomial in terms of the $r(\alpha^i)$, where $r(x)$ is the received word.

Exercises

10-27 Give an encoding polynomial for a $[31 - \deg g(x), 31]$ BCH code for which $d = 9$.

10-28 Show that for a polynomial code, with encoding polynomial $g(x)$, division of a received word by $g(x)$ yields a simple error detection algorithm.

10-29 Suppose $1101100101 \sim 1 + x + x^3 + x^4 + x^7 + x^9$ is a received polynomial for the (5, 15) BCH code given in Section 10.7. Determine the corrected received word and decode the corrected received word.

10-30 Find a primitive polynomial of degree 6 over $Z/(2)$.

10-31 Determine the error locator polynomial in terms of $r(\alpha^i)$ for a triple-error-correcting BCH code.

Universal Algebra

The homomorphism theorems, proved for machines in Sections 5.4 and 5.5, for groups in Section 7.9, and for rings in Section 8.8, have a great deal in common. In all three cases, a homomorphism is a function from a set into another set, which preserves certain operations on the set. In the case of machines, a homomorphism from the machine $(\mathscr{S}, \mathscr{I}, \mathscr{O}, \delta, \theta)$ to the machine $(\mathscr{S}_1, \mathscr{I}, \mathscr{O}, \delta_1, \theta_1)$ is a function ϕ from S to S_1 such that $\phi(\delta(s, a)) = \delta_1(\phi(s), a)$ and $\phi(\theta(s, a) = \theta_1(\phi(s), a)$ for all s in $\mathscr{S}$ and a in $\mathscr{I}$. Thus ϕ preserves the next-state operation and the output operation. For groups, a homomorphism from the group G to the group G_1 is a function ϕ from G to G_1, which preserves the binary operation of the group, that is, $\phi(g_1 \circ g_2) = \phi(g_1) \circ \phi(g_2)$ for all g_1 and g_2 in G. For rings, a homomorphism from the ring R to the ring R_1 is a function ϕ from R to R_1, which preserves the binary operations of addition and multiplication, that is, $\phi(r_1 + r_2) = \phi(r_1) + \phi(r_2)$ and $\phi(r_1 \circ r_2) = \phi(r_1) \circ \phi(r_2)$ for all r_1 and r_2 in R. In each of these cases, an isomorphism is a homomorphism which as a function is one-to-one and onto. We have proved that homomorphic images of machines, groups, and rings, respectively, are constructed by certain congruences. This chapter shows that the concept of homomorphism and congruence is applicable in a general setting which includes homomorphism and congruence of machines, groups, and rings.

A set I is an *index set* for the set X if there is a function from I to X. The image of i in I is denoted by x. The set of positive integers is often used as an index set, and the indexing can be thought of as a listing x_1, x_2, x_3, ... of some of the elements in X.

In order to give a general definition of algebra, we need to extend the notion of operation introduced in the first chapter. It should be no cause for confusion if we here give a more general definition of an *n*-ary operation. Let $X = \{S_i : i \in I\}$ be a set of nonempty sets S_i indexed by $I \neq \varnothing$. If n is a non-negative integer, an *n-ary operation* on X is a function from $S_{i(1)} \times \cdots \times S_{i(n)}$ to S_r, where $i(1)$, $i(2)$, ..., $i(n)$ and r are in I, and where repetitions are allowed. A 0-ary operation is a function from $\{\varnothing\}$ to S, so that a 0-ary operation corresponds to picking a specific element of S, called a distinguished element. The binary operation of multiplication in a semigroup G is a function from $G \times G$ to G. Thus multiplication in G is a 2-ary operation on $X = \{G\}$. If G is a monoid, then the mapping of $\{\varnothing\}$ to G given by $\varnothing \rightarrow e$, where e is the identity element of G, is a 0-ary operation on $X = \{G\}$. We often denote a 0-ary operation by its image, so that we say that e is a 0-ary operation. If G is a group, then the inverse operation, which takes g in G to the unique element g^{-1} in G, is a 1-ary operation on X. If $M = (\mathscr{S}_1, \mathscr{I}_2, \mathcal{O}_3, \delta, \theta)$ is a machine, then δ and θ are 2-ary operations on $\{\mathscr{S}_1, \mathscr{I}_2, \mathcal{O}_2\}$, since δ maps $\mathscr{S}_1 \times \mathscr{I}$ to $\mathscr{S}_1$ and θ maps $\mathscr{S}_1 \times \mathscr{I}$ to $\mathcal{O}_3$. If R is a ring, then multiplication and addition in R correspond to two 2-ary operations on $\{R\}$, since they map $R \times R$ to R. The additive inverse in R is a 1-ary operation, and the distinguished constants 0 and 1 are 0-ary operations. If G is a directed graph, with nodes V_1 and arcs E, and ε is the function from V_1 to $E \times E = S_2$ that determines the initial and terminal nodes of the arc, then ε is a 1-ary operation on $\{V_1, S_2\}$, since ε maps V_1 to S_2. A function f is a *finitary operation* on $\{S_i : i \in I\}$ if f is an *n*-ary operation for some non-negative integer n.

Definition   An algebra is a collection $X = \{S_i : i \in I\}$ of nonempty sets S_i, indexed by a set $I \neq \varnothing$, and a set F of finitary operations on X. We denote the algebra by (X, F).

As we have already observed, semigroups, monoids, groups, machines, rings, and directed graphs are examples of algebras. It is easy to check that Boolean algebras and modules are also algebras.

If we wish to compare different algebras, we must first establish some correspondence between the finitary operations on those algebras. The set of rotations of an equilateral triangle forms a group under composition of mappings. The set of integers forms a group under addition. The set of positive real numbers forms a group under multiplication. In each of these examples, there is one 2-ary operation, and we relate these operations by calling them the group operation. To relate the operations in different algebras and to determine if each operation is 0-ary, 1-ary, 2-ary, and so on, we define an *operator domain* to be a set Ω and a function n from Ω to the set of non-negative integers. The elements of Ω correspond to the operations, and the function n says that the operation corresponding to $\beta \in \Omega$ is $n(\beta)$-ary. Thus to classify the operations for a semigroup, let Ω be a set containing one element, say $\Omega = \{\alpha\}$. The element α corresponds to the semigroup operation, and $n(\alpha)$ is 2, showing that the operation is 2-ary. For a Boolean algebra with operations $\wedge$, $\vee$, and $^-$, plus distinguished elements 0 and 1, we let Ω contain five elements, say $\Omega = \{\alpha, \beta, \gamma, \psi, v\}$, where α corresponds to intersection, β to union, γ to complementation, ψ to 0, and v to 1. The function n in this case has $n(\alpha) = 2$, showing that α is 2-ary; $n(\beta) = 2$, showing that β is 2-ary; $n(\gamma) = 1$, showing that γ is 1-ary; $n(\psi) = 0$, showing that the distinguished element 0 of the Boolean algebra is 0-ary; and $n(v) = 0$, showing that the distinguished element 1 of the Boolean algebra is 0-ary.

Definition   Let Ω be a fixed operator domain. An Ω-algebra is an algebra (X, F) such that there is a one-to-one correspondence $\beta \to f_\beta$ from Ω onto F and f_β is an $n(\beta)$-ary operation.

All groups are $\{\alpha, \beta, \gamma\}$ algebras, where α corresponds to the product operation with $n(\alpha) = 2$, β corresponds to the existence of an identity so that $n(\beta) = 0$, and γ corresponds to the operation of taking an inverse so that $n(\gamma) = 1$. For a ring R, an R-module is an algebra $(\{R, M\}, \{\circ', +', -', 0', 1', \circ, +, -, 0\})$, where $\circ'$ and $+'$ are the 2-ary operations of multiplication and addition, respectively, in the ring, $-'$ is the 1-ary operation giving the additive inverse in R, $0'$ and $1'$ are the 0-ary operations in R determining the additive and multiplicative identities, respectively, in R, $\circ$ is the 2-ary operation $R \times M \to M$ of scalar multiplication, $+$ is the 2-ary operation of module addition, $-$ is the 1-ary operation giving the additive inverse in M, and 0 is the 0-ary operation giving the additive identity of M. Thus an R-module is an Ω-algebra, where Ω is a nine-element operator domain, $\Omega = \{\alpha_1, \alpha_2, \ldots, \alpha_9\}$ with the function n and the correspondence between Ω and the operations given in Figure 11.1.

Definition   Let I be a fixed nonempty set. Two Ω-algebras $(\{S_i : i \in I\}, F)$ and $(\{T_i : i \in I\}, F')$ are similar if, for each $\beta \in \Omega, f_\beta \in F$ and $f'_\beta \in F'$ with $f_\beta : S_{i(1, \beta)} \times \cdots \times S_{i(n(\beta), \beta)} \to S_{r(\beta)}$ and $f'_\beta : T_{i'(1, \beta)} \times \cdots \times T_{i'(n(\beta), \beta)} \to T_{r'(\beta)}$, we have $i(j, \beta) = i'(j, \beta)$ and $r(\beta) = r'(\beta)$ for all $1 \le j \le n(\beta)$.

β	Operation f_β	$n(\beta)$
α_1	$\circ'$	2
α_2	$+'$	2
α_3	$-'$	1
α_4	$0'$	0
α_5	$1'$	0
α_6	$\circ$	2
α_7	$+$	2
α_8	$-$	1
α_9	0	0

Figure 11.1 f_β and $n(\beta)$ for β in the operator domain Ω.

Two similar Ω-algebras thus have the same index sets describing the domain and range of corresponding functions. Any two groups can be considered similar Ω-algebras, as can any two machines and any two modules. It is easy to check that being similar is an equivalence relation on the set of all Ω-algebras. We can now define the concept of homomorphism between similar Ω-algebras.

Definition   Let $A = (\{S_i : i \in I\}, F)$ and $B = (\{T_i : i \in I\}, F')$ be similar Ω-algebras. A homomorphism from A to B is a set of functions ϕ_i from S_i to T_i for each $i \in I$ such that, for each $\beta \in \Omega$, $f_\beta \in F$, with $f_\beta : S_{i(1,\beta)} \times \cdots \times S_{i(n(\beta),\beta)} \to S_{r(\beta)}$, $f'_\beta \in F'$, $s_j \in S_{i(j,\beta)}$ for $1 \le j \le n(\beta)$, we have $\phi_{r(\beta)}(f_\beta(s_1, \ldots, s_{n(\beta)})) = f'_\beta(\phi_{i(1,\beta)}(s_1), \ldots, \phi_{i(n(\beta),\beta)}(s_{n(\beta)}))$.

If each of the mappings ϕ_i described in the definition of homomorphism is onto, then the homomorphism is said to be from the algebra A *onto* the algebra B. If, furthermore, each ϕ_i is one-to-one, then the homomorphism is called an *isomorphism*.

Any i/o machine $(\mathscr{S}, \mathscr{I}, \mathscr{O}, \delta, \theta)$ is an $\{\alpha, \beta\}$ algebra $(\{\mathscr{S}, \mathscr{I}, \mathscr{O}\}, \{\delta, \theta\})$, where $\delta = \delta_\alpha$ is a 2-ary operation from $\mathscr{S} \times \mathscr{I}$ to $\mathscr{S}$ and $\theta = \theta_\beta$ is a 2-ary operation from $\mathscr{S} \times \mathscr{I}$ to $\mathscr{O}$. Any two i/o machines are similar as $\{\alpha, \beta\}$ algebras, and thus a homomorphism from $M = (\{\mathscr{S}, \mathscr{I}, \mathscr{O}\}, \{\delta, \theta\})$ to $M' = (\{\mathscr{S}', \mathscr{I}', \mathscr{O}'\}, \{\delta', \theta'\})$ is a set of three functions $\phi_1 : \mathscr{S} \to \mathscr{S}'$, $\phi_2 : \mathscr{I} \to \mathscr{I}'$, and $\phi_3 : \mathscr{O} \to \mathscr{O}'$ such that $\phi_1(\delta(s, a)) = \delta'(\phi_1(s), \phi_2(a))$ and $\phi_3(\theta(s, a)) = \theta'(\phi_1(s), \phi_2(a))$ for each $s \in \mathscr{S}$ and $a \in \mathscr{I}$. The i/o homomorphism from M to M' introduced in Section 5.5 is defined to be a function ϕ from $\mathscr{S}$ to $\mathscr{S}'$ such that $\phi(\delta(s, a)) = \delta'(\phi(s), a)$ and $\theta(s, a) = \theta'(\phi(s), a)$. This is simply the special case of the general i/o homomorphism introduced above, where $\mathscr{I} = \mathscr{I}'$, $\mathscr{O} = \mathscr{O}'$, $\phi = \phi_1$, and ϕ_2 and ϕ_3 are the identity mappings on $\mathscr{I}$ and $\mathscr{O}$.

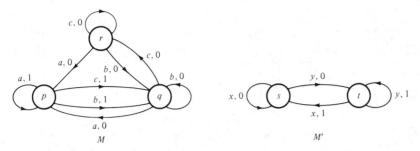

Figure 11.2 i/o machines M and M'.

State	δ			θ		
	a	b	c	a	b	c
p	p	q	q	1	1	1
q	p	q	r	0	0	0
r	p	q	r	0	0	0

Figure 11.3 State table for M.

Figure 11.2 gives the state diagrams of two i/o machines $M = (\{\{p, q, r\},$ $\{a, b, c\}, \{0, 1\}\}, \{\delta, \theta\})$ and $M' = (\{\{s, t\}, \{x, y\}, \{0, 1\}\}, \{\delta', \theta'\})$. The set of mappings $\phi_1, \phi_2,$ and ϕ_3 given by

$$\phi_1(p) = s, \qquad \phi_1(q) = t, \qquad \phi_1(r) = t$$
$$\phi_2(a) = x, \qquad \phi_2(b) = y, \qquad \phi_2(c) = y$$
$$\phi_3(1) = 0, \qquad \phi_3(0) = 1$$

maps the states of M to the states of M', the inputs of M to the inputs of M', and the outputs of M to the outputs of M'. The mappings $\phi_1, \phi_2,$ and ϕ_3, applied to the appropriate elements of the state table of M given in Figure 11.3 yield Figure 11.4. Each entry in Figure 11.4 agrees with the corresponding entry in the state table for M' given in Figure 11.5, hence the set of mappings $\{\phi_1, \phi_2, \phi_3\}$ is an i/o homomorphism from M to M'.

As we have seen, a group G is an $\{\alpha, \beta, \gamma\}$ algebra $(\{G\}, \{\circ, e, ^{-1}\})$, where $\circ : G \times G \to G$, $e : \{\varnothing\} \to G$ and, $^{-1} : G \to G$. A homomorphism from $G = (\{G\}, \{\circ, e, ^{-1}\})$ to $G' = (\{G'\}, \{\circ', e', ^{-1'}\})$ is a function $\phi : G \to G'$ such that $\phi(g \circ h) = \phi(g) \circ' \phi(h)$, $\phi(e) = e'$, and $\phi(g^{-1}) = (\phi(g))^{-1'}$ for all g and h in G. The definition of group homomorphism given in Chapter 7 states that it is a function ϕ from G to G' such that $\phi(g \circ h) = \phi(g) \circ' \phi(h)$ for g and h in G, and it then follows that $\phi(e) = e'$ and $\phi(g^{-1}) = (\phi(g))^{-1'}$. Thus the two definitions are equivalent. Likewise, a homomorphism of the ring R as

State	δ			θ		
	x	y	y	x	y	y
s	s	t	t	0	0	0
t	s	t	t	1	1	1
t	s	t	t	1	1	1

Figure 11.4   Table obtained from Figure 11.3 by taking ϕ_1 (state), ϕ_2 (input) and ϕ_3 (output).

State	δ'		θ'	
	x	y	x	y
s	s	t	0	0
t	s	t	1	1

Figure 11.5   State table for M'.

defined in Chapter 8 is equivalent to an algebra homomorphism of the algebra $(\{R\}, \{\circ, +, -, 0, 1\})$.

Machine congruence is introduced in Chapter 5, semigroup congruence in Chapter 7, and ring congruence in Chapter 8 and, in each of these three cases, a congruence is a partition of the underlying set such that the operations of the algebra induce corresponding operations on the elements of the partition. The concept of congruence is generalized to include each of these three cases.

Definition   Let $A = (\{S_i : i \in I\}, F)$ be an Ω-algebra for some operator domain Ω. Let $\mathscr{P}_i$ be a partition of S_i for each $i \in I$. The set $\{\mathscr{P}_i : i \in I\}$ is a *congruence* for A if, for each $f \in F$ such that $f : S_{i(1)} \times \cdots \times S_{i(n)} \to S_r$, $\{f(p_1, p_2, \ldots, p_n) : p_j \in P_j \text{ for } 1 \le j \le n\}$ is contained in a single subset of the partition $\mathscr{P}_r$ for each P_j in $\mathscr{P}_{i(j)}$, $1 \le j \le n$.

This definition of congruence includes, as special cases, machine congruence, group congruence, and ring congruence.

Let $A = (\{S_i : i \in I\}, F)$ be an Ω-algebra for some operator domain Ω and $\{\mathscr{P}_i : i \in I\}$ be a congruence on A. For each $\alpha \in \Omega$, if $f_\alpha : S_{i(1, \alpha)} \times \cdots \times S_{i(n(\alpha), \alpha)} \to S_{r(\alpha)}$, define $\bar{f}_\alpha : \mathscr{P}_{i(1, \alpha)} \times \cdots \times \mathscr{P}_{i(n(\alpha), \alpha)} \to \mathscr{P}_{r(\alpha)}$ by $\bar{f}_\alpha(P_1, \ldots, P_{n(\alpha)})$ is the unique subset in $\mathscr{P}_{r(\alpha)}$ containing $\{f_\alpha(p_1, \ldots, p_{n(\alpha)}) : p_j \in P_j\}$, where $P_j \in \mathscr{P}_{i(j, \alpha)}$, $1 \le j \le n(\alpha)$. By the definition of congruence, each $\bar{f}_\alpha$ is a well-defined function. Thus $\bar{A} = (\{\mathscr{P}_i : i \in I\}, \{\bar{f}_\alpha : f_\alpha \in F\})$ is an Ω-algebra. Since the indexing of the range and domain of $\bar{f}_\alpha$ is the same as the indexing of the range and domain of f_α, the Ω-algebras A and $\bar{A}$ are similar. In general, if $A = (\{S_i : i \in I\}, F)$ is an Ω-algebra and $\{\mathscr{P}_i : i \in I\}$ is a congruence on A, then we denote the algebra $(\{\mathscr{P}_i : i \in I\}, \{\bar{f}_\alpha : f_\alpha \in F\})$ by $\bar{A}$.

Theorem 11.1 If $\{\mathscr{P}_i : i \in I\}$ is a congruence for the Ω-algebra $A = (\{S_i : i \in I\}, F)$, then the set of mappings ϕ_i, $i \in I$, which take s_i in S_i to the class $[s_i]$ of $\mathscr{P}_i$ containing s_i, is a homomorphism from A onto $\bar{A}$.

Proof Each ϕ_i is clearly a mapping from S_i onto $\mathscr{P}_i$, so it remains to show that, if $f_\alpha : S_{i(1)} \times \cdots \times S_{i(n(\alpha))} \to S_{r(\alpha)}$, then $\phi_{r(\alpha)}(f_\alpha(s_1, \ldots, s_{n(\alpha)})) = \bar{f}_\alpha(\phi_{i(1,\alpha)}(s_1), \ldots, \phi_{i(n(\alpha),\alpha)}(s_{n(\alpha)}))$ for all $s_j \in S_{i(j,\alpha)}$, $1 \leq j \leq n(\alpha)$. However,

$$\bar{f}_\alpha(\phi_{i(1,\alpha)}(s_1), \ldots, \phi_{i(n(\alpha),\alpha)}(s_{n(\alpha)})) = \bar{f}_\alpha([s_1], \ldots, [s_{n(\alpha)}])$$
$$= [f_\alpha(s_1, \ldots, s_{n(\alpha)})] = \phi_{r(\alpha)}(f_\alpha(s_1, \ldots, s_{n(\alpha)})),$$

proving the theorem.

We can now show that, as for machines, groups, and rings, a homomorphism of an Ω-algebra is determined up to isomorphism by a congruence on the Ω-algebra.

Theorem 11.2 Let $A = (\{S_i : i \in I\}, F)$ and $B = (\{T_i : i \in I\}, F')$ be similar Ω-algebras and let $\{\phi_i : i \in I\}$ be a homomorphism from A onto B. Then there is a congruence $\{\mathscr{P}_i : i \in I\}$ on A such that B is isomorphic to $\bar{A}$.

Proof For each $t \in T_i$ and $i \in I$, let $P_t = \{s \in S_i : \phi_i(s) = t\}$. Since ϕ_i is a function from S_i onto T_i, and $T_i \neq \varnothing$, then $\mathscr{P}_i = \{P_t : t \in T_i\}$ is a partition of S_i for each $i \in I$. To see that $\{\mathscr{P}_i : i \in I\}$ is a congruence on A, let $P_j \in \mathscr{P}_{i(j,\alpha)}$ for $1 \leq j \leq n(\alpha)$, where $f_\alpha : S_{i(1,\alpha)} \times \cdots \times S_{i(n(\alpha),\alpha)} \to S_{r(\alpha)}$, $\alpha \in \Omega$. Observe that $\phi_{r(\alpha)}(f(p_1, \ldots, p_{n(\alpha)})) = f'_\alpha(\phi_{i(1,\alpha)}(p_1), \ldots, \phi_{i(n(\alpha),\alpha)}(p_{n(\alpha)}))$ for $p_j \in P_j \in \mathscr{P}_{i(j,\alpha)}$. For $q_j \in P_j$ we have $\phi_{i(j,\alpha)}(q_j) = \phi_{i(j,\alpha)}(p_j)$ by definition of P_j, so that

$$f'_\alpha(\phi_{i(1,\alpha)}(p_1), \ldots, \phi_{i(n(\alpha),\alpha)}(p_{n(\alpha)}))$$
$$= f'_\alpha(\phi_{i(1,\alpha)}(q_1), \ldots, \phi_{i(n(\alpha),\alpha)}(q_{n(\alpha)})) = \phi_{r(\alpha)}(f_\alpha(q_1, \ldots, q_{n(\alpha)})).$$

Thus $f_\alpha(p_1, \ldots, p_{n(\alpha)})$ and $f_\alpha(q_1, \ldots, q_{n(\alpha)})$ are in the same subset of the partition for all p_j and q_j in $P_j \in \mathscr{P}_{i(j,\alpha)}$. This shows that $\{\mathscr{P}_i : i \in I\}$ is a congruence, hence we have an Ω-algebra $\bar{A}$. The mapping ψ_i that takes $t \in T_i$ to P_t is one-to-one from T_i onto $\mathscr{P}_i$. We claim that $\{\psi_i : i \in I\}$ is an isomorphism from B onto $\bar{A}$. To show this, it only remains to show that $\psi_{r(\alpha)}(f'_\alpha(t_1, \ldots, t_{n(\alpha)})) = \bar{f}_\alpha(\psi_{i(1,\alpha)}(t_1), \ldots, \psi_{i(n(\alpha),\alpha)}(t_{n(\alpha)}))$ for all $t_j \in T_{i(j,\alpha)}$, $1 \leq j \leq n(\alpha)$. We have already shown that $\{\mathscr{P}_i : i \in I\}$ is a congruence, so that $\bar{f}_\alpha(\psi_{i(1,\alpha)}(t_1), \ldots, \psi_{i(n(\alpha),\alpha)}(t_{n(\alpha)}))$ is the class $[f_\alpha(s_1, \ldots, s_{n(\alpha)})]$ in $\mathscr{P}_{r(\alpha)}$, where $s_j \in \psi_{i(j,\alpha)}(t_j) = P_{t_j}$.

However,

$$\phi_{r(\alpha)}(f_\alpha(s_1, \ldots, s_{n(\alpha)})) = f'_\alpha(\phi_{i(1,\alpha)}(s_1), \ldots, \phi_{i(n(\alpha),\alpha)}(s_{n(\alpha)})) = f'_\alpha(t_1, \ldots, t_{n(\alpha)}),$$

since $\{\phi_i : i \in I\}$ is a homomorphism and $\phi_{i(j,\alpha)}(s_j) = t_j$ for all $s_j \in \psi_{i(j,\alpha)}(t_j) = P_{t_j}$, $1 \le j \le n(\alpha)$. Thus $[f_\alpha(s_1, \ldots, s_{n(\alpha)})] = P_{f'_\alpha(t_1, \ldots, t_{n(\alpha)})} = \psi_{r(\alpha)}(f'_\alpha(t_1, \ldots, t_{n(\alpha)}))$, which shows that $f_\alpha(\psi_{i(1,\alpha)}(t_1), \ldots, \psi_{i(n(\alpha),\alpha)}(t_{n(\alpha)})) = \psi_{r(\alpha)}(f'_\alpha(t_1, \ldots, t_{n(\alpha)}))$ for all $t_j \in T_{i(j,\alpha)}$, $1 \le j \le n(\alpha)$, proving the theorem.

Exercises

11-1 Show that a Boolean algebra and a ring are similar Ω-algebras.

11-2 By considering a Boolean algebra an Ω-algebra, derive a definition of homomorphism of a Boolean algebra from the general definition of homomorphism of an Ω-algebra. Simplify the definition by showing that some of the conditions follow from the rest.

11-3 Describe an undirected graph as an Ω-algebra. Define a homomorphism of (undirected) graphs that agrees with a homomorphism of graphs as Ω-algebras. Describe all homomorphisms from $a\circ\!\!-\!\!\overset{b}{\circ}\!\!-\!\!\circ c$ to $d\circ\!\!-\!\!\circ e$.

11-4 Prove that, if A and B are finite Boolean algebras, then there exists a homomorphism from A onto B if and only if $|A| \ge |B|$.

11-5 Determine those Boolean algebras that are isomorphic to rings as Ω-algebras.

11-6 Let B be a Boolean algebra. For a and b in B, define $a\theta b$ to be $(a \wedge \bar{b}) \vee (\bar{a} \wedge b)$ and let i be the identity mapping from B to B. Prove that the algebra $(\{B\}, \{\wedge, \theta, i, 0, 1\})$ is a ring, $\wedge$ being multiplication, θ being addition, i being additive inverse, 0 being additive identity, and 1 being multiplicative identity.

11-7 By considering an R-module an Ω-algebra, where R is a ring, give a definition of an R-module homomorphism. Simplify this definition by omitting some conditions that follow from the rest and show that a linear mapping is a special case of homomorphism.

11-8 Let P be a partially ordered set. Define a concept of congruence on P and determine a partial ordering $\bar{P}$ of the set of classes that satisfies $x \ge y$ implies $[x] \ge [y]$ for all x and y in P.

11-9 Give a definition of a homomorphism ϕ from a poset P onto a poset Q such that there is a congruence on P (as defined in Exercise 11-8), a homomorphism ψ from P to $\bar{P}$, and an isomorphism ε from $\bar{P}$ onto Q with $\phi = \varepsilon \cdot \psi$.

11-10 Give a plausible definition of finitary relation.

11-11 A relational system is a set of nonempty sets $\{S_i : i \in I\}$ indexed by $I \ne \varnothing$ and a set of finitary relations on $\{S_i : i \in I\}$ (see Exercise 11-10). Define homomorphism and congruence of relational systems and make a conjecture about their interaction.

Index